MODULAR MATHEMATICS

Foundation GCSE for AQA

Mark Bindley

Edited by: **Brian Gaulter**

The seats on this ride follow the path of a circle.

You can find out about circles on page 400.

OXFORD
UNIVERSITY PRESS

OXFORD
UNIVERSITY PRESS

Great Clarendon Street, Oxford OX2 6DP

Oxford University Press is a department of the University of Oxford.
It furthers the University's objective of excellence in research, scholarship,
and education by publishing worldwide in

Oxford New York

Auckland   Bangkok   Buenos Aires   Cape Town   Chennai
Dar es Salaam   Delhi   Hong Kong   Istanbul   Karachi   Kolkata
Kuala Lumpur   Madrid   Melbourne   Mexico City   Mumbai   Nairobi
São Paulo   Shanghai   Taipei   Tokyo   Toronto

Oxford is a registered trade mark of Oxford University Press
in the UK and in certain other countries

British Library Cataloguing in Publication Data

Data available

ISBN 0 19 914811 2

The authors would like to thank Paul Metcalf for his authoritative coursework guidance.

The publishers would like to thank AQA for their kind permission to reproduce past paper
questions. The AQA accept no responsibility for the answers to the past paper questions
which are the sole responsibility of the publishers.

The photograph on page 209 is reproduced courtesy of Robert Harding
The photograph on page 281 is reproduced courtesy of Quadrant Picture Agency
The photograph on page 321 is reproduced courtesy of Stock Market Picture Library
The Escher drawing on page 356 is reproduced courtesy of Cordon Art

Cartoons by Martin Aston

Typeset by TechSet Ltd. Gateshead, Tyne and Wear.
Printed and bound in Great Britain by Bell & Bain Ltd., Glasgow

About this book

This book is designed to help you get your best possible grade in the **AQA Specification B**, Foundation modular examinations and coursework modules.

How to use this book

The book is arranged so that the content of each module is clear. You can use the tabs at the edge of the page to find the content you need.

The **content modules** – modules 1, 3 and 5 – are broken down into units of work that increase in difficulty throughout the modules.

Each unit starts with an overview of what you are going to learn and a list of what you should already know.

The **'Before you start'** section will help you to remember the key ideas and skills necessary for the exam. The **Check in** questions will help you see what you already know.

At the end of each unit there is a **summary** page.

The **'You should now know'** sections are useful as a quick revision guide and each **Check out** question points out important content that you should remember.

After the summary page you will find a **revision exercise** with past paper questions from AQA. This will help you to prepare for the style of questions you will see in the exam.

At the end of each module you also have two **Practice module tests** – one calculator and one non-calculator. These tests will help you prepare for the real thing.

The **coursework modules** – modules 2 and 4 – are located in a separate unit at the end of the book. The unit tells you what you have to do for your coursework. Each of the Tasks includes **Moderator comments** to help you get better marks.

The numerical **answers** are given at the end of the book. Use these to check you understand what you are doing.

Good luck in your exams!

Module 1 Contents

Module 2: Statistical Coursework

Module 3 Contents

D1 DATA HANDLING 1

Market researchers collect data that is used to shape future products.

This unit will show you how to:

- Design a survey to collect data
- Use tally marks and draw bar charts
- Use pictograms

Before you start:

You should know how to...	Check in D1
1. Use tally marks. For example: ||||| means 5 ||||| ||||| || means 12.	**1.** (a) Write down what these tallies mean: (i) ||| (ii) ||||| ||| (iii) ||||| ||||| |||||	(b) Write these numbers using tally marks: (i) 14 (ii) 6 (iii) 21

Data is another word for information.

One way to collect **data** is to use a survey or questionnaire.

1.1 Designing a survey to collect data

When you design a survey, try to provide tick boxes for as many answers as possible.

Don't use a question like:

What is your favourite type of TV programme? ....

Do use a question like:

- Which is your favourite type of TV programme?
  - ☑ Sport
  - ☐ Drama and films
  - ☐ Soap opera
  - ☐ Chat shows
  - ☐ Comedy
  - ☐ Wildlife and animals
  - ☐ News and documentaries

This will make it much easier to check the data you collect.

Example

Nathan is designing a survey on eye colours. He wants to find out:

- which is the most common eye colour
- whether eye colour distribution is different for men and women
- whether eye colour distribution depends on age.

Design a survey to provide the data he needs.

Tick one box for your eye colour.	Tick one box for your sex.	Tick one box for your age.
☐ Green	☑ Male	☑ 21–30
☐ Brown	☐ Female	☐ 31–40
☑ Blue		☐ 41–50
☐ Grey		☐ 51–60
☐ Other		☐ over 60

Exercise 1A

1. As part of a survey on healthy eating, John wants to find out:

   - How many students in his school consider their health when deciding what to eat for lunch.
   - Whether more boys than girls consider their health when deciding what to eat for lunch.
   - Whether more students in the older year groups consider their health when deciding what to eat for lunch.

   Design three questions which John should include in his survey.

2. As part of a survey on television viewing, Pria wants to find out:

   - How many hours of television people watch during an average day.
   - Whether women watch more television than men.
   - Whether different age groups have different viewing habits.

   Design three questions which Pria should include in her survey.

3. As part of a survey on pop music in her school, Toni wants to find out:

   - Which type of pop music is most popular with students.
   - Whether boys prefer different types of pop music to girls.
   - Whether younger students prefer different types of pop music to older students.

   Design three questions which Toni should include in her survey.

4. As part of a health questionnaire for young people, a Health Authority wants to find out:

   - How many young people smoke cigarettes.
   - If they smoke, how many cigarettes they smoke a day.
   - Whether young people are more likely to smoke cigarettes if one or more of their parents smokes cigarettes.

   Design three questions which the Health Authority should include in its survey.

1.2 Using tally marks and drawing bar charts

Twenty students are given a mark out of 5 for a short test. The results were:

1, 2, 5, 4, 5, 4, 3, 3, 4, 5, 2, 2, 2, 4, 4, 2, 4, 5, 3, 4

This is the **raw data**. It has not been organised in any way.

Tally marks are often used to organise a list of results into a table. The marks for the twenty students can be organised into a table like this.

Mark	Tally	Frequency
0		0
1	|	1
2	卌	5
3	|||	3
4	卌 ||	7
5	||||	4
Total		20

Remember:
The word **frequency** means the number of times something happens.

After the data has been organised, you can draw a **bar chart**.

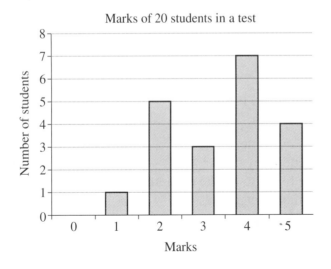

Marks of 20 students in a test

Remember:
All bar charts should have a title and labels on each axis.

Exercise 1B

1. A gamekeeper checks the number of eggs in twenty-five nests. These are his results:

   3, 4, 0, 1, 3, 0, 2, 2, 3, 4, 4, 4, 5, 0, 1, 3, 4, 2, 2, 4, 2, 5, 0, 0, 2

   (a) Use tally marks to organise the results into a table like this:

Number of eggs	Tally	Frequency
0		
1		
2		
3		
4		
5		

   (b) Draw a bar chart using axes like these.

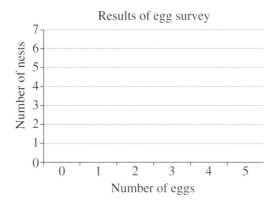

2. Twenty girls and twenty boys are asked whether they considered their health when deciding what to eat for lunch. These are the results:

   Girls: Y, Y, N, N, Y, Y, N, Y, N, Y, N, Y, N, Y, Y, Y, N, Y, N, Y

   Boys: Y, Y, Y, N, N, N, N, N, Y, Y, N, Y, N, N, N, Y, N, Y, Y, N

   (a) Use tally marks to organise the results into two tables with headings like this:

Girls	Tally	Frequency
Yes		
No		

MODULE 1

(b) Draw two bar charts using axes like these.

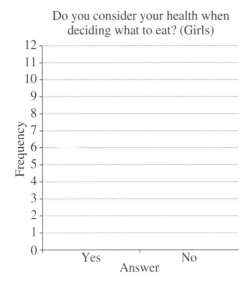

3. In a taste test, 30 people were asked to select their favourite sausage from four brands. The brands were Porkers (P), Sizzlers (S), Yumbos (Y) and Bangers (B). These are the results:

P, B, B, B, B, Y, P, Y, B, Y, P, P, S, B, B, B, S, Y, P, B, P, Y, P, S, P, Y, B, Y, B, P

(a) Use tally marks to organise the results into a table with headings like this:

Type of sausage	Tally	Frequency
Porkers		

(b) Draw a bar chart using axes like these.

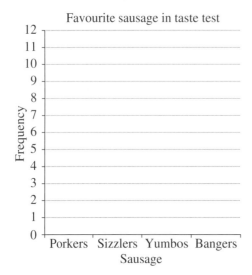

4. Kathy and Kyle both fire twenty-five shots at a target. The
   target has sections which score from 1 to 6 points. These are
   their scores:

   Kathy: 6, 4, 4, 3, 2, 6, 4, 1, 2, 5, 6, 4, 4, 6, 4, 5, 3, 1, 4, 5, 6, 5, 5, 4, 6

   Kyle: 5, 5, 4, 4, 4, 3, 4, 5, 6, 4, 5, 6, 6, 1, 1, 2, 3, 4, 5, 3, 2, 6, 5, 4, 3

   (a) Use tally marks to organise the results into two tables
       with headings like this:

Score	Tally	Frequency
1		
2		

   (b) Draw two bar charts.

5. Twenty men and twenty women answered this question:

   How many hours of television do you watch during an
   average day?

   ☐ A.   less than one hour
   ☐ B.   one to two hours
   ☐ C.   two to three hours
   ☐ D.   three to four hours
   ☐ E.   more than four hours

   These are the results:

   Men: A, A, B, C, D, D, C, E, C, C, A, C, B, C, D, E, C, C, D, A

   Women: B, B, C, C, E, A, D, B, C, C, C, C, C, B, D, D, D, E, A, A

   (a) Use tally marks to organise the results into two tables
       with headings like this:

Numbers of hours watched	Tally	Frequency
Less than one hour		

   (b) Draw two bar charts.

1.3 Pictograms

Pictograms are sometimes used instead of bar charts. Pictures
are used to replace the bars.

For example, the bar chart for student marks can be drawn as this pictogram.

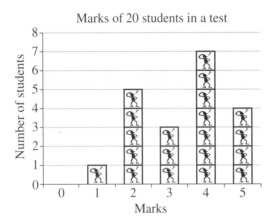

Marks of 20 students in a test

This is data on the number of lions living in a game reserve in six different years.

Year	1995	1996	1997	1998	1999	2000
Number of lions	150	165	172	190	218	205

To show this data with a pictogram, you need a scale because the numbers are large. If you
use one lion symbol to represent 20 lions, the pictogram looks like this:

Lions living in a game reserve

Notice that if the number of lions does not divide exactly by 20, you need to draw part of a lion.

Drawing the same symbol many times can be very tedious. So, unless you are using a computer, always select very simple symbols for pictograms.

Exercise 1C

1. A question about eye colour was answered by twenty people in a survey. The results were:

Green	4
Brown	6
Blue	8
Grey	2
Other	0

   Draw a pictogram to illustrate the results.

2. Thirty people answered a question about the type of house they live in. The results were:

Semi-detached house	10
Detached house	8
Bungalow	3
Terraced house	5
Flat	4

   Draw a pictogram to illustrate the results.

3. In a survey, three hundred people were asked which was their favourite flavour of potato crisps. The results were:

Plain	85
Cheese and Onion	60
Salt and Vinegar	74
Roast Chicken	34
Prawn Cocktail	22
Roast Beef	15
Smoky Bacon	10

   Draw a pictogram to illustrate the results.
   Use a symbol like this to represent 10 first choices.

Summary

1. When you design a survey, try to provide tick boxes for as many answers as possible.

2. **Tally marks** are often used to organise a list of results into a table. After the data has been organised a **bar chart** can be drawn.

3. Pictograms are sometimes sometimes used instead of bar charts. Pictures are used to replace the bars.

Checkout D1

1. As part of a survey on a local superstore, Sangita wants to find out:
   - How long it takes the person answering the survey to travel to the superstore.
   - Whether people who live closer visit the superstore more frequently.
   - Whether people who live closer spend less money per visit than people who live further away.

   Design three questions which Sangita should include in her survey. Each question should have at least four tick boxes for people to choose from.

2. Nina did a survey of the colours of cars passing the school. These are her results:

w	w	r	b	r	r	w	g	g	w
r	b	r	w	w	g	g	r	b	w
b	r	w	b	r	r	g	g	w	w

   Key: w = white
   b = blue
   r = red
   g = green

   (a) Use tally marks to organise Nina's results into a table.
   (b) Draw a bar chart for this data.

3. Draw a pictogram to illustrate Nina's results from Question 2 above.

Revision exercise D1

1. Andy asks his friends what hobbies they have.
   His results are shown in the tally chart.

Hobby	Tally
Computers	𝍷𝍷𝍷 𝍷𝍷𝍷 𝍷𝍷
Football	𝍷𝍷𝍷 𝍷𝍷𝍷 𝍷𝍷𝍷 𝍷𝍷
Music	𝍷𝍷𝍷 𝍷
Other	𝍷𝍷𝍷 𝍷𝍷𝍷𝍷

   (a) How many people chose computers as one of their hobbies?

   (b) Draw a pictogram to show Andy's results.

   Use the symbol 😊 to represent 6 people.

Computers	
Football	
Music	
Other	

[AQA]

2. Susan asks her friends what their favourite school meal is.
   Her results are given in the frequency table.

Favourite school meal	Frequency
Burgers	7
Fish	1
Pasta	3
Salad	4

   (a) Draw a bar chart to show Susan's results.

   (b) How many friends did Susan ask?   [AQA]

3. Jane does a survey about vehicles passing her school. She wants to know about the types of vehicles and their colours.

Design a suitable observation sheet to record this information.
Fill in your observation sheet as if you had carried out this survey.
You should invent suitable data for 25 vehicles.   [NEAB]

4. A survey was conducted to find out which activities 11-year-old pupils do after school.
The results are displayed below.

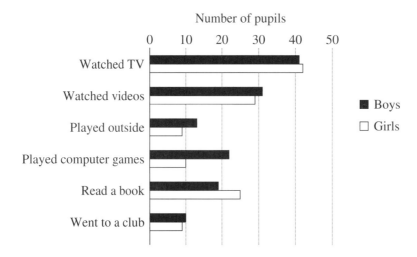

(a) Which activity was chosen most often by both boys and girls?

(b) The survey shows that after school, more boys played outside than girls.
Write down two other findings from the survey that tell us about the differences between what boys and girls did after school.

(c) In another survey, some 16-year-old pupils were asked:
How long did you spend doing your homework last night?

Design an observation sheet to collect this data.

[NEAB]

5. The bar chart shows the percentage sales by petrol
companies in the UK.

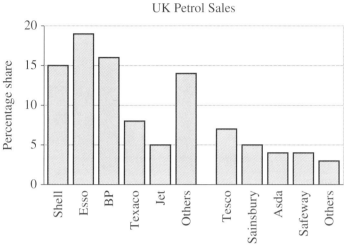

(a) (i)   Which of the garages sells the most petrol?
    (ii) Which supermarket has about 5% of the sales?

(b) The diagram shows how the percentage sales have been
     divided between the well known brands and supermarkets.
     Draw a bar to show what you would expect to happen
     to sales in the year 2000.

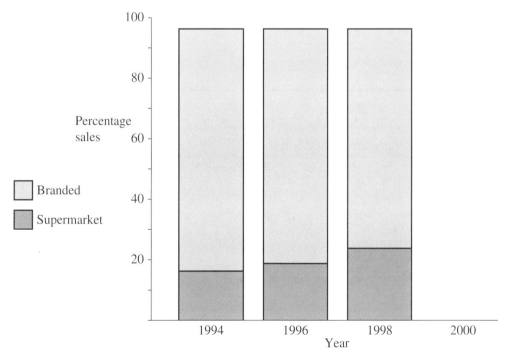

[NEAB]

6. (a) This table shows the maximum temperature recorded one day in May in 20 cities around the world.

City	Temperature °C	City	Temperature °C
Amsterdam	23	Los Angeles	23
Bangkok	35	Madrid	25
Barcelona	21	Mexico City	27
Berlin	20	Moscow	15
Cairo	30	New York	26
Copenhagen	20	Paris	26
Edinburgh	21	Rome	22
Kathmandu	30	San Francisco	16
Lisbon	22	Washington	29
London	25	Zurich	21

(i) Use the data in the table to complete this tally chart.

Temperature °C	Tally	Frequency
11–15		
16–20		
21–25		
26–30		
31–35		

(ii) In how many cities was the temperature higher than the temperature in London?

[NEAB]

D2 DATA HANDLING 2

I don't know why you find the place strange, it has always seemed pretty average to us.

This unit will show you how to:

- Find the mean and the range of a distribution
- Find the median and mode of a distribution
- Construct and use a stem-and-leaf plot
- Find the average of data in tables

Before you start:

You should know how to...	Check in D2
1. Add numbers in your head. Think of a number line... $33 + 45 = 78$ $+40$ $+5$ $33 \quad 73 \; 78$	**1.** Calculate (a) $4 + 5 + 6$ (b) $12 + 15$ (c) $8 + 9 + 11$ (d) $15 + 16 + 17$ (e) $45 + 61$ (f) $23 + 27 + 31$ (g) $32 + 34 + 35 + 36 + 32$
2. Multiply and divide numbers in your head. For example: $420 \div 6$ is like $42 \div 6 = 7$ so $420 \div 6 = 70$.	**2.** Calculate (a) 6×5 (b) 7×3 (c) 9×8 (d) 18×5 (e) $60 \div 5$ (f) $120 \div 3$ (g) $210 \div 7$ (h) $216 \div 9$
3. Write numbers in size order. For example: For example, largest first, 31, 16, 27, 18, 29 becomes 31, 29, 27, 18, 16	**3.** Order these numbers, smallest first (a) 6, 9, 23, 7, 2, 5 (b) 121, 63, 47, 105, 89 (c) 6, 2, 7, 1, 9, 5, 6, 2, 7 (d) 17, 12, 15, 12, 19, 21, 9, 17

2.1 The mean and range of a distribution

Gurpal threw tens sets of three darts at a board. His scores were:

34, 45, 20, 41, 60, 83, 70, 30, 26, 61

A set of values like this is called a **distribution**.

The **range** of a distribution = greatest value − least value
The range of Gurpal's scores = 83 − 20 = 63

The **mean** of a distribution = total of the distribution ÷ number
of values
This distribution has 10 values which add up to 470
The mean of Gurpal's scores = 470 ÷ 10 = 47

You can use the mean and the range to compare two
distributions.
These are Gurpreet's scores when he also threw ten sets of three
darts:

45, 44, 52, 40, 43, 45, 49, 54, 60, 48

The range of Gurpreet's scores = 60 − 40 = 20
The mean of Gurpreet's scores = 480 ÷ 10 = 48

The players are quite evenly matched in terms of their mean
scores. The ranges however show that Gurpreet is the more
consistent player because the range of his scores is much lower.

Exercise 2A

1. Calculate the range and the mean of each distribution.

(a)	4	5	6	7	8						
(b)	5	5	6	6	6	7	7				
(c)	3	4	1	2	3	5	6	4	8		
(d)	3	3	3	2	4	1	5				
(e)	6	7	8	8	8	9	10				
(f)	4	5	3	2	4	5	3	2			
(g)	2	2	2	3	3	4	4	5	5	5	
(h)	2	2	3	4	5	5	5	6	7	8	8	8
(i)	10	10	11	10	9	11	10	12	14	10	
(j)	16	15	13	17	14						
(k)	22	20	25	24	28	20	22				
(l)	102	102	102	103	103	103					
(m)	6	7	7	8	8	8	8	8	9	9	9	9
(n)	15	16	17	14	15	17	18				
(o)	32	32	33	34	35	36	36	37	36	32	

2. In a book sale, Professor Higgins bought:

six books at £5 each
three books at £3 each
one book at £2

(a) What was the total cost of the books?
(b) What was the mean cost of the books?

3. Lisa and Lucy have both completed 10 French homeworks.
These are their marks out of 10.

Lisa   7, 8, 7, 8, 7, 8, 8, 7, 7, 8
Lucy   3, 9, 10, 4, 5, 9, 10, 3, 10, 10

(a) Calculate the range for each person.
(b) Calculate the mean mark for each person.
(c) Say who you think is better at French. Give reasons for
your answer.

4. A scientist weighs two samples of potatoes. The weights in
grams of the samples are:

Sample One   260, 234, 245, 270, 256, 275, 234, 244, 249, 252
Sample Two   270, 230, 295, 218, 280, 278, 211, 276, 284, 254

(a) Calculate the range of each sample.
(b) Calculate the mean of each sample.
(c) Explain how the two samples differ.

5. Sally and Greg are saving to go on holiday. These are the
savings each made over an eight-week period:

Sally   £12   £10   £5   £10   £15   £12   £10   £10
Greg   £2   £20   £18   £0   £5   £4   £20   £15

(a) Calculate the range for each person.
(b) Calculate the mean savings per week for each person.
(c) Is there a difference between the ways that Greg and
Sally are saving?

6. Alexandra and Emmanuel play an 18-hole round of golf.
These are their scores.

Alexandra   7, 8, 6, 5, 5, 7, 8, 9, 7, 5, 10, 9, 9, 12, 8, 8, 15, 6
Emmanuel   9, 9, 9, 9, 10, 10, 8, 8, 9, 9, 8, 10, 9, 8, 10, 5, 5, 8

(a) Calculate the range for each person.
(b) Calculate the mean shots per hole for each person.
(c) Who do you think is the best player? Give a reason for
your answer.

2.2 The median of a distribution

Kelly sometimes travels to school by bus. These are the number of times she has used the bus in the last 9 weeks:

> Last one to the bus pays.

3, 4, 2, 3, 3, 2, 1, 0, 3

The **median** of a distribution is the value in the middle **when the values are arranged in order**.

If this distribution is arranged in order it becomes:

0, 1, 2, 2, *3*, 3, 3, 3, 4

The middle value is 3. The median number of times Kelly uses the bus is 3.
The range of the distribution = 4 − 0 = 4

You can use the median and the range to compare two distributions.
These are the number of times Gavin has used the bus in the last 9 weeks:

4, 4, 5, 1, 2, 4, 3, 5, 4

If this distribution is arranged in order it becomes:

1, 2, 3, 4, *4*, 4, 4, 5, 5

The middle value is 4. The median number of times Gavin uses the bus is 4.
The range of the distribution = 5 − 1 = 4

You can say that, on average, Gavin uses the bus more often than Kelly.

These are the number of times Nisha has used the bus in the last ten weeks:

5, 1, 1, 4, 4, 3, 2, 3, 5, 4

There are an even number of values in this distribution, so there is no exact middle value. The median is found like this:

1, 1, 2, 3, *3*, *4*, 4, 4, 5, 5

Median = (3 + 4) ÷ 2 = 3·5

Exercise 2B

1. Calculate the median of each distribution.

(a)	4	5	6	7	8							
(b)	5	5	6	6	6	7	7					
(c)	3	4	1	2	3	5	6	4	8			
(d)	3	3	3	2	4	1	5					
(e)	6	7	8	8	8	9	10					
(f)	4	5	3	2	4	5	3	2				
(g)	2	2	2	3	3	4	4	5	5	5		
(h)	2	2	3	4	5	5	5	6	7	8	8	8
(i)	10	10	11	10	9	11	10	12	14	10		
(j)	16	15	13	17	14							
(k)	22	20	25	24	28	20	22					
(l)	102	102	102	103	103	103						
(m)	6	7	7	8	8	8	8	8	9	9	9	9
(n)	15	16	17	14	15	17	18					
(o)	32	32	33	34	35	36	36	37	36	32		

2. During one week, two country vets each buy petrol every day. These are the number of litres that each buys.

Day	Vet 1	Vet 2
Monday	40	22
Tuesday	10	24
Wednesday	35	23
Thursday	12	20
Friday	36	26

(a) Find the range for each vet.
(b) Find the median for each vet.
(c) Describe the differences between the two distributions.

3. A netball team wins a tournament after playing five matches. These are the scores in their matches.

24 12   34 5   15 14   20 17   18 14

(a) Find the median number of goals the team scores.
(b) Find the range of the goals the team scores.
(c) Find the median number of goals scored against the team.
(d) Find the range of the goals scored against the team.

4. The midday temperatures in two different seaside resorts for a week during July were:

Skegness   22°C   21°C   23°C   24°C   26°C   24°C   24°C
Eastbourne   28°C   30°C   24°C   20°C   19°C   26°C   30°C

(a) Find the median midday temperature and the range for Skegness.
(b) Find the median midday temperature and the range for Eastbourne.
(c) Describe the differences between the midday temperatures in the two resorts.

5. The scores of the players in two cricket teams during a game were:

Team 1   64, 32, 85, 52, 30,   0, 10, 24,   0, 24, 31
Team 2   29, 45, 26, 43, 42, 35, 40, 14, 28, 28, 26

(a) Find the median score and the range for Team 1.
(b) Find the median score and the range for Team 2.
(c) Which team won the match?

6. A shop prices researcher buys half a kilogram of tomatoes in eight different supermarkets in two different areas. These are her results.

North West   54p, 64p, 58p, 45p, 53p, 62p, 48p, 50p
South West   64p, 60p, 62p, 48p, 67p, 54p, 56p, 65p

(a) Find the median price and the range for the North West.
(b) Find the median price and the range for the South West.
(c) Compare the price of tomatoes in the two areas.

2.3 Stem-and-leaf plots

A stem-and-leaf plot is a frequency diagram that can help you to find the median value easily.

> A stem-and-leaf plot may be called a stem plot or a stem-and-leaf diagram.

Example

This data shows the number of words in sentences taken from two newspapers. Show the data as a stem-and-leaf plot and find the median for The Recorder.

The Chronicle
37, 44, 21, 18, 34, 25, 30, 19, 22, 31
40, 38, 27, 34, 18, 19, 33, 41, 32, 27
35, 28, 22, 26, 33, 36, 41, 35, 23, 19

The Recorder
16, 23, 5, 22, 24, 31, 18, 22, 17, 25
28, 24, 29, 31, 19, 25, 30, 8, 21, 19
24, 18, 26, 33, 38, 28, 30, 22, 4, 21

MODULE 1

Stem-and-leaf plot to show the number of words in a sentence

```
           The Chronicle                    The Recorder
                              4 |
             4  1  1  0       4 |
             8  7  6  5  5    3 | 8
     4  4  3  3  2  1  0      3 | 0  0  1  1  3
             8  7  7  6  5    2 | 5  5  6  8  8  9
                3  2  2  1    2 | 1  1  2  2  2 (3  4) 4  4
             9  9  9  8  8    1 | 6  7  8  8  9  9
                              1 |
                              0 | 5  8
                              0 | 4
```

These are the units digits (The leaves)   These are the units digits (The leaves)

↑ This column has the tens digit (The stem)

To find the median:

There are 30 numbers so the middle number will be between the 15th and 16th values.

So the median is between 23 and 24. It is 23.5 words per sentence.

Exercise 2C

1. Use the stem-and-leaf plot above to find the median number of words used in a sentence for The Chronicle.

2. This data gives the number of sandwiches sold each day by two shops.

Kwik Bite	Lunch Box
36, 42, 28, 21, 51, 43, 29, 35, 41, 40	55, 39, 44, 48, 42, 39, 38, 32, 47, 56
27, 44, 35, 29, 44, 31, 35, 56, 38, 43	49, 56, 48, 46, 49, 38, 44, 41, 52, 53
26, 37, 46, 38, 29, 28, 29, 41, 37, 33	56, 42, 47, 45, 37, 30, 49, 54, 51, 46

(a) Show the two sets of data on a stem-and-leaf plot.

(b) For each shop find the median value for the data.

(c) Which shop seems to have the better sandwich trade? Explain your answer.

2.4 The mode

These are the shoe sizes of a group of 30 children:

3, 4, 5, 4, 4, 3, 4, 5, 6, 7, 7, 6, 5, 4, 3, 4, 5, 4, 6,
4, 5, 3, 3, 6, 7, 7, 4, 4, 5, 6

The data can be organised into this tally chart.

Size	Tally	Frequency
3	JHT	5
4	JHT JHT	10
5	JHT I	6
6	JHT	5
7	JHT	4

Remember:
The value which occurs
the most in a distribution
is called the **mode** or
modal value.

The modal shoe size is 4, because this size occurs the most
number of times.

Exercise 2D

1. The ages of a group of pupils taking part in a school visit were:

    11, 11, 12, 13, 13, 11, 12, 12, 13, 12, 11, 11, 12, 13,
    12, 12, 11, 11, 13, 11

    Find the mode of these ages.

2. The number of goals scored in eleven Premier League
   matches one Saturday was:

    1, 0, 0, 2, 3, 5, 2, 4, 5, 2, 3

    Find the modal number of goals scored.

3. Chantal and Lindsey have both completed ten homeworks
   for their GCSE Drama course. These are their marks.

   Chantal   6, 8, 8, 9, 7, 9, 8, 9, 10, 10
   Lindsey   7, 7, 7, 6, 6, 8, 6, 8, 7, 8

   (a) Find the mode and the range for Chantal's marks.
   (b) Find the mode and the range for Lindsey's marks.

4. Adam and Josef both shoot at a target 15 times. These are their scores.

   Adam   3, 4, 5, 4, 5, 6, 5, 7, 8, 5, 3, 5, 6, 8, 7
   Josef   4, 6, 5, 6, 5, 4, 6, 4, 7, 8, 8, 5, 6, 6, 6

   (a) Find the mode and the range for Adam's scores.
   (b) Find the mode and the range for Josef's scores.

5. This table shows the number of people (in thousands) visiting a museum during each season of a year.
   (a) How many people visited the museum during the year?
   (b) Which was the modal season?

Season	Visitors (thousands)
Spring	8
Summer	15
Autumn	10
Winter	3

6. Thirty people take part in a taste test. They are asked to select their favourite flavour ice-cream from a choice of Strawberry (S), Vanilla (V), Chocolate (C), Pistachio (P) and Mint Choc-Chip (M). These are the results:

   V, V, V, P, M, S, C, C, V, V, C, P, S, S, M, P, M, S, M,
   V, M, V, V, M, S, P, S, S, M, P

   Find the modal choice for favourite flavour.

2.5 Finding the mean, the median, the mode and the range

You need to remember which average is which. This might help you:

- The mean is mean because you have to work it out.
- The median is the middle.
- The mode is the most fashionable item.

Exercise 2E

1. Find the mean, median, mode and range of each distribution.
   (a) 2, 4, 5, 3, 8, 10, 3
   (b) 28, 28, 27, 25, 23, 23, 24, 26, 23, 25, 23
   (c) 2, 4, 5, 3, 3, 2, 2, 3, 3
   (d) 8, 8, 8, 0, 7, 6, 6, 7, 9, 9, 7, 22, 7

2. Philip keeps a check on eleven students at his driving school. This is the number of attempts each student needs before they pass the test:

   0, 0, 1, 1, 2, 2, 4, 5, 6, 6, 6

   (a) Find the mean number of attempts before passing.
   (b) Find the median number of attempts before passing.
   (c) Find the modal number of attempts before passing.
   (d) Find the range of the number of attempts before passing.

3. The midday temperature is recorded each day during a week in January. These are the results:

   $^-4°C$, $^-3°C$, $^-3°C$, $0°C$, $1°C$, $1°C$, $1°C$,

   (a) Find the mean midday temperature during the week.
   (b) Find the median midday temperature during the week.
   (c) Find the modal midday temperature during the week.
   (d) Find the range of the midday temperatures during the week.

4. Roberta and Robert saved some of their pocket money each week to go on holiday. This is a list of how much they saved each week.

   Roberta   £2, £2.50, £3, £1, £2, £3.50, £2, £1, £3, £2.50
   Robert   £1, £5, £0.50, £6, £0.25, £0.75, £5, £1, £1, £4

   (a) Find the mean, median, mode and range of the amounts which Roberta saved each week.
   (b) Find the mean, median, mode and range of the amounts which Robert saved each week.

5. Eunice works in a zoo. One of her jobs is to look after a group of 10 baby snakes. She measures the snakes each week to check their growth. These are the results for two successive weeks.

   Week One   125 mm, 134 mm, 128 mm, 120 mm, 125 mm,
              125 mm, 128 mm, 125 mm, 120 mm, 130 mm
   Week Two   137 mm, 144 mm, 142 mm, 145 mm, 145 mm,
              145 mm, 148 mm, 145 mm, 143 mm, 144 mm

   (a) Find the mean, median, mode and range of the distribution of lengths for week one.
   (b) Find the mean, median, mode and range of the distribution of lengths for week two.

6. Tommy is testing two makes of oven for a consumer magazine. He sets the temperature control to 200°C and then measures the actual temperature inside the ovens every five minutes for one hour. These are his results.

   Oven One
   Temperature (°C)   189, 191, 195, 195, 195, 195, 199, 200, 200, 200, 202, 203

   Oven Two
   Temperature (°C)   198, 200, 200, 202, 202, 203, 204, 205, 205, 205, 206, 206

   (a) Find the mean, median, mode and range of the distribution of temperatures for oven one.
   (b) Find the mean, median, mode and range of the distribution of temperatures for oven two.

2.6 Data in tables

Ricky fired 40 shots at a target. This table shows his results.

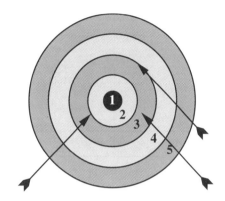

Score	Frequency
1	6
2	4
3	12
4	15
5	3

The **range** of Ricky's scores $= 5 - 1 = 4$

Ricky's **modal** score was 4, because this is his most frequent score.

With forty values, the median is between the 20th and 21st values. Imagine the table written out as a long list, starting 1, 1, 1, 1, 1, 1, 2, 2, 2, 2, 3, …. You will see that the 20th and 21st scores are both 3. Ricky's **median** score is 3.

To find the mean score from the table you need to add an extra column for the score multiplied by the frequency.

Score	Frequency	Score × Frequency
1	6	1 × 6 = 6
2	4	2 × 4 = 8
3	12	3 × 12 = 36
4	15	4 × 15 = 60
6	3	6 × 3 = 18
Totals	40	128

The table shows that Ricky scored a total of 128 points with his 40 shots.
Ricky's mean score $= 128 \div 40 = 3{\cdot}2$

Exercise 2F

1. The table below shows the distribution of children per family on an estate of 50 houses.

Number of children	Number of houses	Number of children × Number of houses
0	14	
1	15	
2	18	
3	3	
4	0	
Totals		

(a) What is the modal number of children per house?
(b) What is the range of the number of children per house?
(c) In a distribution of 50 values, where is the median value?
(d) What is the median number of children per house?
(e) Copy and complete the table.
(f) Calculate the mean number of children per house.

2. Amy collects eggs each morning from her pet hens. This table shows the number of eggs she collected each day during April.

Number of eggs	Frequency	Number of eggs × Frequency
0	4	
1	1	
2	7	
3	4	
4	4	
5	4	
6	3	
7	1	
8	1	
9	1	
Totals		

(a) What was the modal number of eggs that Amy collected?
(b) What was the range of the number of eggs that Amy collected?
(c) In a distribution of 30 values, where is the median value?
(d) What is the median number of eggs that Amy collected?
(e) Copy and complete the table.
(f) Calculate the mean number of eggs that Amy collected.

3. A spelling test has ten words. These are the results for a class of 20 pupils.

Number correct	Frequency	Number correct × Frequency
0	0	
1	0	
2	0	
3	1	
4	1	
5	2	
6	3	
7	4	
8	5	
9	3	
10	1	
Totals		

(a) What is the modal number of correct answers?
(b) What is the range of the number of correct answers?
(c) In a distribution of 20 values, where is the median value?
(d) What is the median number of correct answers?
(e) Copy and complete the table.
(f) Calculate the mean number of correct answers.

4. This table shows the number of tests taken by 100 driving school students before passing.

Number of tests taken	Frequency	Number of tests taken × Frequency
1	43	
2	31	
3	17	
4	6	
5	2	
6	1	
Totals		

(a) What is the modal number of tests taken?
(b) What is the range of the number of tests taken?

(c) In a distribution of 100 values, where is the median value?
(d) What is the median number of tests taken?
(e) Copy and complete the table.
(f) Calculate the mean number of tests taken.

5. Zippo Mints come in a packet with a label saying, 'Average contents 34 sweets'. The number of sweets in 25 packets is checked by a trading standards officer. These are her results:

Number of sweets	Number of packets	Number of sweets × Number of packets
30	4	
31	1	
32	2	
33	4	
34	8	
35	3	
36	3	
Totals		

(a) What is the modal number of sweets per packet?
(b) What is the range of the number of sweets per packet?
(c) In a distribution of 25 values, where is the median value?
(d) What is the median number of sweets per packet?
(e) Copy and complete the table.
(f) Calculate the mean number of sweets per packet.
(g) Are Zippo Mints entitled to claim, 'Average contents 34 sweets'?

Summary

1. A set of values is called a **distribution**.
   The **range** of a distribution
   = greatest value − least value
   The **mean** of a distribution
   = total of the distribution
   ÷ number of values

Checkout D2

1. Find the mean and the range of each set of numbers.
   (a) 3   3   6   5   3
   (b) 1   2   1   1   1   3   3   6
   (c) 10   11   11   15   11   10   10   10
   (d) 14   14   13   16   16   16   12   14   15   16

2. The **median** of a distribution is the value in the middle **when the values are arranged in order**.

2. Find the median of each set of numbers in Question 1.

---

3. The value which occurs the most in a distribution is called the **mode** or **modal value**.

3. Find the mode of each set of numbers in Question 1.

---

4. An examination question may ask you to work out the mean, the median, the mode and the range.

4. A doctor keeps a check on eleven patients at her surgery. This is the number of times each patient visits her during one month:

      0 0 0 1 2 2 3 4 5 7 9

(a) Find the mean number of visits.
(b) Find the median number of visits.
(c) Find the modal number of visits.
(d) Find the range of the number of visits.

---

5. An examination question may ask you to work out the mean, the median, the mode and the range for data arranged in a table.

5. The table below shows the distribution of children per family on an estate of 50 houses.

Number of children	Number of houses	Number of children × Number of houses
0	1	
1	23	
2	19	
3	6	
4	1	
Totals		

(a) What is the modal number of children per house?
(b) What is the range of the number of children per house?
(c) In a distribution of 50 values, where is the median value?
(d) What is the median number of children per house?
(e) Copy and complete the table.
(f) Calculate the mean number of children per house.

Revision exercise D2

1. The handspans of some children were measured.
The measurements, in centimetres, are shown.

    15   13   16   15   14   14   15   12
    12   14   13   15   13   15   13

(a) (i)   What is the range of the children's handspans?
    (ii) Calculate the mean handspan.

A second group of children have handspans with the same
mean as the first group. The range of their handspans is 7 cm.

(b) Describe **one** difference between the handspans of the
    two groups.   [SEG]

2. A milkman delivers pints of milk to houses in a street.
The street has 20 houses.
The number of pints of milk he delivers to each house is shown.

    2   1   3   2   2   2   4   1   1   2
    4   1   2   2   3   1   2   1   3   4

(a) Calculate the mean number of pints delivered.

(b) What is the range of the number of pints delivered? [SEG]

3. Pat carried out a survey.
She asked each pupil in her class how many postcards they
received last August.
Her results are shown in the vertical line graph.

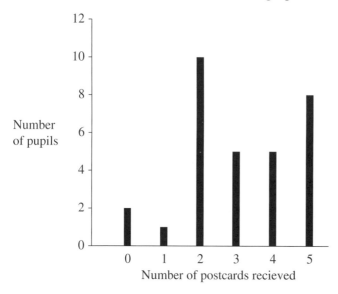

Number
of pupils

Number of postcards recieved

(a) What is the modal number of postcards received?

(b) How many pupils took part in the survey?

(c) How many postcards were received altogether? [NEAB]

4. A teacher asks all his class,

'How many children are there in your family?'

Here are their replies.

(a) How many children are in the class?

(b) What is the most common number of children in the family for this class?

(c) Calculate the mean number of children per family in this class.
Give your answer to 1 decimal place.   [NEAB]

Number of children in the family	Number of replies
1	7
2	12
3	5
4	2
5	0

5. The number of pages in each chapter of a book are

12, 21, 15, 26, 17, 35, 20, 32

Construct a stem and leaf diagram to show these numbers.   [AQA]

6. The number of people staying in a campsite in the New Forest during the first 14 nights in August were recorded in the table.

Draw a stem and leaf diagram to show the data.

Date	Forest campsite
August 1	34
August 2	28
August 3	36
August 4	31
August 5	27
August 6	29
August 7	19
August 8	25
August 9	38
August 10	27
August 11	41
August 12	45
August 13	36
August 14	32

D3 DATA HANDLING 3

Statistics are all around us:

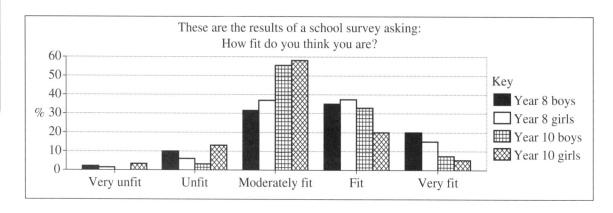

This unit will show you how to:

- Use frequency tables for grouped data
- Draw bar charts and frequency polygons
- Draw and interpret pie charts

Before you start:

You should know how to...	Check in D3
1. Use a protractor. 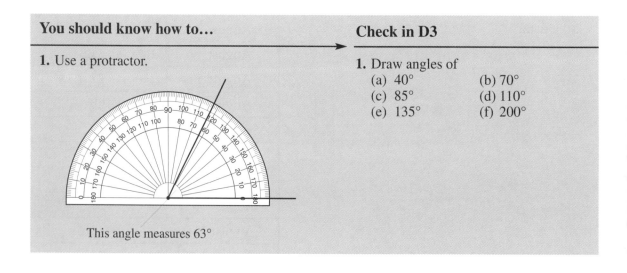 This angle measures 63°	**1.** Draw angles of (a) 40° (b) 70° (c) 85° (d) 110° (e) 135° (f) 200°

3.1 Grouped data, bar charts and frequency polygons

These are the marks of 30 students in a maths examination marked out of 50.

22	32	29	7	13	41	34	28	27	39
18	33	45	28	39	31	17	41	35	28
15	8	33	47	21	27	34	36	33	29

Data with lots of different values is usually organised into a **frequency table**. The data could be organised into this frequency table.

Mark	Frequency
1 to 10	2
11 to 20	4
21 to 30	9
31 to 40	11
41 to 50	4

Hint:
Frequency means total.

The table can be illustrated with a bar chart like this:

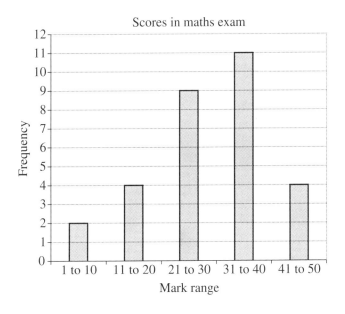

MODULE 1

Or with a **frequency polygon** like this:

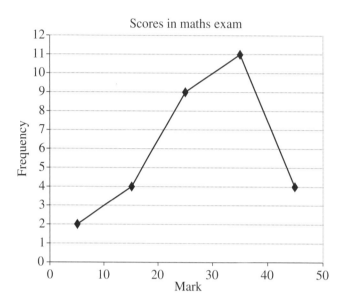

You draw a frequency polygon by:

- plotting points over the **middle** of each group
- joining the points with straight lines.

Exercise 3A

1. Lisa Jones and Orla Carli both make twenty car journeys in one week. The distances they travel (in miles) are:

    Lisa: 7, 8, 10, 15, 11, 17, 16, 20, 1, 14, 13, 13, 12, 11, 3, 2, 6, 7, 24, 23

    Orla: 3, 6, 7, 8, 9, 10, 11, 15, 14, 13, 18, 16, 20, 23, 7, 12, 6, 6, 7, 13

    (a) Copy and complete the frequency table.

Distance (miles)	Frequency
1 to 5	
6 to 10	
11 to 15	
16 to 20	
21 to 25	

(b) Draw two bar charts to illustrate the data. Use axes like these:

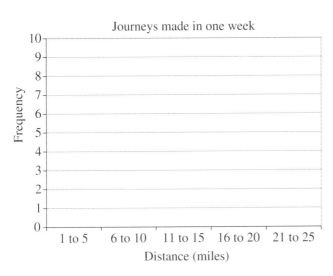

(c) Draw two frequency polygons to illustrate the data. Draw **both** frequency polygons on **one** set of axes like these. Remember to plot points above the **middle** of each group.

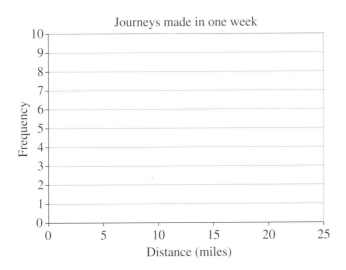

2. Thirty members of a health club are weighed, to the nearest kilogram, before and after a three-month healthy eating scheme. These are the results.

Before: 77, 81, 82, 84, 84, 86, 86, 88, 88, 88, 90, 91, 92, 93, 93, 94, 95, 95, 96, 96, 97, 97, 97, 98, 99, 100, 101, 101, 104, 105

After: 77, 78, 78, 80, 82, 83, 84, 85, 86, 86, 87, 87, 88,
            90, 90, 91, 91, 91, 92, 92, 93, 93, 93, 94, 94, 95,
            95, 96, 96, 98

Organise the data into a table with headings like this:

Weight (kilograms)	Frequency (before)	Frequency (after)
76 to 80		
81 to 85		
86 to 90		
91 to 95		
96 to 100		
101 to 105		

3. A history test is marked out of 20. These are the marks for two different classes who take the test.

Class 9Y   1, 3, 4, 7, 9, 9, 10, 11, 11, 12, 12, 12, 13, 13, 14,
           15, 15, 15, 15, 15, 16, 16, 16, 16, 17, 17, 17, 18,
           19, 20

Class 9Q   7, 7, 8, 8, 9, 9, 9, 9, 9, 9, 9, 10, 10, 10, 11, 11, 12,
           12, 12, 12, 13, 13, 13, 13, 14, 14, 15, 15, 16, 20

(a) Organise the data into a table with headings like this:

Mark	Frequency (9Y)	Frequency (9Q)
0 to 2		
3 to 5		
6 to 8		
9 to 11		

(b) Draw two bar charts to illustrate the data.

(c) Draw two frequency polygons to illustrate the data. Draw **both** frequency polygons on **one** set of axes. Remember to plot points above the **middle** of each group.

4. A bus company uses a 20-seat mini-bus to run excursions to a theme park. On two different days the ages of the passengers in the mini-bus were:

Day 1 4, 13, 23, 2, 3, 14, 4, 9, 17, 5, 6, 6, 6, 7, 8, 17, 4, 27, 4, 9

Day 2 24, 28, 35, 36, 31, 29, 13, 16, 16, 28, 38, 34, 17, 18, 23, 32, 36, 28, 4, 7

(a) Organise the data into a table with headings like this:

Age	Frequency (Day 1)	Frequency (Day 2)
0 to 4		
5 to 9		
10 to 14		
15 to 19		

(b) Draw two bar charts to illustrate the data.

(c) Draw two frequency polygons to illustrate the data. Draw **both** frequency polygons on **one** set of axes. Remember to plot points above the **middle** of each group.

3.2 Pie charts drawn with a protractor

A **pie chart** is a good way to show how something is shared out. This pie chart shows how Bill spent a day. It shows how 24 hours are shared out between different activities.

To draw a pie chart with a protractor, you need to find the angle for each sector. The pie chart for Bill's day was drawn from this table.

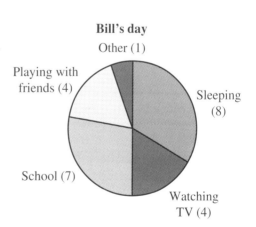

Bill's day

Activity	Time (hours)
School	7
Sleeping	8
Playing with friends	4
Watching TV	4
Other	1
Total	24

There are 360° in a circle. This means that each hour is represented by 360 ÷ 24 = 15°. A column for angles was added to the table.

Activity	Time (hours)	Angle
School	7	7 × 15° = 105°
Sleeping	8	8 × 15° = 120°
Playing with friends	4	4 × 15° = 60°
Watching TV	4	4 × 15° = 60°
Other	1	1 × 15° = 15°
Total	24	360°

To draw a pie chart follow these steps:

- Draw a suitable sized circle
- Draw one line from the centre to the edge of the circle
- From this starting line, use a protractor to measure the first sector
- Add each sector in turn until the pie chart is complete
- Label the pie chart clearly.

Exercise 3B

1. Rajinder completed a survey on the pets owned by her class. In total, her class owned 36 pets. Rajinder wanted to draw a pie chart and calculated that each pet would be represented by 360 ÷ 36 = 10°. Rajinder started to complete this table.

Pets owned	Frequency	Angle
Dog	5	5 × 10° = 50°
Cat	7	
Mouse	10	
Fish	8	
Hamster	6	
Totals	36	360°

(a) Copy and complete the table.
(b) Draw the pie chart.

2. A junior school class of 30 pupils completed a survey on how each pupil came to school. To draw a pie chart they calculated that each pupil would be represented by $360 \div 30 = 12°$. They started to complete this table.

Ways of coming to school	Number of pupils	Angle
Parent's car	10	$10 \times 12° = 120°$
Friend's car	4	
Bus	2	
Walk	8	
Cycle	6	
Totals	30	$360°$

(a) Copy and complete the table.
(b) Draw the pie chart.

3. Every householder in a district has to pay a tax to the local council. The council wants to prepare a pie chart to show how the tax is spent. This table shows how every £180 of spending is made up.

Type of spending	Amount	Angle
Highways and planning	£14	$14 \times 2 = 28°$
Sports and recreation	£28	
Environmental health	£32	
Housing	£27	
Administration	£47	
Emergencies	£32	
Totals	£180	$360°$

(a) Why has £14 been multiplied by 2 to calculate the pie chart angle?
(b) Copy and complete the table.
(c) Draw the pie chart.

4. A plastic moulding company owns two factories. A manager wishes to prepare two pie charts to compare the running costs of the two factories. He starts to draw up these tables which show how every £90 spent in the two factories is accounted for.

Expenditure	Factory A	Angle
Wages	£30	$30 \times 4 = 120°$
Raw materials	£40	
Overheads	£20	
Totals	£90	360°

Expenditure	Factory B	Angle
Wages	£25	$25 \times 4 = 100°$
Raw materials	£35	
Overheads	£30	
Totals	£90	360°

(a) Why has £30 been multiplied by 4 in the first table to calculate the pie chart angle?

(b) Copy and complete the tables.

(c) Draw the two pie charts.

5. A museum is open all year. A manager wants to compare the number of visitors in two different years. She starts to draw up these tables which show the numbers of visitors in spring, summer, autumn and winter.

Season	Visitors 1999 (thousands)	Angle
Spring	7	$7 \times 9 = 63°$
Summer	18	
Autumn	9	
Winter	6	
Totals	40	360°

Season	Visitors 2000 (thousands)	Angle
Spring	8	$8 \times 6 = 48°$
Summer	31	
Autumn	14	
Winter	7	
Totals	60	360°

(a) Why has 7 been multiplied by 9 in the first table to calculate the pie chart angle?
(b) Why has 8 been multiplied by 6 in the second table to calculate the pie chart angle?
(b) Copy and complete the tables.
(c) Draw the two pie charts.

6. Sunshine Desserts is developing a new range of sponge puddings. These are the results of taste tests with two different groups of people. The results will be illustrated with two pie charts.

Flavour	Number of first choices (Test 1)	Angle
Strawberry	54	
Raspberry	47	
Orange	21	
Apple	23	
Pear	35	
Totals		

Flavour	Number of first choices (Test 2)	Angle
Strawberry	32	
Raspberry	44	
Orange	34	
Apple	40	
Pear	30	
Totals		

(a) Copy and complete the tables.
(b) Draw the two pie charts.

3.3 Pie charts drawn with a pie chart scale

If the data for a pie chart is presented as percentages, it is easier to draw the pie chart using a **pie chart scale**. A pie chart scale is a circular measure divided up from 0% to 100%.

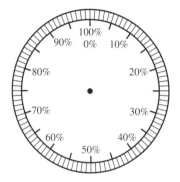

Stacey asked 50 pupils how they travelled to school.
This table shows her results.

Type of transport	Number	Percentage
Bus	23	46%
Walk	14	28%
Car	8	16%
Bike	5	10%
Totals	50	100%

Using a pie chart scale, this pie chart can be drawn to illustrate the table.

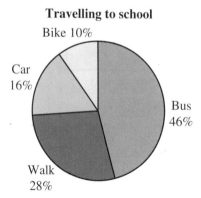

Travelling to school

You work out percentages by:
- Dividing each frequency by the total of the frequencies
- Multiplying the answer by 100.

Exercise 3C

1. The BBC estimates that the money collected from licence fees is spent in this way:

   Capital costs   25%
   BBC1   35%
   BBC2   20%
   Radio   20%

   Draw a pie chart to illustrate this data.

2. This table shows results from the General Household Survey of 1994.

Type of dwelling	Frequency
Detached house	20%
Semi-detached house	31%
Terraced house	28%
Flat or maisonette (purpose built)	15%
Flat or maisonette (converted)	5%
With business or shop	1%
Totals	100%

   Draw a pie chart to illustrate the data in the table

3. In a taste test in a GCSE Food class, students were asked to vote for their favourite sausage. Four brands were compared. Sammy-Jo Afford started to draw up this table of results.

Brand	Votes	Percentage
Pork	5	$5 \div 25 \times 100 = 20\%$
Pork with apple	10	$10 \div 25 \times 100 = 40\%$
Pork with herbs	6	
Vegetarian	4	
Totals	25	100%

   (a) Copy and complete the table.
   (b) Draw a pie chart to illustrate the data in the table.

4. A youth club offers four different activities: football, snooker, table tennis and aerobics. All the club members are asked which is their favourite activity. The results are shown in this table.

Activity	Number of first choices	Percentage
Football	30	$30 \div 150 \times 100 = 20\%$
Snooker	15	
Table tennis	45	
Aerobics	60	
Totals	150	100%

(a) Copy and complete the table.
(b) Draw a pie chart to illustrate the data in the table.

5. A group of Year 7 pupils and a group of Year 11 pupils are asked how they think a £1 000 donation to the school should be spent. These tables show the results.

Spending idea	Votes from Year 7	Percentage
Computer for the library	48	$48 \div 200 \times 100 = 24\%$
Sports equipment	84	
Staging for school productions	46	
Display boards in the school entrance	22	
Totals	200	100%

Spending idea	Votes from Year 11	Percentage
Computer for the library	45	$45 \div 180 \times 100 = 25\%$
Sports equipment	63	
Staging for school productions	54	
Display boards in the school entrance	18	
Totals	180	100%

(a) Copy and complete the tables.
(b) Draw two pie charts to illustrate the data in the tables.

6. Shaun is designing a CD holder for his GCSE Technology examination. Before he completes a final design he uses a questionnaire to test his ideas. One question Shaun uses is:

What finish would you prefer for the product?

Polished wood ☐   Stained wood ☐   Painted ☐

These tables show the responses to the question from a group of pupils and a group of adults.

Finish	Choices (pupils)	Percentage
Polished wood	6	
Stained wood	36	
Painted	18	
Totals		

Finish	Choices (adults)	Percentage
Polished wood	15	
Stained wood	24	
Painted	21	
Totals		

(a) Copy and complete the tables.
(b) Draw two pie charts to illustrate the data in the tables.

3.4 Reading information from pie charts

Pie charts are used to show information. You need to be able to understand this information.

Exercise 3D

1. A shop sells a sweatshirt in four sizes: small, medium, large and extra large. This pie chart shows the weekly sales of different sizes.
  (a) What percentage of the sweatshirts sold were small?
  (b) Which was the most popular size?
  (c) The shop sold a total of 25 sweatshirts. How many of these were large?

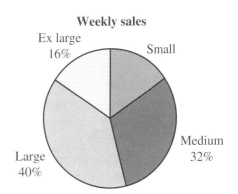

Weekly sales
Ex large 16%
Small
Medium 32%
Large 40%

    (d) How many medium sweatshirts were sold?

    (e) Show the same information in a bar chart.

2. An office manager calculates that her average working day is divided up in the way shown in this pie chart.

    (a) What is the size of the angle which represents working?

    (b) There are 24 hours in the manager's day. How many hours does she spend sleeping?

    (c) How many hours does the manager spend travelling?

    (d) How many hours does the manager spend working?

    (e) Show the same information in a bar chart.

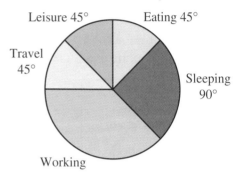

Division of the day

3. This pie chart shows the monthly rainfall for a seaside town during the tourist season.

    (a) Equal amounts of rain fell during September and April. What is the size of the angle which represents the rainfall in April?

    (b) A total of 90 mm of rain fell during the whole tourist season. What angle in the pie chart would represent a rainfall of 1 mm?

    (c) What was the rainfall in May?

    (d) What was the rainfall in September?

    (e) Show the same information in a bar chart.

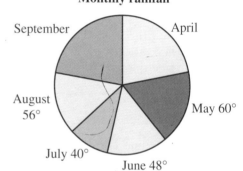

Monthly rainfall

4. This pie chart shows the distribution of men, women, boys and girls among the members of a swimming club.

    (a) What percentage of the club members are girls?

    (b) Six of the members are men. How many members does the club have?

    (c) How many of the members are girls?

    (d) How many members are boys?

    (e) How many of the members are women?

    (f) Show the same information in a bar chart.

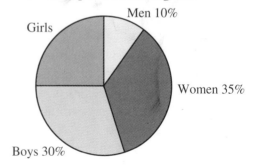

Membership of a swimming club

5. This pie chart shows the results of a class
   survey on pet ownership.
   (a) What is the size of the angle which
       represents cats?
   (b) The survey found that 1 person owned a
       fish. How many pupils owned snakes?
   (c) How many pupils owned dogs?
   (d) How many pupils owned birds?
   (e) Show the same information in a bar
       chart.

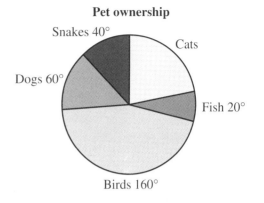

Pet ownership

6. After a survey in a small village this pie chart
   was drawn to show the different ways in which
   houses were heated.
   (a) What percentage of the houses are heated
       by coal?
   (b) 20 houses are heated by gas. How many
       houses are heated by coal?
   (c) How many of the houses are heated by
       electricity?
   (d) How many of the houses are heated by oil?
   (e) How many houses are there in the village?
   (f) Show the same information in a bar chart.

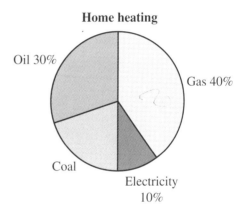

Home heating

Summary

1. Data with lots of
   different values is
   usually organised into a
   frequency table. The
   tables can be illustrated
   with **bar charts** or
   frequency polygons.

Checkout D3

1. Lisa Jones and Orla Carli both make twenty car journeys
   in one week. The distances they travel (in miles) are:

   Lisa: 3, 4, 7, 15, 6, 7, 8, 9, 4, 11, 5, 16, 7, 8, 11, 12, 4, 4,
           17, 3

   Orla: 2, 4, 15, 22, 2, 1, 5, 7, 8, 9, 13, 14, 15, 23, 14, 18,
           22, 7, 6, 24

(a) Organise the data into two tables with headings like this:

Distance (miles)	Frequency
1 to 5	
6 to 10	
11 to 15	
16 to 20	
21 to 25	

(b) Draw two bar charts to illustrate the data. Use axes like these:

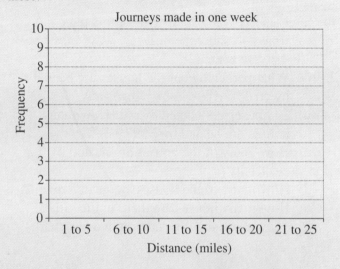

(c) Draw two frequency polygons to illustrate the data. Draw **both** frequency polygons on **one** set of axes like these. Remember to plot points above the **middle** of each group.

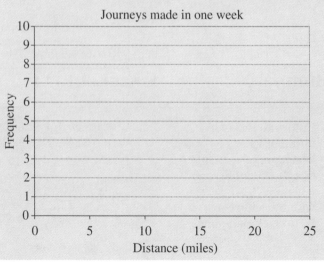

2. A **pie chart** is a good way to show how something is shared out.
To draw a pie chart with a protractor, first calculate the angle for each sector.

2. A heritage park is open all year. This table shows the numbers of visitors in spring, summer, autumn and winter.

Season	Visitors (thousands)	Angle
Spring	10	$10 \times 6 = 60°$
Summer	25	
Autumn	16	
Winter	9	
Totals	60	360°

(a) Why has 10 been multiplied by 6 in the table to calculate the pie chart angle?

(b) Copy and complete the table.

(c) Draw the pie chart.

3. If the data for a pie chart is presented as percentages, it is easier to draw the pie chart with a **pie chart scale**. A pie chart scale is a circular measure divided up from 0% to 100%.

3. In a taste test in a GCSE Food class, students were asked to vote for their favourite pizza. Four toppings were compared. Carla started to draw up this table of results.

Topping	Votes	Percentage
Cheese and tomato	4	$4 \div 25 \times 100 = 16\%$
Pepperoni and ham	12	$12 \div 25 \times 100 = 48\%$
Garlic and mushroom	3	
Roast vegetable	6	
Totals	25	100%

(a) Copy and complete the table.

(b) Draw a pie chart to illustrate the data in the table.

4. Sometimes you will be asked to read information from a pie chart.

4. (a) This pie chart shows the results of a survey into school transport.

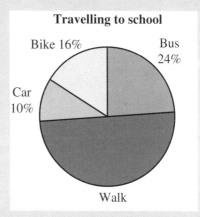

Travelling to school

(i) What percentage of children walked to school?
(ii) 20 children came by car, how many came by bus?
(iii) Show the same information with a bar chart.

(b) This pie chart shows the results of a survey into the sporting activities a group of Year 10 boys took part in each week.

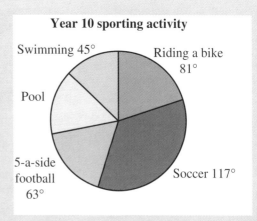

Year 10 sporting activity

(i) What is the pie chart angle that represents pool?
(ii) 5 boys went swimming. How many degrees represent each boy in the pie chart?
(iii) How many boys played soccer?
(iv) How many boys played five-a-side football?
(v) How many boys went for a bike ride?
(vi) Show the same information with a bar chart.

Revision exercise D3

1. 400 members of a Sports Club are asked, "What is your favourite sport?" The pie chart shows the results.

(a) What percentage chose tennis?

(b) How many members chose volleyball?

(c) **Calculate** the size of the angle for football. **Show all your working.**　　　[NEAB]

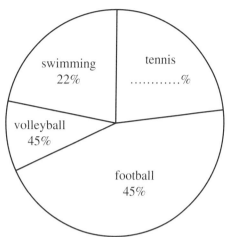

2. The pie chart shows the different types of trees in a wood.

(a) What fraction of the trees in the wood are Ash?

There are 459 Oak trees in the wood.

(b) How many trees are there in the wood altogether?

(c) How many Elm trees are there?　　[SEG]

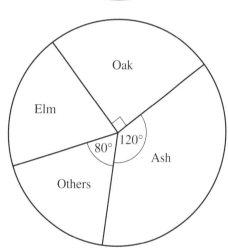

3. The grouped frequency table shows the number of hours that 25 students spent sleeping on a particular night.

Hours spent sleeping	7 to under 8	8 to under 9	9 to under 10	10 to under 11	11 to under 12
Frequency	4	6	8	3	4

(a) Draw a frequency polygon to illustrate these data.

(b) Write down the modal class.

(c) From the polygon, explain how you know that the mean number of hours that the students spent sleeping is less than 10.　　　[AQA]

4. An insurance company investigated the causes of 2400 motoring accidents. A summary of their findings is given below.

Cause of accident	Number of accidents
Speeding	840
Weather conditions	360
Mechanical failure	240
Other	960
TOTAL	2400

(a) Draw a clearly labelled pie chart to represent this information.
This graph shows the time of day when these accidents happened.

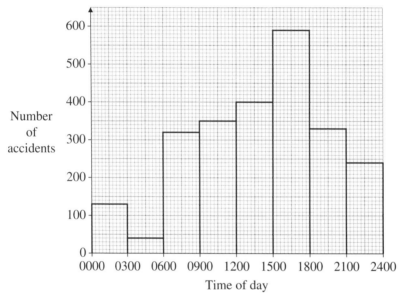

(b) Suggest a reason why more accidents happened between 1500 and 1800 than at other times of the day.

(c) (i) How many accidents happened between 2100 and 2400?

$12\frac{1}{2}$ of the accidents which happened between 2100 and 2400 involved drivers who had been drinking.

(ii) How many accidents between 2100 and 2400 involved drivers who had been drinking?

5. One Saturday a newsagent sells the following:

National daily newspapers 510
Echo 360
Magazines and comics 210

Draw a clearly labelled pie chart to represent these sales.   [SEG]

D4 DATA HANDLING 4

People are different shapes and sizes.

This unit will show you how to:

- Distinguish between constants and variables
- Draw scatter diagrams and the line of best fit
- Describe the correlation between two variables

Before you start:

You should know how to...	Check in D4
1. Plot points on a grid. For example, to plot (6, 3)	**1.** On a clean copy of the grid plot each set of points. Join the points together in order. What shape do you get?

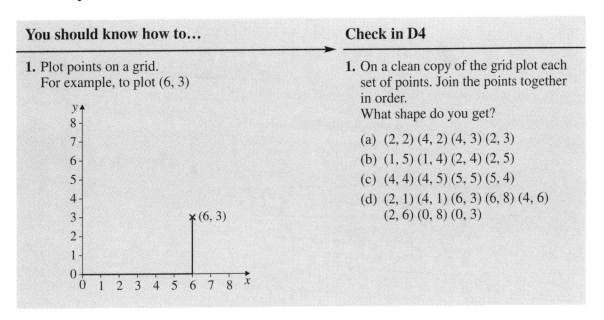

(a) (2, 2) (4, 2) (4, 3) (2, 3)

(b) (1, 5) (1, 4) (2, 4) (2, 5)

(c) (4, 4) (4, 5) (5, 5) (5, 4)

(d) (2, 1) (4, 1) (6, 3) (6, 8) (4, 6) (2, 6) (0, 8) (0, 3)

4.1 Variables

Variables are properties which can change. For example, look at this car.

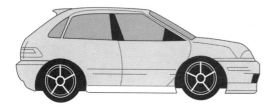

Some of the variables which can be associated with a car are:

- make
- model
- price
- top speed
- colour
- engine size
- weight
- number of gears
- number of seats

Exercise 4A

1. One variable which could be associated with a dog is 'breed'.

List five more variables which can be associated with a dog.

2. One variable which could be associated with a person is 'shoe size'.

List five more variables which can be associated with a person.

3. One variable which can be associated with a book is 'number of pages'.

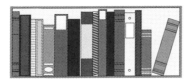

List five more variables which can be associated with a book.

4. One variable which can be associated with a house is 'number of bedrooms'.

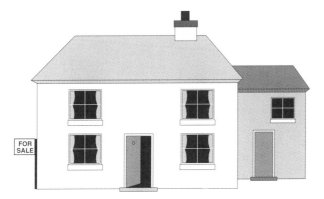

List five more variables which can be associated with a house.

4.2 Correlation

Two variables are **positively correlated** if, as one increases, the other tends to increase.

Two variables are **negatively correlated** if, as one increases, the other tends to decrease.

Two variables are **not correlated** if, as one increases, it tends to have no effect on the other.

Example 1

Do tall men tend to have bigger feet than short men?

If your answer to this question is, 'yes they do', you are saying:

> In men, height and shoe size are **positively correlated**.
> As height increases, shoe size will also tend to increase.

Example 2

I want to buy a Ford Escort. Will older cars tend to cost less than newer cars?

If your answer to this question is, 'yes they will', you are saying:

> In Ford Escorts, age and price are **negatively correlated**. As the age of a car increases, its value tends to decrease.

Example 3

Is there a link between being good at mathematics and being a good dancer?

If your answer to this question is, 'no there is not', you are saying:

> Skills in mathematics and dancing are **not correlated**. There is no connection between the two skills.

Exercise 4B

In each of the following examples, say whether you think the two variables are:

- positively correlated
- negatively correlated
- not correlated

1. The number of bedrooms in a house and its market value.
2. The age of a used motorbike and its value.
3. The height of a man and his weight.
4. The length of a woman's hair and her shoe size.
5. The age of a child and the time they take to run 50 metres.
6. The age of an adult and the time they take to run 50 metres.
7. The age of an adult and the colour of their car.
8. The value of a centre forward and the number of goals he scores each season.
9. The value of a goalkeeper and the number of goals he lets in each season.
10. The annual winnings of a tennis star and her shoe size.

4.3 Scatter diagrams

These are the test scores for 10 students in mathematics and science.

Student	A	B	C	D	E	F	G	H	I	J
Maths	3	7	6	8	9	2	4	7	9	8
Science	2	6	7	9	7	3	6	8	8	7

Looking at the table, you might decide that marks in mathematics and science seem to be positively correlated. One way to show the correlation is to draw a graph like this, called a **scatter diagram**.

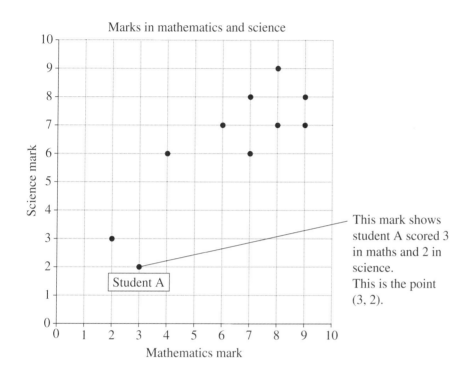

The scatter diagram shows a positive correlation because the points are in a 'sausage shaped' area, going upwards from left to right. These scatter diagrams show positive, negative and no correlation.

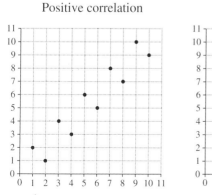

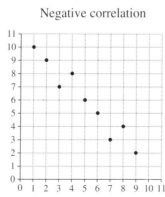

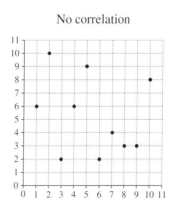

MODULE 1

Exercise 4C

1. This table records the year group of 10 students and the number of days they were absent from school in one year.

Year	7	7	8	8	9	9	10	10	11	11
Absence	0	2	3	2	3	4	6	2	5	8

(a) Copy and complete this scatter diagram to show the data in the table.

(b) What correlation does your completed scatter diagram show?

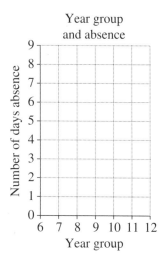

2. A food stall owner recorded the average temperature for ten weeks and the number of cans of soup powder she used during each week. These are her results.

Temp	1°C	1°C	3°C	3°C	4°C	4°C	6°C	7°C	10°C	12°C
Cans	10	6	8	6	5	6	4	2	2	1

(a) Copy and complete this scatter diagram to show the data in the table.

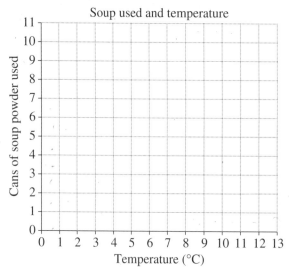

(b) What correlation does your completed scatter diagram show?

3. Lucy did a survey on the age and value of a certain type of used car. She collected this data.

Age (years)	1	1	2	2	3	4	4	5	6	7
Value (nearest thousand pounds)	9	8	7	5	6	3	4	4	2	2

(a) Copy and complete this scatter diagram to show the data in the table.

(b) What correlation does your completed scatter diagram show?

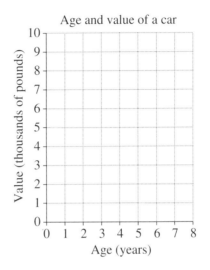

Age and value of a car

4. Ten teachers take part in a 100-metre race on Sports Day. This table shows the age of the teachers (in years) and their time (in seconds) to run the race.

Age	24	25	31	33	35	42	46	48	51	56
Time	14	12	18	16	12	20	22	24	26	30

(a) Copy and complete this scatter diagram to show the data in the table.

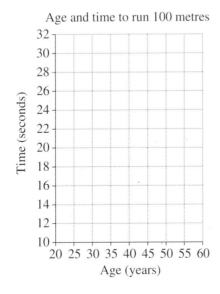

Age and time to run 100 metres

(b) What correlation does your completed scatter diagram show?

5. Adrian collects this data on car engine sizes in litres and average fuel consumption in kilometres per litre.

Engine size	1	1	1·5	1·5	2	2	2	2·5	3	3·5
Fuel consumption	15	14	12	13	15	11	10	9	9	8

(a) Copy and complete this scatter diagram to show the data in the table.

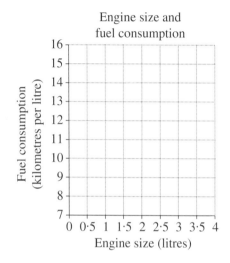

(b) What correlation does your completed scatter diagram show?

4.4 Line of best fit

When a scatter diagram shows two variables are highly correlated, you can draw a **line of best fit**.

This is the straight line which goes through the point representing the mean of each set of data, passing close to as many points as possible.

Example

This table shows the ages of 10 children and their times to run 100 m.

Child	A	B	C	D	E	F	G	H	I	J
Age	8	4	11	8	6	7	5	4	9	10
Time (seconds)	17	23	14	15	20	20	22	26	15	16

(a) Draw a scatter diagram and add the line of best fit.
(b) Estimate the time a child of 8 years and 6 months would take to run 100 m.

(a) You draw the scatter diagram and then position the line of best fit, balancing points above the line with points below the line.

(b) Draw a line up from the age axis to the line of best fit and then across to the time axis. You can estimate that a child of 8 years 6 months will run 100 m in about 17 seconds.

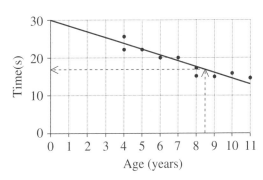

Exercise 4D

1. This scatter graph shows the correlation between the engine capacity (in cubic centimetres) and the top speed (in miles per hour) of a group of cars. A line of best fit has been added.

   (a) Comment on any correlation.
   (b) Estimate the top speed of cars with engine capacities of:
   (i) $2\,000$ cm^2 (ii) $3\,500$ cm^3
   (iii) $4\,500$ cm^3 (iv) $1\,000$ cm^3
   (c) Estimate the engine capacity of a car with a top speed of:
   (i)   100 miles/h   (ii) 130 miles/h   (iii) 90 miles/h   (iv) 110 miles/h

2. Draw the line of best fit for the graphs you drew in Exercise 4C if such a line is appropriate.

Summary

1. **Variables** are properties which can change.

2. Two variables are **positively correlated** if, as one increases, the other tends to increase.
   Two variables are **negatively correlated** if, as one increases, the other tends to decrease.
   Two variables are **not correlated** if, as one increases, it tends to have no effect on the other.

Checkout D4

1. One variable which could be associated with a wild bird is 'wingspan'. List five more variables which could be associated with a wild bird.

2. In each of the following examples, say whether you think the two variables are:
   • positively correlated
   • negatively correlated
   • not correlated
   (a) The average daily temperature and the number of ice creams a shop sells.
   (b) The average daily temperature and the number of overcoats a shop sells.
   (c) The average daily temperature and the number of computers a shop sells.

3. One way to show correlation is to draw a graph called **a scatter diagram**.

3. This table shows the ages (in years) of a group of 10 children and the time (in seconds) they take to run 100 metres.

Age	4	4	5	6	6	7	8	9	10	11
Time	24	22	20	18	20	17	19	15	16	14

(a) Copy and complete this scatter diagram to show the data in the table.

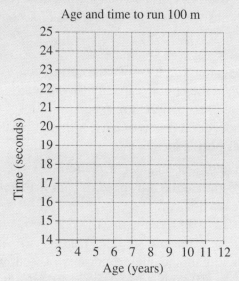

Age and time to run 100 m

(b) What correlation does your scatter diagram show?

Revision exercise D4

1. These are the prices charged for different journeys by taxi.

Length of journey (km)	1	2	3	5	8	13	14	18
Cost (£)	1·80	2·30	2·50	2·80	5·40	7·50	8·40	10·30

(a) Draw a scatter diagram to show this information.

(b) What does your diagram tell you about the relationship between the length of a journey and its cost?

[NEAB]

2. A number of women do aerobics for one minute.
Their ages and pulse rates are shown in the table.

Age (years)	16	17	22	25	38	42	43	50
Pulse rate (per minute)	82	78	83	90	99	97	108	107

(a) Use this information to draw a scatter graph.

(b) What type of correlation is there between the
ages and pulse rates of these women?   [SEG]

3. The table shows the number
of pages and the cost of six
books bought in the UK.

Pages	Cost (£)
120	6.00
180	7.50
240	9.50
250	8.50
290	11.00
320	10.50

(a) Plot a scatter graph of these data.

(b) What type of correlation is shown by the scatter
graph?   [AQA]

4. The table shows the times taken by each of seven
motorists to complete a journey.

Length of journey (km)	25	40	50	65	90	90	100
Time taken (hours)	0·5	0·8	1·2	1	1·3	1·8	1·2

(a) Use this information to draw a scatter graph.

(b) Draw a line of best fit.

(c) (i) Use your line of best fit to estimate the time
taken by a motorist to complete a journey of
length 130 km.

(ii) Give **one** reason why your estimate may not
be very accurate.   [SEG]

5. The scatter graph shows the number of pages in, and the cost of, six books.

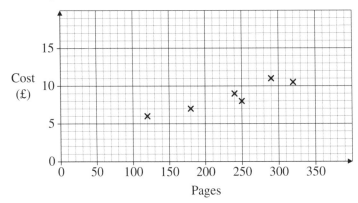

(a) Draw a line of best fit through the points on the scatter graph.

(b) Describe the relationship shown in the scatter graph.

(c) Explain how you know that the relationship is quite strong.   [AQA]

6. The Mathematics scores and Science scores of 8 students are shown in the table.

Student	A	B	C	D	E	F	G	H
Mathematics score	44	18	51	60	25	10	35	40
Science score	34	21	46	50	18	15	29	39

(a) Use the data to plot a scatter diagram.

(b) What does the scatter diagram suggest about the connection between the scores in Mathematics and Science?   [SEG]

7. A salesman has recorded the distance that he travelled each day for twenty working days.
The grouped frequency table shows his results.

(a) Draw a frequency polygon to illustrate these data.

Distance from Coventry (miles)	Frequency
0 and under 100	6
100 and under 200	8
200 and under 300	2
300 and under 400	2
400 and under 500	2

The salesman has plotted a scattergraph to show the distance that he travelled in the morning, plotted against that he travelled in the afternoon, for each of the twenty days.

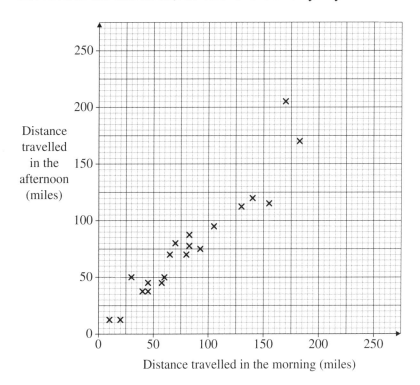

Distance travelled in the morning (miles)

(b) Draw a line of best fit through the points on the scattergraph.

(c) Use your line of best fit to estimate the distance that the salesman will travel in the afternoon if he travels 50 miles in the morning.

(d) Use your line of best fit to estimate the distance that the salesman will travel in the afternoon if he travels 250 miles in the morning.

(e) Explain why you would expect your answer to part (c) to be more reliable than your answer to part (d).

[SEG]

D5 DATA HANDLING 5

You use probability to describe how likely something is to happen.

ROUND THE WORLD
HOPPING
CHALLENGE

My estimated probability is zero, what do you think?

This unit will show you how to:

- Understand simple probability
- Draw probability scales
- Work out probabilities when two things happen

Before you start:

You should know how to...	Check in D5
1. Simplify fractions. For example: $\frac{12}{20} \overset{\div 4}{\underset{\div 4}{=}} \frac{3}{5}$	**1.** Simplify: (a) $\frac{4}{6}$ (b) $\frac{8}{10}$ (c) $\frac{3}{15}$ (d) $\frac{12}{18}$ (e) $\frac{20}{100}$ (f) $\frac{25}{75}$
2. Change a fraction to a decimal. For example: $\frac{3}{8} = 3 \div 8 = 0.375$	**2.** Change into decimals: (a) $\frac{1}{4}$ (b) $\frac{2}{5}$ (c) $\frac{5}{8}$ (d) $\frac{4}{25}$
3. Change a decimal into a percentage. For example: $0.175 = 17.5\%$	**3.** Write as percentages: (a) 0.25 (b) 0.75 (c) 0.5 (d) 0.4 (e) 0.125 (f) 0.09

5.1 Simple probability

Elizabeth, Daniel and Steve are going to roll a dice to see who will go first in a game. The highest score goes first.

Elizabeth rolls the dice first and scores a 3.

Before he rolls the dice, Daniel wants to know what is the **probability** that he will beat Elizabeth.

Bet you don't beat that.

There are six possible results when you roll a dice: 1, 2, 3, 4, 5 and 6. Three of these, 4, 5 and 6, will allow Daniel to beat Elizabeth.

The probability that Daniel will beat Elizabeth $= \frac{3}{6} = \frac{1}{2}$

Daniel rolls a 4. Steve will start first if he rolls a 5 or a 6.

The probability that Steve starts first $= \frac{2}{6} = \frac{1}{3}$

Probabilities can be written as fractions, decimals or percentages.

The probability that Daniel beats Elizabeth $= \frac{1}{2} = 0.5 = 50\%$

The probability that Steve starts first $= \frac{1}{3}$
$= 0.333$ (to 3 decimal places) $= 33.3\%$

Example 1

What is the probability of selecting a letter at random from the word TEACHER and getting a vowel?

There are three vowels (e, a, e) out of seven letters.

The probability $= \frac{3}{7} = 0.428 = 42.8\%$

Example 2

What is the probability of cutting a deck of cards and getting a red king or a black ace?

There are two red kings and two black aces out of 52 cards.

The probability $= \frac{4}{52} = 0.076 = 7.6\%$

Exercise 5A

In this exercise, give every answer first as a fraction, then as a decimal correct to 3 decimal places and finally as a percentage.

1. Bob tossed a one pound coin. What is the probability that he gets:
   (a) a head   (b) a tail?

2. Toni rolls a dice. What is the probability that she gets:
   (a) a six
   (b) an even number
   (c) less than five
   (d) a one or a two?

3. A bag contains 2 mints, 3 toffees and 5 fruit chews. If one
   sweet is selected at random, what is the probability of
   getting:
   (a) a mint
   (b) a toffee
   (c) a fruit chew
   (d) a mint or a toffee?

4. One letter is selected at random from the word
   SUCCESSFUL. What is the probability that the letter is:
   (a) an S
   (b) an E
   (c) a C or a U
   (d) a vowel
   (e) neither a C nor an S?

5. On a supermarket shelf there are 20 jars of Tom's favourite
   coffee. Tom does not notice that 5 of these are
   decaffeinated. If Tom picks a jar at random, what is the
   probability that the coffee is:
   (a) decaffeinated
   (b) not decaffeinated?

6. In a class there are 14 girls and 16 boys. 3 of the girls and 2
   of the boys wear glasses. If a pupil is selected at random
   from the class, what is the probability that the pupil is:
   (a) a girl
   (b) a boy
   (c) a girl who wears glasses
   (d) a pupil who wears glasses?

7. In a cupboard a family has a box filled with packets of
   crisps. There are 5 cheese and onion flavour, 8 plain and 7
   salt and vinegar flavour. If a bag is selected at random, what
   is the probability that the flavour will be:
   (a) cheese and onion
   (b) plain
   (c) salt and vinegar
   (d) not plain?

8. A pencil case contains 15 felt tips, 9 crayons and 1 pencil.
   In a hurry, Mrs Smith grabs one item from the case at
   random to write down a phone message. What is the
   probability that the phone message is written down with:
   (a) a felt tip
   (b) a crayon
   (c) a pencil
   (d) a felt tip or a pencil?

9. A pack of 52 cards is cut. What is the probability that the
   cut card is:
   (a) red   (b) a two   (c) a red queen   (d) a club   (e) the ace of hearts?

10. This pie chart shows the ways that 50 houses
in a small village are heated.
If a house is selected at random, what is the
probability that it is heated by:

(a) coal

(b) oil

(c) electricity

(d) gas?

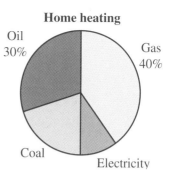

Home heating

Oil 30%   Gas 40%   Coal   Electricity

11. A class completed a survey on how each pupil came to
school. This table shows their results.

Ways of coming to school	Number of pupils
Parent's car	10
Friend's car	4
Bus	2
Walk	8
Cycle	6

If a pupil is selected at random, what is the probability that
their way of coming to school is:

(a) by bus   (b) by parent's car   (c) by cycle   (d) not by walking?

12. This bar chart shows the marks that a group of students scored in a test.

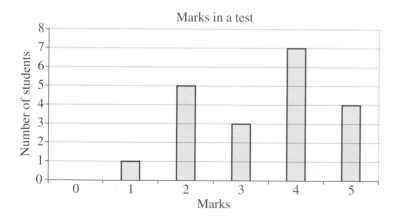

If a student is selected from the group at random, what is the
probability that their test mark was:

(a) 2   (b) 1   (c) more than 3   (d) less than 5?

5.2 Probabilities of 0 and 1

If something cannot happen it has a probability of 0 or 0%.

For example, if there are five red beads in a bag and one is selected at random,

the probability that the selected bead is green $= \frac{0}{5} = 0 = 0\%$

If something is certain to happen it has a probability of 1 or 100%.

For example, if there are five red beads in a bag and one is selected at random,

the probability that the selected bead is red $= \frac{5}{5} = 1 = 100\%$

Example

Vicky Jones is driving in a strange town looking for a friend's new house. She gets lost and decides to stop and ask the next person she sees for directions. If the probability that the person is female is 0·6, what is the probability that the person is male?

The probability that the person is either male or female $= 1$
The probability that the person is male $= 1 - 0.6 = 0.4$

Exercise 5B

1. The probability that Nicola wins a race is $\frac{1}{5}$. What is the probability that she does not win the race?

2. Every day, Carla buys either a coffee or a hot chocolate during her morning break. The probability that she buys a coffee is 0·65. What is the probability that she buys a hot chocolate?

3. A bag contains red and green beads. The probability of selecting a red bead from the bag is $\frac{1}{4}$. What is the probability that a bead selected at random is:
   (a) either red or green   (b) green   (c) yellow?

4. The probability that it rains tomorrow is $\frac{1}{8}$. What is the probability that it stays dry tomorrow?

5. If a sweet is selected at random from a bag, the probability that it is not a mint is 75%. What is the probability that the sweet is a mint?

6. The probability that a milling machine breaks down during a night shift is 12%. What is the probability that the machine does not break down during a night shift?

7. A machine makes compact discs. The probability that the machine makes a perfect disc is 0·98. What is the probability that the machine makes a faulty disc?

8. The probability that Janet is late for school tomorrow is 22%. What is the probability that Janet is not late for school tomorrow?

9. A bag contains red and green beads. The probability that a bead selected at random is red is 45%. What is the probability that a bead selected at random is:

   (a) either red or green   (b) green   (c) yellow?

10. In a seaside town, the probability of a wet day during June is $\frac{7}{30}$. What is the probability of a dry day during June?

11. A bag contains blue and green beads. If two beads are selected from the bag, the probability that they are the same colour is $\frac{5}{9}$. What is the probability that the beads are different colours?

12. The probability that Mr Jones is delayed by a level crossing on his way to work is 60%. What is the probability that Mr Jones is not delayed by the level crossing?

13. If a sweet is selected at random from a bag, the probability that it is a fruit chew is 0·3. The probability that it is a toffee is 0·25. What is the probability that it is neither a fruit chew nor a toffee?

14. Every day, Malcolm either wears black, grey or brown socks. The probability that he wears black socks is 0·5. The probability that he does not wear grey socks is 0·7. What is the probability that he wears brown socks?

15. A box of crisps has a mixture of cheese and onion flavour, plain and salt and vinegar flavour. The probability of selecting a bag at random and getting cheese and onion flavour is 0·2. The probability of selecting a bag at random and getting salt and vinegar flavour is 0·5. What is the probability of selecting a bag at random and getting plain crisps?

MODULE 1

5.3 Probability scales

Probabilities are sometimes shown on a **probability scale**.
This is a number line from 0 to 1.

Example

The probability that it will rain tomorrow is 0·4. Mark the
probabilities that it will rain or stay dry tomorrow on a
probability scale.

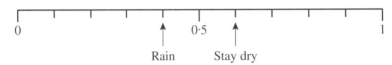

Exercise 5C

1. A bag contains 3 red beads and 7 green beads. One bead is
   selected at random from the bag.
   (a) What is the probability that the bead is red?
   (b) What is the probability that the bead is green?
   (c) Copy this probability scale and mark both probabilities on it.

2. There are 1 000 combinations on a bike lock.
   (a) If somebody tries 100 combinations, what is the
       probability that they will open the lock?
   (b) Copy this probability scale and mark this probability on it.

3. Juanita has eight pairs of earrings, three silver, one gold and
   four jewelled. She cannot decide which pair to wear so she
   chooses a pair at random.
   (a) What is the probability that she picks a silver pair
       of earrings?
   (b) What is the probability that she picks the gold pair of earrings?

(c) What is the probability that she picks a jewelled pair of earrings?

(d) Copy this probability scale and mark all three probabilities on it.

4. Carlos was late for school on 38 days out of 190 last year.

(a) On any school day last year, what was the probability that Carlos was late?

(b) On any school day last year, what was the probability that Carlos was not late?

(c) Copy this probability scale and mark both probabilities on it.

5. There are 100 red, yellow and green beads in a bag. If a bead is selected at random, the probability that it is red is 0·6 and the probability that it is green is 0·3.

(a) What is the probability that a bead selected at random from the bag is yellow?

(b) Copy this probability scale and mark all three probabilities on it.

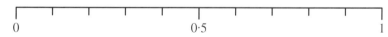

6. Amit walked to school with Callum on 48 days out of 60 last term.

(a) On any day last term, what was the probability that Amit walked to school with Callum? Give your answer as a decimal.

(b) On any day last term, what was the probability that Amit did not walk to school with Callum? Give your answer as a decimal.

(c) Copy this probability scale and mark both probabilities on it.

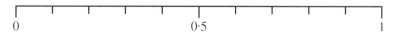

7. The probability that Mrs Jones buys a newspaper on her way to work is 30%.

   (a) What is the probability that Mrs Jones does not buy a newspaper on her way to work?
   (b) Copy this probability scale and mark both probabilities on it.

8. A restaurant offers a choice of one vegetable from peas, carrots, broccoli and green beans. Experience has shown that the probability that a customer picks broccoli is 10%. A customer is twice as likely to pick carrots and three times as likely to pick green beans.

   (a) What is the probability that a customer picks peas?
   (b) Copy this probability scale and mark all four probabilities on it.

5.4 Probabilities when two things happen

A school canteen offers a choice of fish pie, sausages or chilli, served with either a baked potato or chips. If William picks a meal at random, what is the probability that he picks sausages and chips?

Today's Specials

Fish Pie
Sausages
Chilli

All served with Chips
or
Baked potatoes

There are six possible meal combinations:

fish pie with chips	fish pie with baked potato
sausages with chips	sausages with baked potato
chilli with chips	chilli with baked potato

The probability that William picks sausages and chips
$= \frac{1}{6} = 0{\cdot}167 = 16{\cdot}7\%$

If two separate choices are involved, always carefully list all the outcomes before trying to answer the question.

A tree diagram can help you identify all the outcomes:

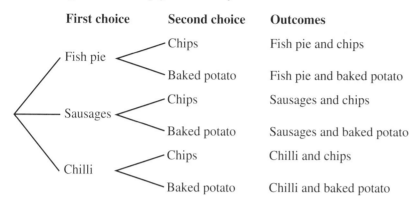

First choice	Second choice	Outcomes
Fish pie	Chips	Fish pie and chips
	Baked potato	Fish pie and baked potato
Sausages	Chips	Sausages and chips
	Baked potato	Sausages and baked potato
Chilli	Chips	Chilli and chips
	Baked potato	Chilli and baked potato

Example

Susan flips two coins.

(a) Copy and complete this table to show all the possible outcomes.

	Second coin head	Second coin tail
First coin head	head head	
First coin tail		

(b) What is the probability that the result is a head and a tail?

(a) This is the completed table:

	Second coin head	Second coin tail
First coin head	head head	head tail
First coin tail	tail head	tail tail

A tree diagram can be used instead of the table:

First flip	Second flip	Outcomes
Head	Head	Head and head
	Tail	Head and tail
Tail	Head	Tail and head
	Tail	Tail and tail

(b) There are two results out of four which give a head and a tail.

The probability that the result is a head and a tail $= \frac{2}{4} = \frac{1}{2} = 0{\cdot}5 = 50\%$

Exercise 5D

1. Wilma wants to make a sandwich with one filling. She has cheese, ham, chicken and prawns for the filling. She also as a choice of wholemeal or white bread.

   (a) Copy and complete this list of all the possible sandwiches that Wilma can make.

   cheese with white bread   cheese with wholemeal bread
   ham with white bread

   (b) How many different types of sandwich can Wilma make?

   (c) If Wilma chooses her filling and bread at random, what is the probability that she will make a prawn sandwich with wholemeal bread?

2. Shaina is choosing her outfit to wear to a school disco. She has four tops, one red, one blue, one black and one silver. She also has three skirts, one red, one white and one gold.

   (a) Copy and complete this list of all the outfits that Shaina could wear:

   red top with red skirt   red top with white skirt   red top with gold skirt
   blue top with red skirt   blue top with white skirt

   (b) How many diferent outfits can Shaina wear?

   (c) If Shaina chooses her top and skirt at random, what is the probability that she will wear a silver top with a white or gold skirt?

3. A bag contains two red beads and one white bead. A bead is selected at random from the bag, replaced, and then another bead is selected.

   (a) Copy and complete this table showing all the possible pairs of beads.

	R	R	W
R	RR		
R			RW
W		WR	

   (b) There are 9 possible outcomes when the two beads are selected. How many of these outcomes give two red beads?

   (c) What is the probability that the two beads selected will be:
   (i) both red   (ii) both white   (iii) different colours?

4. One bag contains 2 yellow beads and 1 green bead. Another bag contains 1 yellow bead, 1 green bead and 1 blue bead. A bead is selected at random from both bags.

(a) Copy and complete this table showing all possible pairs of beads.

	Y	Y	G
Y			YG
G		GY	
B	BY		

(b) There are 9 possible outcomes when the two beads are selected. How many of these outcomes give two yellow beads?

(c) What is the probability that the two beads selected will be:
   (i)   both yellow   (ii)   both green   (iii) one blue and one green
   (iv) one yellow and one blue (v)   different colours?

5. Jorina has two spinners, each marked with the numbers from 1 to 4.

The spinners are used for a board game. Both arrows are spun and the score is the sum of the two numbers pointed to. The score shown is $3 + 1 = 4$.

(a) Copy and complete this table showing all the possible scores.

+	1	2	3	4
1			4	
2	3			
3		5		
4				8

(b) There are 16 possible outcomes when the spinners are spun. How many of these give a score of 5?

(c) What is the probability of scoring 5?

(d) What is the probability of scoring:
   (i) 2   (ii) 3   (iii) 4   (iv) 6   (v) 7   (vi) 8?

6. Jorina has another game with two different spinners marked with numbers like this:

Both arrows are spun and the score is the sum of the two numbers pointed to. The score shown is $7 + 2 = 9$.

(a) Copy and complete this table showing all the possible scores.

+	1	3	5	7
2	3			
4			9	
6		9		
8				15

(b) There are 16 possible outcomes when the spinners are spun. How many of these give a score of 5?
(c) What is the probability of scoring 5?
(d) What is the probability of scoring:
    (i) 3   (ii) 7   (iii) 9   (iv) 11   (v) an odd number   (vi) an even number?

7. Lee rolls two dice, each numbered from 1 to 6.
(a) Copy and complete this table showing all the possible scores.

+	1	2	3	4	5	6
1	2					
2						8
3		5				
4				8		
5			8			
6					11	

(b) There are 36 possible outcomes when the dice are rolled. How many of these give a score of 7?
(c) What is the probability of scoring 7?
(d) What is the probability of scoring:
    (i) 3   (ii) 8   (iii) 5   (iv) 9   (v) 1   (vi) an even number?

Summary

Checkout D5

1. Probabilities can be written as fractions, decimals or percentages. If a single coin is flipped the probability that it comes down heads is:
$\frac{1}{2} = 0.5 = 50\%$

1. A single letter is selected from the word SURREALISM. What is the probability that the letter is:
   (a) an S   (b) an M   (c) a vowel   (d) not a vowel?

2. If something cannot happen it has a probability of 0 or 0%. If something is certain to happen it has a probability of 1 or 100%.

2. Melissa will pick either potato chips or a baked potato to go with her cheese salad. The probability that she will pick a baked potato is 0·6. What is the probability that Melissa picks:
   (a) chips   (b) cabbage   (c) cooked potatoes?

3. Probabilities are sometimes shown on a **probability scale**. This is a number line from 0 to 1.

3. A bag contains 2 red beads and 8 green beads. One bead is selected at random from the bag.
   (a) What is the probability that the bead is red?
   (b) What is the probability that the bead is green?
   (c) Copy this probability scale and mark both probabilities on it.

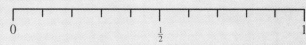

0                                $\frac{1}{2}$ 1

4. If two separate choices are involved, always carefully list all the outcomes before trying to answer the question.

4. One bag contains 2 purple beads and 1 red bead. Another bag contains 1 purple bead and 2 red beads. A bead is selected at random from both bags.
   (a) Copy and complete this table showing all possible pairs of beads.

	P	P	R
P			PR
R		RP	
R	RP		

   (b) There are 9 possible outcomes when the two beads are selected. How many of these outcomes give two red beads?
   (c) What is the probability that the two beads selected will be:
      (i) both red   (ii) both purple
      (iii) one purple and one red?

Revision exercise D5

1. Quickstrike guarantee that their boxes will contain 42, 43, 44, 45 or 46 matches.
    The probabilities for the number of matches in one of their boxes are:

Number of matches per box	42	43	44	45	46
Probability	$\frac{1}{10}$	$\frac{1}{10}$		$\frac{4}{10}$	$\frac{1}{10}$

(a) Complete the table.

(b) What is the probability that I will get at least 45 matches if I buy one box of Quickstrike?   [NEAB]

2. Brenda has a bag of fruit sweets.
    There are 4 lemon, 1 orange, 8 strawberry and 7 pear sweets.
    Brenda chooses 1 sweet at random.
    What is the probability that it is:

(a) the orange sweet?

(b) a pear sweet?

(c) not a pear sweet?   [NEAB]

3. A fair spinner has eight sides.
    The sides are numbered 1, 2, 2, 3, 3, 4, 5 and 6.

The spinner is spun once.

(a) What is the probability that the spinner lands on a 3?

Michael and Sheila play a game using the spinner.
The spinner is spun once.
Michael wins if the spinner lands on 1 or 2 or 3.
Sheila wins if it lands on 4 or 5 or 6.

(b) What is the probability that Sheila will win the game?

(c) Explain why this game is **not** fair.   [SEG]

4. The probability that someone gets flu next winter is 0·3.
What is the probability that someone **does not** get flu
next winter?   [NEAB]

5. The table shows information about some cars.

Make	Colour	Mileage
Vauxhall	blue	8 606
Ford	white	12 214
Vauxhall	white	5 567
Rover	red	11 984
Rover	blue	9 085
Vauxhall	red	6 984
Ford	blue	8 763
Vauxhall	white	14 675

A car is chosen from the list at random.

(a) What is the probability that it has a mileage of more than 10 000?

(b) What is the probability that it is a white Ford?

(c) A Vauxhall car is chosen at random.
The probability that it is blue is 0·25.
What is the probability that it is **not** blue?   [SEG]

6 (a) A fair coin is thrown.
What is the probability of getting a head?

(b) A bag contains 4 blue balls and 7 red balls.
A ball is chosen at random.
What is the probability that it is blue?

(c) Another bag contains only yellow, green and black counters.

(i) Fill in the table to show the probability
of getting a green counter.

Counter	Yellow	Green	Black
Probability	0·4		0·2

(ii) What does this tell you about the numbers
of counters in the bag?   [NEAB]

MODULE 1

Module 1   Practice Calculator Test

1. This spinner is used in a game.

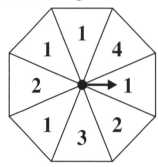

The spinner is spun once.

(a) Which number is the spinner most likely to land on?

(b) Which numbers is the spinner equally likely to land on?

(c) What is the probability that the spinner will land on 5?

(3 marks)   [NEAB]

2. Ahmed is growing sunflowers.
After a few weeks, he measures how high the sunflowers
have grown.
The heights of the 17 sunflowers measured in centimetres are:

11, 19, 21, 17, 14, 16, 12, 20, 14, 18, 12, 15, 16, 18, 17, 11, 20.

What is the median height of Ahmed's sunflowers?

(2 marks)

3. Charles wants to estimate the total number of words in a book.
To do this he selects 20 printed pages at random.
He counts the number of words on each of these pages.
His results are shown below:

500 401 202 570 406   67 431 426 419   96
429 192 372 598 323 184 439 458 445 124

(a) What is the range of this data?

(b) Calculate the mean number of words per page.

(c) His book has 326 printed pages.
Use your answer to (b) to estimate how many words
there are in this book.

(6 marks)   [NEAB]

4. In one week Ronnie rents out 90 items from his shop as shown in the table.

Item	Frequency	
Televisions	35	
Videos	30	
Computers	17	
Other equipment	8	

Draw a pie chart for all the week's rentals. **(4 marks)** [NEAB]

5. "Bridgit" and "Pong K'I" are two Chinese games.
Each game is for two players.

A class of children played each other at these games.
The table shows the number of wins obtained by some of the children.

Child	Ann	Ben	Ciri	Dawn	Erin	Fay	Gil	Hue	Ian	Jo
Number of wins at Bridgit	14	7	10	5	12	7	10	3	5	12
Number of wins at Pong K'I	1	10	5	14	3	12	7	16	12	5

(a) Plot these results as a scatter diagram on a copy of the grid.

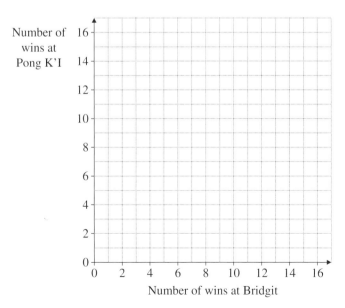

(b) What does the scatter diagram tell you? **(3 marks)** [NEAB]

Module 1   Practice Non-Calculator Test

1. The pictogram shows the time it takes a train to travel from London to three other cities.

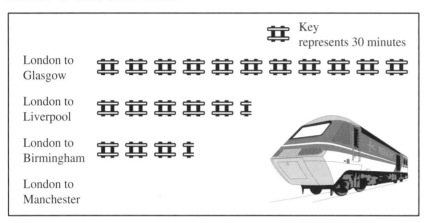

(a) How long does it take to travel from London to Glasgow?

(b) How much longer does it take to go from London to Liverpool than to go from London to Birmingham?

(c) The train from London to Manchester takes 2 hours 30 minutes.
Draw this information on the pictogram.

(3 marks)   [NEAB]

2. Brenda has seven cards.
The cards are numbered as shown.

(a) Brenda chooses one card at random.
What is the probability of her getting an even number?

(2 marks)   [SEG]

3. There are 30 people in a class.
They are asked how many pets they have.
Here are the results.

```
1 4 7 3 1 0 0 1 3 8 3 5 1 0 2
8 1 4 2 1 7 5 1 0 2 4 1 6 3 5
```

(a) Complete the frequency table for this data.

Number of pets	Tally	Frequency
0–1		
2–3		
4–5		
6–7		
8–9		

(b) Draw a bar chart to show this data.

(5 marks) [NEAB]

4. The table shows information about a group of children.

		Boys	Girls
Wears glasses	Yes	5	3
	No	14	10

(a) A boy in the group is chosen at random.
What is the probability that he wears glasses?

(b) A child in the group is chosen at random.
The probability that the child wears glasses is 0·25.
What is the probability that the child does **not**
wear glasses?

(3 marks) [SEG]

5. The weights of packets, in kg, received by a village post
office was recorded as:

3·4, 2·6, 6·3, 3·6, 2·5, 4·1, 2·7, 4·9

Using a key 4|3 to mean 4·3, draw a stem and leaf diagram
to show this data.

(2 marks)

6. A school wants to open a snack bar.
They want to sell sandwiches, pizzas, soup, jacket
potatoes and salad.

(a) Design a data collection sheet that could be used to
find out from pupils in the school what they would buy.

(b) Invent the first 30 entries on your data sheet.

(3 marks) [NEAB]

N1 NUMBER 1

People use numbers everyday, particularly when spending money!

This unit will show you how to:

- Read place value in whole numbers
- Write numbers in figures and words
- Round to the nearest whole number
- Understand significant figures
- Add and subtract whole numbers
- Understand negative numbers
- Add and subtract negative numbers

1.1 Place value in whole numbers

Dry Gulch had a population of 5 127 people.

> The number 5 127 has four digits.
> The **5** digit represents **5 000** people
> The **1** digit represents **100** people
> The **2** digit represents **20** people
> The **7** digit represents **7** people

After the gold ran out, Dry Gulch became a ghost town and the sign had to be changed.

> In 1 275:
> The **1** digit represents **1 000** people
> The **2** digit represents **200** people
> The **7** digit represents **70** people
> The **5** digit represents **5** people

After oil was discovered the town sign was changed again.

> In 7 512:
> The **7** digit represents **7 000** people
> The **5** digit represents **500** people
> The **1** digit represents **10** people
> The **2** digit represents **2** people

Exercise 1A

1. What does the underlined digit represent in each of these numbers?

   (a) 3$\underline{4}$5   (b) 67$\underline{5}$ (c) $\underline{8}$03   (d) 80$\underline{3}$ (e) 8$\underline{0}$3
   (f) 1 $\underline{2}$91   (g) $\underline{3}$ 905   (h) 2 2$\underline{2}$2   (i) 7 38$\underline{4}$ (j) $\underline{6}$ 073
   (k) 3 $\underline{0}$57   (l) 5 67$\underline{8}$ (m) 3 $\underline{3}$75   (n) 9 1$\underline{7}$9   (o) $\underline{2}$ 135
   (p) 6 22$\underline{1}$ (q) 5 6$\underline{6}$4   (r) 1 $\underline{9}$99   (s) $\underline{3}$ 212   (t) 8 21$\underline{0}$

In Questions **2** to **9**, write down the value represented by each digit of the number.

2. 348 people saved as a boat sinks.

3. 903 pigeons lost after a race in stormy weather.

4. 2 658 students pass a new examination.

5. 7 190 cars cross to Calais in one day.

6. 3 527 dogs entered for a show.

7. 1 411 cats caught in a ruined building.

8. 8 006 fish stolen from a garden centre.

9. 12 467 people attend a home game.

10. Using the digits 5, 8 and 2, different three-digit numbers can be made like 528, 285 and 852.

    (a) Write down all the three-digit numbers you can make with 5, 8 and 2.

    (b) Write your numbers in order, from the smallest to the largest.

11. Using the digits 7, 3 and 9, different three-digit numbers can be made like 379, 739 and 937.

    (a) Write down all the three-digit numbers you can make with 7, 3 and 9.

    (b) Write your numbers in order, from the smallest to the largest.

12. Using the digits 1, 0, 6 and 4, different four-digit numbers can be made like 1 604, 6 041 and 4 160.

    (a) Write down all the four-digit numbers you can make with 1, 0, 6 and 4.

    (b) Write your numbers in order, from the smallest to the largest.

1.2 Writing numbers in figures and words

You need to know these numbers in words:

1	2	3	4	5	6	7	8	9
one	two	three	four	five	six	seven	eight	nine

11	12	13	14	15	16	17	18	19
eleven	twelve	thirteen	fourteen	fifteen	sixteen	seventeen	eighteen	nineteen

10	20	30	40	50	60	70	80	90
ten	twenty	thirty	forty	fifty	sixty	seventy	eighty	ninety

100	1 000	1 000 000
one hundred	one thousand	one million

You can use these numbers to write large numbers in words.

MODULE 3

Example

Write these numbers in words:

(a) 234   (b) 4 743   (c) 57 690

(a)   234   (b)   4 743

two hundred and thirty-four   four thousand seven hundred and forty-three

(c)   57 690

fifty-seven thousand six hundred and ninety

Exercise 1B

1. Write each number in figures.

   (a) Three hundred and seventy-four.
   (b) Two hundred and eleven.
   (c) Five hundred and forty-eight.
   (d) Six hundred and nine.
   (e) Seven hundred and sixty.
   (f) One hundred and twenty-five.
   (g) Three thousand seven hundred and fifteen.
   (h) Six thousand four hundred and nineteen.
   (i) Fourteen thousand nine hundred and ninety.
   (j) Seventeen thousand eight hundred and fifty-four.
   (k) Twenty-four thousand five hundred and nineteen.
   (l) Forty-eight thousand six hundred and sixty.
   (m) Eighty-six thousand eight hundred and eighty-six.
   (n) Sixty-eight thousand and sixty-eight.
   (o) Ninety-two thousand and three.
   (p) Two hundred and twelve thousand one hundred and thirteen.
   (q) Three hundred and eighteen thousand seven hundred and sixteen.
   (r) Six hundred and eight thousand three hundred and thirty-nine.
   (s) Five hundred and eighty thousand two hundred and ninety-seven.
   (t) Six hundred thousand four hundred and four.

2. Write each number in words.

(a) 358	(b) 217	(c) 677	(d) 469	(e) 111
(f) 2 519	(g) 6 085	(h) 9 801	(i) 7 442	(j) 5 613
(k) 15 723	(l) 18 459	(m) 34 098	(n) 67 112	(o) 10 111
(p) 231 214	(q) 616 270	(r) 109 710	(s) 100 000	(t) 857 243

MODULE 3

3. John is doing a project on trees' heights. He has collected
this data.

Beech 161 ft
Sitka Spruce 216 ft
Giant Sequoia 272 ft
Ponderosa Pine 223 ft
Californian Redwood 366 ft
Black Cottonwood 147 ft

Douglas Fir 302 ft
Western Larch 177 ft
Noble Fir 278 ft
Hemlock 163 ft
Cedar 219 ft

John writes a list of trees in order of size. He writes the
heights in words. Write out John's list, starting with:

Californian Redwood: Three hundred and sixty-six feet.

4. Zeelam has collected this data about the diameter of the Sun
and the planets.

Sun 865 500 miles
Earth 7 962 miles
Saturn 74 600 miles
Neptune 30 800 miles
Mercury 3 032 miles

Mars 4 217 miles
Venus 7 521 miles
Jupiter 88 700 miles
Uranus 32 200 miles
Pluto 3 700 miles

Write Zeelam's list in order, starting with the smallest
diameter. Write all the diameters in words.

←—7 962 miles—→

1.3 Approximation to the nearest 10

There are 33 passengers
on this bus

33 is nearer
30 than 40

There are 37 passengers
on this bus

37 is nearer
40 than 30

There are 35 passengers
on this bus

35 is exactly
halfway between
30 and 40

To the nearest 10 …

There are 30
people on the bus

There are 40
people on the bus

There are 40
people on the bus

Remember: If the number is
halfway, you always round up.

The exact number of CDs could be either:

45, 46, 47, 48, 49, 50, 51, 52, 53 or 54.

If you had 55 CDs, you'd round the number up to 60.

Exercise 1C

1. Approximate each of these numbers to the nearest 10.

   (a) 13   (b) 17   (c) 11   (d) 28   (e) 26
   (f) 21   (g) 44   (h) 48   (i) 45   (j) 59
   (k) 53   (l) 55   (m) 75   (n) 72   (o) 76
   (p) 91   (q) 95   (r) 99   (s) 59   (t) 85

2. Approximate each of these numbers to the nearest 10.

   (a) 255   (b) 254   (c) 256   (d) 323   (e) 487
   (f) 136   (g) 135   (h) 134   (i) 797   (j) 973
   (k) 308   (l) 305   (m) 304   (n) 214   (o) 217
   (p) 594   (q) 595   (r) 793   (s) 898   (t) 996

3. A keen supporter says,
   'To the nearest 10, I have 60 players' autographs'.

   From this list, write down all the numbers which could not
   be the exact number of autographs.

   63, 57, 54, 65, 55, 64, 59, 69, 52, 60

4. Make a list of all the exact numbers that each statement
   could represent.

   (a) To the nearest 10, I own 80 videos.
   (b) To the nearest 10, there are 130 passengers on the boat.
   (c) To the nearest 10, I own 300 books.
   (d) To the nearest 10, there are 360 shopping days left
       before Christmas.
   (e) To the nearest 10, there are 1 000 students at this school.

1.4 Approximation to the nearest 100

Larger numbers can be rounded to the nearest 100.

This DJ owns 828 CDs

I own about 800 CDs.

828 is closer to 800 than 900

This DJ owns 872 CDs

I own about 900 CDs.

872 is closer to 900 than 800

This DJ owns 850 CDs

I own about 900 CDs.

Numbers in the middle are always rounded up

To the nearest 100 …

   … 828 is 800   … 872 is 900   … 850 is 900

If a store manager said, 'To the nearest 100, we sold 700 Christmas Cards last week', then the exact number of cards sold could be any number between 650 and 749.

Exercise 1D

1. Approximate each of these numbers to the nearest 100.

(a) 334	(b) 567	(c) 872	(d) 450	(e) 449
(f) 451	(g) 752	(h) 725	(i) 750	(j) 619
(k) 243	(l) 257	(m) 250	(n) 760	(o) 748
(p) 683	(q) 545	(r) 554	(s) 913	(t) 950

2. Approximate each of these numbers to the nearest 100.

(a) 999	(b) 1 356	(c) 1 365	(d) 1 342	(e) 1 309
(f) 1 635	(g) 3 429	(h) 4 349	(i) 4 371	(j) 8 087
(k) 5 031	(l) 5 099	(m) 5 050	(n) 3 789	(o) 3 923
(p) 2 987	(q) 7 950	(r) 8 950	(s) 8 949	(t) 12 999

3. A bingo club manager says, 'To the nearest 100, there are 600 people here tonight'. From this list, write down the numbers which could not be the exact number of people.

   600, 611, 550, 660, 581, 518, 650, 549, 590, 649

MODULE 3

4. The statement, 'To the nearest 100, there are 1 500 people in the theatre', means that the exact number of people could be any number between 1 450 and 1 549. For each statement write down the two numbers that the approximation could be between.

(a) To the nearest 100, there are 200 nails in the packet.
(b) To the nearest 100, there are 500 tickets available.
(c) To the nearest 100, there are 800 students attending this school.
(d) To the nearest 100, there are 2 900 spectators watching the game.
(e) To the nearest 100, there are 55 600 voters in this constituency.

5. Alisha collected this data on the areas (in square miles) of the ten largest islands in the world:

Ellesmere (Canada) 81 930	Greenland 840 000
Great Britain 88 756	Borneo 286 967
Victoria (Canada) 82 119	Honshu (Japan) 88 930
New Guinea 316 856	Baffin (Canada) 183 810
Madagascar 227 000	Sumatra 182 866

Write out a list of the islands in order of size, starting with the largest. Write each island's area correct to the nearest 100 square miles.

1.5 Approximation to the nearest 1 000

Much larger numbers can be rounded to the nearest 1 000.

55 897 people attend a football match. A newspaper reports, '56 000 watch United beat Rangers'.
55 897 is closer to 56 000 than to 55 000.

If 55 223 people attend the match, the report would be, '55 000 watch United beat Rangers'.
55 223 is closer to 55 000 than to 56 000.

Remember that numbers in the middle are always rounded up.
If 55 500 people attend the match, the report would be, '56 000 watch United beat Rangers'.

If a magazine publisher says, 'To the nearest 1 000, we sell 65 000 copies every week', then the exact number of copies sold could be any number between 64 500 and 65 499.

Exercise 1E

1. Approximate each of these numbers to the nearest 1 000.

   (a) 3 860   (b) 2 113   (c) 1 925   (d) 1 213
   (e) 1 500   (f) 6 278   (g) 5 750   (h) 6 311
   (i) 4 591   (j) 7 500   (k) 8 490   (l) 6 499
   (m) 2 500   (n) 7 501   (o) 6 606   (p) 7 199
   (q) 9 483   (r) 9 500   (s) 9 678   (t) 9 999

2. Approximate each of these numbers to the nearest 1 000.

   (a) 10 678   (b) 18 390   (c) 19 500   (d) 12 399
   (e) 15 939   (f) 25 499   (g) 59 501   (h) 23 500
   (i) 32 259   (j) 21 529   (k) 45 188   (l) 25 678
   (m) 500 900   (n) 235 289   (o) 567 730   (p) 234 156
   (q) 349 500   (r) 499 500   (s) 999 500   (t) 949 678

3. The statement, 'To the nearest 1 000 square kilometres, the area of Lake Superior is 82 000 square kilometres', means that the exact area is between 81 500 square kilometres and 82 499 square kilometres.

   For each statement write down the two numbers that the approximation could be between.

   To the nearest 1 000:

   (a) there are 6 000 students in this University.
   (b) there are 5 000 secondary schools in England.
   (c) the distance from England to New Zealand is 19 000 miles.
   (d) there are 55 000 voters in this constituency.

4. Simon collected this data on the attendances at 10 football matches.

   Arsenal 38 098   Manchester United 55 216
   Everton 39 206   Wimbledon 10 106
   Middlesbrough 34 626   Coventry 23 098
   Southampton 15 253   Newcastle 36 783
   Blackburn 27 536   Sheffield Wednesday 33 513

   Write out a list of attendances in order of size, starting with the smallest. Round each attendance to the nearest 1 000 spectators.

1.6 Approximation to one significant figure

In the number 5 283, the digit 5 has the greatest value, 5 000.

5 is the most **significant figure**.

In the number 12 345, the digit 1 has the greatest value, 10 000.

1 is the most **significant figure**.

You can give any number approximated to one significant figure.

Examples

23 is	20 to 1 s.f.
65 is	70 to 1 s.f.
268 is	300 to 1 s.f.
4 394 is	4 000 to 1 s.f.
55 897 is	60 000 to 1 s.f.

Hint:
s.f. is short for significant figure.

Remember:
If the second digit is 5 or more you round up.

Exercise 1F

Write each number correct to 1 significant figure:

1. 17	**2.** 24	**3.** 36	**4.** 43
5. 57	**6.** 75	**7.** 72	**8.** 85
9. 92	**10.** 99	**11.** 130	**12.** 183
13. 247	**14.** 283	**15.** 321	**16.** 389
17. 490	**18.** 409	**19.** 686	**20.** 668
21. 1 325	**22.** 2 341	**23.** 3 684	**24.** 5 099
25. 6 832	**26.** 7 500	**27.** 8 300	**28.** 5 628
29. 15 431	**30.** 14 531		

1.7 The addition table

This table shows all the additions from $1 + 1$ to $10 + 10$.

+	1	2	3	4	5	6	7	8	9	10
1	2	3	4	5	6	7	8	9	10	11
2	3	4	5	6	7	8	9	10	11	12
3	4	5	6	7	8	9	10	11	12	13
4	5	6	7	8	9	10	11	12	13	14
5	6	7	8	9	10	11	12	13	14	15
6	7	8	9	10	11	12	13	14	15	16
7	8	9	10	11	12	13	14	15	16	17
8	9	10	11	12	13	14	15	16	17	18
9	10	11	12	13	14	15	16	17	18	19
10	11	12	13	14	15	16	17	18	19	20

For example:
$5 + 9 = 14$

MODULE 3

Exercise 1G

Answer all the questions without using a calculator or written calculations. Try to memorise the addition table but look up answers if you need to.

1. (a) $7 + 3$ (b) $6 + 2$ (c) $3 + 5$ (d) $9 + 6$ (e) $2 + 7$
   (f) $6 + 5$ (g) $4 + 3$ (h) $7 + 8$ (i) $9 + 1$ (j) $8 + 5$
   (k) $4 + 8$ (l) $5 + 7$ (m) $8 + 8$ (n) $4 + 9$ (o) $6 + 4$
   (p) $7 + 6$ (q) $9 + 9$ (r) $7 + 9$ (s) $8 + 9$ (t) $8 + 6$
   (u) $8 + 2$ (v) $6 + 6$ (w) $5 + 9$ (x) $7 + 4$ (y) $7 + 7$

2. (a) $10 + 3$ (b) $7 + 10$ (c) $10 + 5$ (d) $9 + 10$ (e) $4 + 10$
   (f) $10 + 8$ (g) $6 + 10$ (h) $10 + 10$ (i) $10 + 2$ (j) $3 + 2 + 10$
   (k) $6 + 3 + 10$ (l) $2 + 5 + 10$ (m) $10 + 4 + 5$ (n) $10 + 2 + 5$ (o) $10 + 4 + 4$
   (p) $3 + 10 + 3$ (q) $2 + 10 + 6$ (r) $1 + 10 + 7$ (s) $8 + 10 + 1$ (t) $5 + 5 + 10$
   (u) $10 + 4 + 1$ (v) $2 + 10 + 2$ (w) $1 + 10 + 2$ (x) $10 + 1 + 6$ (y) $10 + 1 + 3$

3. (a) $20 + 10$ (b) $30 + 10$ (c) $40 + 10$ (d) $60 + 10$ (e) $70 + 10$
   (f) $10 + 50$ (g) $20 + 30$ (h) $30 + 50$ (i) $30 + 60$ (j) $70 + 40$
   (k) $80 + 30$ (l) $90 + 50$ (m) $70 + 60$ (n) $50 + 80$ (o) $70 + 30$
   (p) $60 + 50$ (q) $80 + 70$ (r) $90 + 80$ (s) $80 + 60$ (t) $40 + 90$
   (u) $70 + 90$ (v) $70 + 50$ (w) $50 + 40$ (x) $60 + 90$ (y) $80 + 40$

4. (a) 20 + 30 + 7   (b) 40 + 10 + 5   (c) 20 + 20 + 8
  (d) 60 + 30 + 9   (e) 60 + 40 + 5   (f) 50 + 40 + 3
  (g) 50 + 70 + 1   (h) 20 + 80 + 6   (i) 60 + 90 + 8
  (j) 40 + 70 + 7   (k) 50 + 30 + 7   (l) 80 + 50 + 2
  (m) 90 + 40 + 6   (n) 70 + 30 + 6   (o) 80 + 80 + 5
  (p) 10 + 3 + 70   (q) 70 + 8 + 10   (r) 20 + 5 + 90
  (s) 50 + 6 + 60   (t) 60 + 3 + 60   (u) 60 + 9 + 50
  (v) 90 + 7 + 90   (w) 4 + 30 + 40   (x) 1 + 30 + 80

5. (a) 20 + 11   (b) 30 + 16   (c) 10 + 19   (d) 20 + 13   (e) 50 + 19
  (f) 40 + 12   (g) 30 + 17   (h) 80 + 15   (i) 60 + 16   (j) 70 + 19
  (k) 90 + 11   (l) 90 + 16   (m) 90 + 17   (n) 100 + 15   (o) 120 + 13
  (p) 120 + 18   (q) 150 + 12   (r) 110 + 14   (s) 110 + 11   (t) 180 + 18
  (u) 170 + 17   (v) 160 + 15   (w) 180 + 13   (x) 190 + 17   (y) 190 + 11

6. (a) 60 + 70 + 3 + 4   (b) 90 + 50 + 1 + 2   (c) 70 + 90 + 2 + 4
  (d) 40 + 80 + 3 + 3   (e) 80 + 90 + 5 + 2   (f) 90 + 30 + 4 + 4
  (g) 20 + 70 + 2 + 6   (h) 70 + 80 + 4 + 5   (i) 70 + 70 + 3 + 5
  (j) 80 + 7 + 50 + 2   (k) 90 + 6 + 40 + 3   (l) 60 + 4 + 40 + 4
  (m) 10 + 40 + 5 + 5   (n) 20 + 30 + 8 + 5   (o) 10 + 80 + 7 + 6
  (p) 20 + 40 + 8 + 7   (q) 30 + 30 + 6 + 5   (r) 30 + 50 + 8 + 9
  (s) 70 + 50 + 6 + 8   (t) 60 + 60 + 9 + 7   (u) 30 + 90 + 8 + 4
  (v) 90 + 60 + 9 + 5   (w) 30 + 80 + 8 + 9   (x) 90 + 90 + 9 + 9

1.8 Adding whole numbers 'in your head'

Anthony is playing darts. He has scored 67 with his first two darts and hits 18 with his third dart. What is his total score?

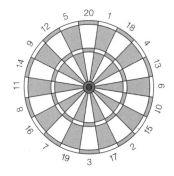

To find the total score without a calculator or a written calculation, think of a number line:

67 + 18:

start at 67 → — add 10 → — add 8 →

```
60        70        80        90
```

67 +10 → 77 +8 → 85

so 67 + 18 = 85.

You may need to note down some steps but try to do as much of the calculation as you can 'in your head'.

Example

John and Chantal are going on holiday. John has saved £83 and Chantal has saved £78. How much have they saved altogether?

83 + 78:

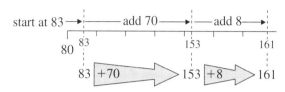

Hint:

Your number line doesn't have to be to scale.

So 83 + 78 = 161.

They have saved £161 altogether.

Exercise 1H

Answer all the questions without using a calculator.

1. (a) 16 + 13   (b) 12 + 25   (c) 41 + 37   (d) 55 + 23   (e) 84 + 16
   (f) 29 + 34   (g) 56 + 17   (h) 45 + 37   (i) 19 + 37   (j) 26 + 38
   (k) 17 + 11   (l) 13 + 21   (m) 22 + 22   (n) 34 + 51   (o) 28 + 62
   (p) 55 + 27   (q) 19 + 19   (r) 17 + 17   (s) 8 + 55   (t) 48 + 27
   (u) 95 + 23   (v) 97 + 26   (w) 86 + 75   (x) 94 + 53   (y) 98 + 67

2. A seaside stall displays this sign.

   What is the total cost of:
   (a) A tea and a sandwich   (b) A roll and a soft drink
   (c) A coffee and a roll   (d) A hot dog and a soft drink
   (e) A coffee and a sandwich   (f) A burger and a soft drink
   (g) A tea and a hot dog   (h) Two teas
   (i) Two coffees   (j) Two hot dogs
   (k) Two burgers and a soft drink   (l) Two hot dogs and two teas
   (m) A roll, a sandwich and a tea   (n) A tea, a coffee and a hot dog
   (o) Two soft drinks and a burger   (p) Two teas and three hot dogs?

Tea..............	45 p
Coffee.........	55 p
Sandwich...	87 p
Roll..............	68 p
Burger.......	125 p
Hot Dog......	110 p
Soft Drink...	35 p

3. Sonny is saving to buy a stereo which costs £215. He keeps a record of his weekly savings like this:

Saved this week	Total so far
£12	£12
£17	£29
£9	£38

   Copy and complete Sonny's record for the next ten weeks, when he saves: £22, £35, £5, £16, £17, £24, £18, £6, £11 and £23. If the final total is not £215, check for mistakes.

4. Maggie has collected this data on the number of days in each month:

January 31 February 28 March 31 April 30 May 31 June 30
July 31 August 31 September 30 October 31 November 30 December 31

Maggie starts a table like this.

By end of month	Days passed
January	31
February	59

Copy and complete Maggie's table. If the final total is not 365 days, check for mistakes.

1.9 Subtracting whole numbers 'in your head'

Most people work out subtractions by thinking about the addition table. If you want to work out $17 - 8$, you need to remember that $8 + 9 = 17$, so

$$17 - 8 = 9$$

Example

Melissa had 13 CDs but gave 7 to her brother. How many has she got left?

Remember that $7 + 6 = 13$
so $13 - 7 = 6$

Melissa has 6 CDs left.

To answer a more difficult question like $55 - 38$, you can think like this:

Start at 38 and find what to add on to get 55.

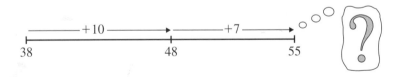

so the difference is 17 and

$$55 - 38 = 17$$

Exercise 1I

Do these subtraction questions in your head.

1. (a) $7 - 4$ (b) $9 - 3$ (c) $11 - 8$ (d) $9 - 3$ (e) $9 - 4$
   (f) $12 - 3$ (g) $16 - 7$ (h) $14 - 6$ (i) $11 - 5$ (j) $10 - 3$
   (k) $12 - 7$ (l) $15 - 8$ (m) $11 - 9$ (n) $13 - 7$ (o) $13 - 5$
   (p) $18 - 9$ (q) $16 - 8$ (r) $15 - 7$ (s) $13 - 6$ (t) $16 - 9$
   (u) $15 - 6$ (v) $14 - 8$ (w) $17 - 8$ (x) $15 - 9$ (y) $14 - 7$

2. (a) $25 - 3$ (b) $47 - 5$ (c) $65 - 2$ (d) $89 - 7$ (e) $47 - 6$
   (f) $46 - 6$ (g) $27 - 5$ (h) $88 - 4$ (i) $34 - 3$ (j) $55 - 1$
   (k) $57 - 2$ (l) $48 - 5$ (m) $123 - 2$ (n) $156 - 4$ (o) $187 - 4$
   (p) $239 - 6$ (q) $67 - 7$ (r) $88 - 5$ (s) $83 - 3$ (t) $29 - 8$
   (u) $46 - 2$ (v) $56 - 5$ (w) $78 - 6$ (x) $76 - 3$ (y) $99 - 9$

3. (a) $55 - 30$ (b) $67 - 50$ (c) $56 - 20$ (d) $49 - 20$ (e) $98 - 50$
   (f) $76 - 40$ (g) $83 - 30$ (h) $72 - 60$ (i) $34 - 20$ (j) $85 - 40$
   (k) $97 - 40$ (l) $77 - 30$ (m) $49 - 30$ (n) $27 - 10$ (o) $74 - 50$
   (p) $83 - 60$ (q) $97 - 70$ (r) $55 - 40$ (s) $55 - 10$ (t) $85 - 70$
   (u) $99 - 60$ (v) $81 - 20$ (w) $96 - 80$ (x) $73 - 10$ (y) $88 - 50$

4. (a) $65 - 32$ (b) $37 - 24$ (c) $86 - 34$ (d) $38 - 14$ (e) $59 - 26$
   (f) $54 - 33$ (g) $68 - 27$ (h) $59 - 37$ (i) $43 - 12$ (j) $82 - 21$
   (k) $56 - 15$ (l) $77 - 37$ (m) $58 - 46$ (n) $39 - 12$ (o) $93 - 52$
   (p) $58 - 38$ (q) $47 - 16$ (r) $85 - 74$ (s) $67 - 33$ (t) $68 - 22$
   (u) $95 - 53$ (v) $76 - 32$ (w) $99 - 35$ (x) $88 - 33$ (y) $69 - 24$

5. (a) $22 - 5$ (b) $43 - 4$ (c) $27 - 8$ (d) $32 - 6$ (e) $84 - 6$
   (f) $65 - 7$ (g) $82 - 4$ (h) $73 - 5$ (i) $54 - 7$ (j) $46 - 7$
   (k) $35 - 6$ (l) $84 - 5$ (m) $33 - 6$ (n) $76 - 8$ (o) $75 - 8$
   (p) $37 - 9$ (q) $48 - 9$ (r) $31 - 4$ (s) $51 - 5$ (t) $62 - 7$
   (u) $91 - 6$ (v) $63 - 8$ (w) $34 - 9$ (x) $82 - 8$ (y) $61 - 9$

6. (a) $34 - 15$ (b) $83 - 24$ (c) $55 - 27$ (d) $86 - 17$ (e) $42 - 15$
   (f) $54 - 26$ (g) $72 - 43$ (h) $84 - 37$ (i) $93 - 15$ (j) $24 - 18$
   (k) $73 - 66$ (l) $87 - 28$ (m) $92 - 14$ (n) $76 - 38$ (o) $74 - 39$
   (p) $43 - 18$ (q) $55 - 26$ (r) $76 - 39$ (s) $95 - 28$ (t) $46 - 19$
   (u) $52 - 27$ (v) $93 - 39$ (w) $84 - 48$ (x) $58 - 29$ (y) $95 - 39$

7. Paul needs to cook a large turkey for 240 minutes. He checks the oven and bastes the bird after these time gaps (in minutes):

    18, 25, 23, 31, 42, 17, 56 and 28.

    He keeps a record of how much cooking time is left every time he checks.

Time passed between checks	Time left
18 mins	222 mins
25 mins	197 mins

Copy and complete Paul's table. If your final answer is not zero minutes, check for mistakes.

8. Nisha is conducting an experiment. She is measuring the temperature of wax as it cools.

She records the temperature every 5 minutes for one hour. This is her data (in degrees centigrade):

    176, 155, 138, 124, 112, 98, 96, 95, 81, 64, 43, 31, 29

She presents her results in this table:

Time (mins)	Temp (°C)	Temp fall (°C)
0	176	–
5	155	21
10	138	17

Copy and complete Nisha's table.

1.10 Adding whole numbers with written calculations

If additions are too difficult to do in your head, you do them on paper.

Example

Find (a) 125 + 33   (b) 634 + 128   (c) 543 + 877

(a)   125
   + 33
   ─────
     158   Align the units

(b)   634
   + 128
   ─────
     762
        1

4 + 8 = 12
12 is 2 units
and 1 ten

(c)   543
   + 877
   ─────
     1420
      1 1 1

3 + 7 = 10
0 units
1 ten

40 + 70 + 10
= 120
= 2 tens and 1 hundred

500 + 800 + 100
= 1400
= 4 hundreds and 1 thousand

MODULE 3

Exercise 1J

Answer all the questions without using a calculator.

1. (a) 27 + 52   (b) 45 + 54   (c) 87 + 12   (d) 62 + 35   (e) 182 + 14
   (f) 623 + 64   (g) 721 + 58   (h) 805 + 72   (i) 922 + 34   (j) 732 + 45
   (k) 426 + 123   (l) 130 + 209   (m) 321 + 567   (n) 203 + 86   (o) 921 + 17
   (p) 342 + 503   (q) 267 + 131   (r) 555 + 333   (s) 240 + 559   (t) 322 + 657
   (u) 703 + 196   (v) 750 + 239   (w) 57 + 102   (x) 84 + 304   (y) 39 + 150

2. (a) 23 + 47   (b) 56 + 38   (c) 27 + 38   (d) 19 + 35   (e) 13 + 67
   (f) 345 + 35   (g) 606 + 77   (h) 801 + 59   (i) 623 + 68   (j) 208 + 17
   (k) 245 + 83   (l) 415 + 92   (m) 365 + 84   (n) 423 + 87   (o) 278 + 191
   (p) 367 + 162   (q) 750 + 67   (r) 831 + 88   (s) 922 + 90   (t) 271 + 168
   (u) 237 + 128   (v) 481 + 395   (w) 506 + 149   (x) 422 + 17   (y) 645 + 274

3. (a) 45 + 67   (b) 27 + 95   (c) 56 + 44   (d) 31 + 89   (e) 89 + 34
   (f) 108 + 97   (g) 237 + 74   (h) 528 + 79   (i) 187 + 78   (j) 249 + 76
   (k) 347 + 875   (l) 238 + 194   (m) 375 + 96   (n) 231 + 99   (o) 346 + 185
   (p) 453 + 278   (q) 653 + 279   (r) 593 + 308   (s) 607 + 296   (t) 372 + 548
   (u) 456 + 789   (v) 487 + 798   (w) 689 + 987   (x) 567 + 583   (y) 234 + 766

4. This table shows the numbers of motorbikes, vans and cars which used a ferry during one week.

	Motorbikes	Vans	Cars
Monday	32	36	102
Tuesday	27	41	156
Wednesday	19	63	134
Thursday	37	54	98
Friday	56	21	89

(a) How many vehicles used the ferry on Monday?
(b) How many motorbikes used the ferry on Wednesday, Thursday and Friday?
(c) How many cars used the ferry during the week?
(d) How many vans used the ferry during the week?
(e) How many vehicles used the ferry during the week?

5. A group of students are saving each month for a school trip. The table shows their savings for the first four months.

	Month 1	Month 2	Month 3	Month 4
John	£25	£32	£21	£27
Hitesh	£38	£30	£26	£19
Ajay	£30	£27	£23	£28
Elizabeth	£35	£12	£33	£24
Amy	£50	£14	£17	£26
Deryn	£20	£26	£25	£37

(a) How much has John saved?
(b) How much has Hitesh saved?
(c) How much is saved in the first month?
(d) How much is saved in the third month?
(e) How much have Elizabeth and Deryn saved altogether?

1.11 Subtracting whole numbers with written calculations

If subtractions are too difficult to do in your head, you do them on paper.

Example

Find (a) $346 - 23$ (b) $852 - 38$ (c) $541 - 179$

(a)
$$
\begin{array}{r}
346 \\
-\ 23 \\
\hline
323
\end{array}
$$

Subtract from the units end

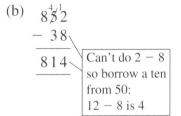

(b) Can't do $2 - 8$ so borrow a ten from 50: $12 - 8$ is 4

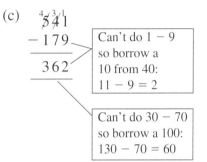

(c) Can't do $1 - 9$ so borrow a 10 from 40: $11 - 9 = 2$

Can't do $30 - 70$ so borrow a 100: $130 - 70 = 60$

MODULE 3

Exercise 1K

Answer all the questions without using a calculator.

1. (a) $87 - 56$ (b) $35 - 11$ (c) $56 - 32$ (d) $89 - 37$ (e) $58 - 14$
    (f) $123 - 12$ (g) $156 - 42$ (h) $245 - 23$ (i) $562 - 51$ (j) $347 - 25$
    (k) $340 - 120$ (l) $225 - 103$ (m) $453 - 142$ (n) $567 - 231$ (o) $698 - 377$
    (p) $452 - 132$ (q) $567 - 365$ (r) $777 - 234$ (s) $859 - 457$ (t) $750 - 430$
    (u) $806 - 701$ (v) $888 - 652$ (w) $999 - 457$ (x) $999 - 363$ (y) $789 - 678$

2. (a) $363 - 46$ (b) $271 - 35$ (c) $186 - 28$ (d) $137 - 18$ (e) $317 - 209$
    (f) $456 - 28$ (g) $362 - 29$ (h) $267 - 49$ (i) $583 - 69$ (j) $523 - 79$
    (k) $415 - 207$ (l) $367 - 249$ (m) $832 - 126$ (n) $555 - 247$ (o) $231 - 118$
    (p) $415 - 270$ (q) $367 - 294$ (r) $832 - 261$ (s) $555 - 274$ (t) $231 - 181$
    (u) $603 - 183$ (v) $207 - 196$ (w) $203 - 109$ (x) $305 - 127$ (y) $504 - 239$

3. (a) $234 - 79$ (b) $385 - 58$ (c) $271 - 92$ (d) $350 - 87$ (e) $321 - 58$
    (f) $621 - 156$ (g) $356 - 189$ (h) $450 - 195$ (i) $567 - 398$ (j) $278 - 189$
    (k) $452 - 177$ (l) $365 - 276$ (m) $680 - 543$ (n) $891 - 693$ (o) $673 - 285$
    (p) $451 - 252$ (q) $346 - 199$ (r) $670 - 191$ (s) $687 - 488$ (t) $713 - 615$
    (u) $708 - 89$ (v) $303 - 125$ (w) $502 - 163$ (x) $700 - 371$ (y) $800 - 259$

4 Thomas and Yasmin are timing the competitors in a marathon. These are the times (in minutes) of the first twenty runners:

175, 183, 189, 193, 195, 198, 200, 203, 206, 211, 214, 217, 221, 225, 232, 238, 245, 249, 251, 254

Yasmin starts to draw up a table like this:

Runner	Time behind winner
1st	–
2nd	+ 8 minutes
3rd	+ 14 minutes

Copy and complete Yasmin's table.

1.12 Temperature

Temperatures are measured in degrees Celsius (°C).

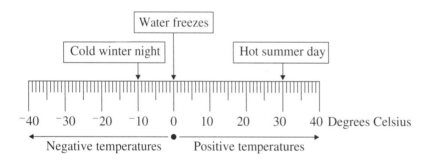

Example

A weather station records the lowest temperature each day.
These are the results for six days in December:

$^-5$°C, 2°C, $^-1$°C, 4°C, $^-3$°C, 0°C

Arrange the results into order, starting with the lowest.

Think of a number line:

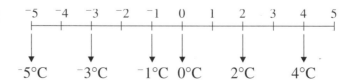

Exercise 1L

1. Arrange each list of temperatures into order, starting with the lowest.

   (a) 7°C, ⁻6°C, ⁻8°C, 2°C, 5°C, ⁻7°C

   (b) 6°C, ⁻7°C, ⁻2°C, 0°C, 1°C, ⁻1°C, ⁻3°C, 5°C

   (c) 4°C, 7°C, 6°C, 8°C, 0°C, 9°C, 3°C, 4°C, 5°C, 9°C

   (d) 0°C, ⁻1°C, 2°C, 3°C, ⁻2°C, ⁻3°C, 1°C, ⁻4°C, 4°C, 5°C

   (e) ⁻20°C, 30°C, 40°C, ⁻30°C, ⁻40°C, ⁻50°C, 0°C, 10°C, 50°C, ⁻10°C

   (f) ⁻13°C, ⁻17°C, 11°C, 8°C, ⁻9°C, ⁻6°C, 11°C, ⁻20°C, ⁻7°C, ⁻19°C

   (g) 21°C, 43°C, ⁻17°C, ⁻29°C, 32°C, ⁻56°C, 81°C, ⁻73°C, 65°C, ⁻16°C

   (h) 65°C, 76°C, 82°C, 90°C, 34°C, 67°C, 0°C, 55°C, 39°C, 93°C

   > **Hint:**
   > Use the number line to help you.

2. These are some of the highest and lowest temperatures recorded on the Earth. Write the list in order, starting with the highest temperature.

⁻45°C	The coldest temperature ever recorded in Europe (Finland)
46°C	The hottest temperature recorded in Europe (Spain)
53·1°C	The hottest temperature recorded in Australia (Cloncurry)
⁻68°C	The coldest temperature recorded in Siberia (Oymyakon)
58°C	The hottest temperature recorded on Earth (Libya)
⁻88·3°C	The coldest temperature recorded on Earth (Antarctica)
⁻58·3°C	The coldest temperature recorded in Canada (Ellesmere Island)
56·7°C	The hottest temperature recorded in the USA (Death Valley)

1.13 Temperature changes

The temperature is 5°C.

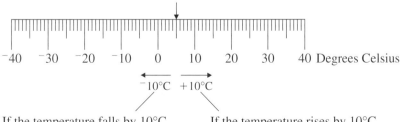

If the temperature falls by 10°C the new temperature will be ⁻5°C
5°C − 10°C = ⁻5°C

If the temperature rises by 10°C the new temperature will be 15°C
5°C + 10°C = 15°C

The temperature is ⁻5°C.

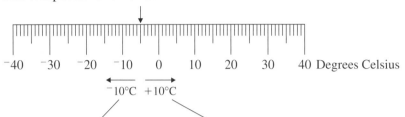

If the temperature falls by 10°C
the new temperature will be ⁻15°C
⁻5°C − 10°C = ⁻15°C

If the temperature rises by 10°C
the new temperature will be 5°C
⁻5°C + 10°C = 5°C

Examples

8°C + 7°C = 15°C
8°C − 7°C = 1°C
⁻8°C + 7°C = ⁻1°C
⁻8°C − 7°C = ⁻15°C

4°C + 6°C = 10°C
4°C − 6°C = ⁻2°C
⁻4°C + 6°C = 2°C
⁻4°C − 6°C = ⁻10°C

Exercise 1M

1. (a) 5°C + 8°C   (b) 5°C − 8°C   (c) ⁻5°C + 8°C   (d) ⁻5°C − 8°C
2. (a) 2°C + 3°C   (b) 2°C − 3°C   (c) ⁻2°C + 3°C   (d) ⁻2°C − 3°C
3. (a) 4°C + 7°C   (b) 4°C − 7°C   (c) ⁻4°C + 7°C   (d) ⁻4°C − 7°C
4. (a) 9°C + 2°C   (b) 9°C − 2°C   (c) ⁻9°C + 2°C   (d) ⁻9°C − 2°C
5. (a) 1°C + 10°C   (b) 1°C − 10°C   (c) ⁻1°C + 10°C   (d) ⁻1°C − 10°C
6. (a) 5°C + 6°C   (b) 5°C − 6°C   (c) ⁻5°C + 6°C   (d) ⁻5°C − 6°C
7. (a) 11°C + 6°C   (b) 11°C − 6°C   (c) ⁻11°C + 6°C   (d) ⁻11°C − 6°C
8. (a) 13°C + 8°C   (b) 13°C − 8°C   (c) ⁻13°C + 8°C   (d) ⁻13°C − 8°C
9. (a) 9°C + 3°C   (b) 9°C − 3°C   (c) ⁻9°C + 3°C   (d) ⁻9°C − 3°C
10. (a) 15°C + 5°C   (b) 15°C − 5°C   (c) ⁻15°C + 5°C   (d) ⁻15°C − 5°C
11. (a) 7°C + 12°C   (b) 7°C − 12°C   (c) ⁻7°C + 12°C   (d) ⁻7°C − 12°C
12. (a) 10°C + 10°C   (b) 10°C − 10°C   (c) ⁻10°C + 10°C   (d) ⁻10°C − 10°C
13. (a) 7°C + 7°C   (b) 7°C − 7°C   (c) ⁻7°C + 7°C   (d) ⁻7°C − 7°C
14. (a) 14°C + 4°C   (b) 14°C − 4°C   (c) ⁻14°C + 4°C   (d) ⁻14°C − 4°C
15. (a) 10°C + 20°C   (b) 10°C − 20°C   (c) ⁻10°C + 20°C   (d) ⁻10°C − 20°C
16. (a) 20°C + 10°C   (b) 20°C − 10°C   (c) ⁻20°C + 10°C   (d) ⁻20°C − 10°C
17. (a) 18°C + 9°C   (b) 18°C − 9°C   (c) ⁻18°C + 9°C   (d) ⁻18°C − 9°C

MODULE 3

18. (a) $15°C + 25°C$ (b) $15°C - 25°C$ (c) $^-15°C + 25°C$ (d) $^-15°C - 25°C$

19. (a) $13°C + 7°C$ (b) $13°C - 7°C$ (c) $^-13°C + 7°C$ (d) $^-13°C - 7°C$

20. (a) $31°C + 23°C$ (b) $31°C - 23°C$ (c) $^-31°C + 23°C$ (d) $^-31°C - 23°C$

1.14 Adding negative numbers

Adding a negative number is the same as subtracting.

Example 1

$$8 + {}^-7 = 8 - 7 = 1$$
$$3 + {}^-6 = 3 - 6 = {}^-3$$
$${}^-5 + {}^-9 = {}^-5 - 9 = {}^-14$$
$${}^-1 + {}^-5 = {}^-1 - 5 = {}^-6$$

With any two numbers, you can now make and solve six different problems.

Example 2

Starting with 7 and 2:

$$7 + 2 = 9$$
$$7 - 2 = 5$$
$$7 + {}^-2 = 5$$
$${}^-7 + 2 = {}^-5$$
$${}^-7 - 2 = {}^-9$$
$${}^-7 + {}^-2 = {}^-9$$

Starting with 4 and 10:

$$4 + 10 = 14$$
$$4 - 10 = {}^-6$$
$$4 + {}^-10 = {}^-6$$
$${}^-4 + 10 = 6$$
$${}^-4 - 10 = {}^-14$$
$${}^-4 + {}^-10 = {}^-14$$

Exercise 1N

Use a number line to help you work out these.

1. (a) $4 + 5$ (b) $4 - 5$ (c) $4 + {}^-5$
     (d) $^-4 + 5$ (e) $^-4 - 5$ (f) $^-4 + {}^-5$

2. (a) $5 + 7$ (b) $5 - 7$ (c) $5 + {}^-7$
     (d) $^-5 + 7$ (e) $^-5 - 7$ (f) $^-5 + {}^-7$

3. (a) $8 + 2$ (b) $8 - 2$ (c) $8 + {}^-2$
     (d) $^-8 + 2$ (e) $^-8 - 2$ (f) $^-8 + {}^-2$

4. (a) $3 + 9$ (b) $3 - 9$ (c) $3 + {}^-9$
     (d) $^-3 + 9$ (e) $^-3 - 9$ (f) $^-3 + {}^-9$

5. (a) $6 + 9$ (b) $6 - 9$ (c) $6 + {}^-9$
     (d) $^-6 + 9$ (e) $^-6 - 9$ (f) $^-6 + {}^-9$

6. (a) $10 + 6$ (b) $10 - 6$ (c) $10 + {}^-6$
     (d) $^-10 + 6$ (e) $^-10 - 6$ (f) $^-10 + {}^-6$

7. (a) $5 + 3$ (b) $5 - 3$ (c) $5 + {}^-3$
     (d) $^-5 + 3$ (e) $^-5 - 3$ (f) $^-5 + {}^-3$

MODULE 3

8. (a) $6 + 1$ (b) $6 - 1$ (c) $6 + {}^-1$
   (d) ${}^-6 + 1$ (e) ${}^-6 - 1$ (f) ${}^-6 + {}^-1$

9. (a) $7 + 10$ (b) $7 - 10$ (c) $7 + {}^-10$
   (d) ${}^-7 + 10$ (e) ${}^-7 - 10$ (f) ${}^-7 + {}^-10$

10. (a) $5 + 2$ (b) $5 - 2$ (c) $5 + {}^-2$
   (d) ${}^-5 + 2$ (e) ${}^-5 - 2$ (f) ${}^-5 + {}^-2$

11. (a) $11 + 3$ (b) $11 - 3$ (c) $11 + {}^-3$
   (d) ${}^-11 + 3$ (e) ${}^-11 - 3$ (f) ${}^-11 + {}^-3$

12. (a) $7 + 14$ (b) $7 - 14$ (c) $7 + {}^-14$
   (d) ${}^-7 + 14$ (e) ${}^-7 - 14$ (f) ${}^-7 + {}^-14$

1.15 Subtracting negative numbers

Subtracting a negative number is the same as adding.

Example 1

$$8 - {}^-7 = 8 + 7 = 15$$
$$3 - {}^-6 = 3 + 6 = 9$$
$${}^-5 - {}^-9 = {}^-5 + 9 = 4$$
$${}^-1 - {}^-5 = {}^-1 + 5 = 4$$

With any two numbers, you can now make and solve eight different problems.

Example 2

Starting with 6 and 3:

$$6 + 3 = 9$$
$$6 - 3 = 3$$
$$6 + {}^-3 = 3$$
$$6 - {}^-3 = 6 + 3 = 9$$
$${}^-6 + 3 = {}^-3$$
$${}^-6 - 3 = {}^-9$$
$${}^-6 + {}^-3 = {}^-9$$
$${}^-6 - {}^-3 = {}^-6 + 3 = {}^-3$$

Starting with 8 and 12:

$$8 + 12 = 20$$
$$8 - 12 = {}^-4$$
$$8 + {}^-12 = {}^-4$$
$$8 - {}^-12 = 8 + 12 = 20$$
$${}^-8 + 12 = 4$$
$${}^-8 - 12 = {}^-20$$
$${}^-8 + {}^-12 = {}^-20$$
$${}^-8 - {}^-12 = {}^-8 + 12 = 4$$

Hint:

For 8 and 12
the **difference** is 4,
the **sum** is 20.
There are only four
possible answers:
4 or ${}^-4$, 20 or ${}^-20$.

Exercise 10

Use a number line to work out these.

1. (a) $10 + 5$ (b) $10 - 5$ (c) $10 + {}^-5$ (d) $10 - {}^-5$
   (e) ${}^-10 + 5$ (f) ${}^-10 - 5$ (g) ${}^-10 + {}^-5$ (h) ${}^-10 - {}^-5$

2. (a) $7 - 6$ (b) ${}^-7 + 6$ (c) $7 + {}^-6$ (d) ${}^-7 - {}^-6$
   (e) ${}^-7 + {}^-6$ (f) $7 + 6$ (g) $7 - {}^-6$ (h) ${}^-7 - 6$

3. (a) ${}^-4 - 3$ (b) $4 - {}^-3$ (c) $4 + 3$ (d) ${}^-4 + 3$
   (e) ${}^-4 - {}^-3$ (f) $4 + {}^-3$ (g) ${}^-4 + {}^-3$ (h) $4 - 3$

4. (a) $6 + 6$ (b) $^-6 + 6$ (c) $6 - 6$ (d) $^-6 - 6$

    (e) $6 + ^-6$ (f) $^-6 + ^-6$ (g) $6 - ^-6$ (h) $^-6 - ^-6$

5. (a) $10 + 2$ (b) $10 - 2$ (c) $10 + ^-2$ (d) $10 - ^-2$

    (e) $^-10 + 2$ (f) $^-10 - 2$ (g) $^-10 + ^-2$ (h) $^-10 - ^-2$

6. (a) $1 - 8$ (b) $^-1 + 8$ (c) $1 + ^-8$ (d) $^-1 - ^-8$

    (e) $^-1 + ^-8$ (f) $1 + 8$ (g) $1 - ^-8$ (h) $^-1 - 8$

7. (a) $^-7 - 3$ (b) $7 - ^-3$ (c) $7 + 3$ (d) $^-7 + 3$

    (e) $^-7 - ^-3$ (f) $7 + ^-3$ (g) $^-7 + ^-3$ (h) $7 - 3$

8. (a) $10 + 9$ (b) $^-10 + 9$ (c) $10 - 9$ (d) $^-10 - 9$

    (e) $10 + ^-9$ (f) $^-10 + ^-9$ (g) $10 - ^-9$ (h) $^-10 - ^-9$

9. (a) $9 + 4$ (b) $9 - 4$ (c) $9 + ^-4$ (d) $9 - ^-4$

    (e) $^-9 + 4$ (f) $^-9 - 4$ (g) $^-9 + ^-4$ (h) $^-9 - ^-4$

10. (a) $2 - 1$ (b) $^-2 + 1$ (c) $2 + ^-1$ (d) $^-2 - ^-1$

    (e) $^-2 + ^-1$ (f) $2 + 1$ (g) $2 - ^-1$ (h) $^-2 - 1$

11. (a) $^-16 - 3$ (b) $16 - ^-3$ (c) $16 + 3$ (d) $^-16 + 3$

    (e) $^-16 - ^-3$ (f) $16 + ^-3$ (g) $^-16 + ^-3$ (h) $16 - 3$

12. (a) $9 + 9$ (b) $^-9 + 9$ (c) $9 - 9$ (d) $^-9 - 9$

    (e) $9 + ^-9$ (f) $^-9 + ^-9$ (g) $9 - ^-9$ (h) $^-9 - ^-9$

MODULE 3

1.16 Going overdrawn

The amount of money that is in your bank account is called the **balance**.

Taking money out of your account is called **making a withdrawal**.

Paying money into your account is called **making a deposit**.

Writing a cheque to pay for something is the same as making a withdrawal.

If you withdraw more money than is in your account, your account is **overdrawn** and you owe the bank money.

Example 1

(a) Ms Jones has a balance of £230 in her bank account.
If she writes a cheque for £350, how much is she overdrawn?
£350 is £120 more than £230, so Ms Jones has $^-$£120 in her account. She is £120 *overdrawn*.

(b) Mr Smith was £455 overdrawn but then made a deposit of £600.
What is his new balance?
Mr Smith's balance before he paid in the £600 was $^-$£455.
£600 is £145 more than £455, so Mr Smith's new balance is £145.

Exercise 1P

Copy and complete this table.

	Balance	Change	New balance
1.	£340	deposit £400	
2.	£235	deposit £1 675	
3.	£389	withdraw £350	
4.	£1 745	withdraw £705	
5.	£3 450	cheque £2 775	
6.	£209	cheque £209	
7.	⁻£400	deposit £500	
8.	⁻£783	deposit £800	
9.	⁻£1 000	deposit £1 200	
10.	⁻£275	deposit £645	
11.	£500	withdraw £650	
12.	£456	withdraw £457	
13.	£371	withdraw £567	
14.	⁻£300	deposit £200	

1.17 Timetables

To travel by train or bus you need to be able to read a timetable.

Here is a train timetable:

London Kings Cross	Dep	10.00	10.30	11.30	12.00	12.30	13.00	13.30	14.00	14.30	15.00
Stevenage	..	..	..	..	12.01	..	..	..	14.01	..	..	..
Peterborough	Arr	11.15	11.45	12.47	13.15	13.44	14.14	14.47	15.15	15.44	16.14
	Dep	11.15	11.45	12.48	13.15	13.44	14.14	14.48	15.15	15.44	16.14
Grantham	..	..	..	12.14	13.15	..	14.11	..	15.15	..	16.11	..
Newark North Gate	..	..	..	12.26	13.27	..	14.23	..	15.27	..	16.23	..
Retford	..	..	..	..	13.54	..	..	..	15.54	..	..	..
Doncaster	Arr	12.47	13.22	14.29	14.47	15.19	15.44	16.29	16.47	17.19	17.44
	Dep	12.47	13.23	14.29	14.47	15.20	15.44	16.29	16.47	17.20	17.44
Wakefield Westgate	..	..	..	13.49	14.48	..	15.49	..	16.48	..	17.39	..
Leeds	Arr	..	14.13	15.13	..	16.13	..	17.13	..	18.13	..

Note:

Timetables are based on the 24-hour clock.

For example:
13.44 means 1.44 pm
17.39 means 5.39 pm.

You cannot use a calculator to work with times.

It is better to use a number line.

Example

A bus leaves Warwick at 13.05 and arrives in Birmingham at 14.23. How long was the journey? Draw a timeline:

So the journey took 1 hour 17 minutes.

Exercise 1Q

Look at the timetable on page 26 and answer the questions (assume that all trains run to schedule).

1. Bethany wants to travel from London Kings Cross to Leeds. She needs to be in Leeds by 2.30 pm. What is the latest train that she could catch from London?

2. Colin is travelling from Peterborough to Wakefield Westgate, and gets on the same train as Bethany.
   (a) At what time does he leave Peterborough?
   (b) How long is Colin's journey? Give your answer in hours and minutes.

3. How much longer is Bethany's journey than Colin's journey?

4. Greg gets on the 14.00 train from London Kings Cross. He wants to travel to Newark North Gate but he will need to change at Peterborough.
   (a) How long must he wait on the platform at Peterborough?
   (b) What time does he arrive in Newark North Gate?

MODULE 3

Summary

1. Each digit in a number has a place value.

2. Numbers can be written in words or figures.

3. Whole numbers can be approximated to the nearest 10, 100 or 1 000.

Checkout N1

1. What place value does each underlined digit have?
   (a) 4<u>7</u>8   (b) 2 <u>8</u>97

2. (a) Write three thousand nine hundred and ninety-four in figures.
   (b) Write 7 843 in words.

3. (a) Approximate to the nearest 10.
   (i) 78 (ii) 95 (iii) 231
   (b) Approximate to the nearest 100.
   (i) 710 (ii) 350 (iii) 2 483
   (c) Approximate to the nearest 1 000.
   (i) 3 500 (ii) 22 897 (iii) 45 123

4. You can approximate a number to one significant figure (s.f. for short).

4. Give each number correct to 1 s.f.
(a) 37   (b) 42
(c) 321   (d) 584
(e) 1 731   (f) 2 399

---

5. You should work out simple calculations in your head.

5. (a) $5 + 9$ (b) $4 + 3 + 10$
(c) $50 + 60$ (d) $30 + 60 + 5$
(e) $40 + 16$ (f) $20 + 5 + 30 + 7$
(g) $12 + 26$ (h) $34 + 28$
(i) $14 - 8$ (j) $48 - 5$
(k) $55 - 40$ (l) $68 - 27$
(m) $35 - 7$ (n) $73 - 56$

---

6. Work out harder calculations on paper.

6. (a) $231 + 427$ (b) $178 + 219$
(c) $89 + 34$ (d) $234 + 766$
(e) $87 - 55$ (f) $453 - 142$
(g) $363 - 46$ (h) $832 - 261$
(i) $452 - 177$ (j) $687 - 488$

---

7. Negative temperatures are below 0°C.
You arrange temperatures using a number line:

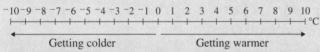

7. Arrange these temperatures in order, starting with the lowest.
$^-4°C, 7°C, 3°C, 2°C, ^-3°C,$
$4°C, 0°C, 1°C, ^-2°C, ^-1°C$

---

8. You can calculate temperature changes using a number line.

8. Work out:
(a) $15°C + 8°C$
(b) $15°C - 8°C$
(c) $^-15°C + 8°C$
(d) $^-15°C - 8°C$

---

9. Adding a negative number is the same as subtracting.
$$8 + {}^-7 = 8 - 7 = 1 \qquad ^-5 + {}^-9 = {}^-5 - 9 = {}^-14$$

9. Find:
(a) $6 + 11$ (b) $6 - 11$
(c) $6 + {}^-11$ (d) $^-6 + 11$
(e) $^-6 - 11$ (f) $^-6 + {}^-11$

---

10. Subtracting a negative number is the same as adding.
$$8 - {}^-7 = 8 + 7 = 15 \qquad ^-5 - {}^-9 = {}^-5 + 9 = 4$$

10. Work out:
(a) $^-7 - 3$ (b) $7 - {}^-3$
(c) $7 + 3$ (d) $^-7 + 3$
(e) $^-7 - {}^-3$ (f) $7 + {}^-3$
(g) $^-7 + {}^-3$ (h) $7 - 3$

Revision exercise N1

1. (a) Write 7582
     (i) to the nearest ten,
     (ii) to the nearest hundred.

   (b) Write 7582 in words.   [SEG]

2. (a) There are 3600 seconds in one hour.
     In the number 3600, the 3 stands for three thousands.
     What does the 6 stand for?

   (b) 7428 people attend a concert.
     What does the 2 stand for?

   (c) There are 59 150 entries for an examination.
     Write this number in words.   [NEAB]

3. The temperatures, in degrees Celsius, in eight towns in Finland were

     15, -10, 11, 8, -17, 9, 2, -5

Arrange these temperatures in order, starting with the warmest.   [SEG]

4. The cooking time for meat is worked out using the following formula.

     Cooking time = time per pound × weight in pounds

   (a) The time per pound for beef is 25 minutes.
     A piece of beef weighs 5 pounds.
     What is the cooking time for this piece of beef?
     Give your answer in hours and minutes.

   (b) The cooking time for a piece of pork is 150 minutes.
     The time per pound for pork is 25 minutes.

     What is the weight of this piece of pork?   [SEG]

5. Simon paid a cheque for £174 into his bank account.
Simon's bank account is now £94·07 overdrawn.
What was the balance on his account before Simon paid in this cheque?   [SEG]

6. Mary's bank account is £25·37 overdrawn.
She pays in £60 in cash. What is the new balance in her bank account?   [SEG]

MODULE 3

7. These are the starting times of television programmes.

     5.10   The Saint; Part One
     6.45   News
     6.55   World of Animals
     7.25   Film

(a) How long is the programme "World of Animals"?

(b) The film is 1 hour 50 minutes long.
What time does the film end?

(c) "The Saint" is shown in three parts on different days.
Each part is 1 hour 35 minutes long.
How long is "The Saint" altogether?
Give your answer in hours and minutes.   [SEG]

8. Place the following numbers in order of size starting with the largest.

     17, 34, −21, −11, 132

                               [SEG]

9. These cards are used to make 3-figure numbers.

(a) Using each of these cards once, write down the number that is nearest to 400.

(b) Use all three cards to write down a 3-figure number that is a multiple of 8.

(c) Use all three cards to write down a 3-figure number that is a square number.   [NEAB]

10. (a) Write the following numbers in figures

     (i) Ten thousand one hundred and twenty five.

     (ii) One thousand and eighty six.

(b) The attendance at a local football match was 2 743.
Write this number to the nearest 100.   [NEAB]

MODULE 3

11. Place the following numbers in order of size, starting with the largest.

219 17 52 41 81 115   [SEG]

12. Peter is setting his video recorder for a programme which starts at 8.45 pm. He knows that the programme should last for 1 hour and 25 minutes and he wants to allow an extra 5 minutes, in case the programme finishes late. At what time should Peter set his video recorder to finish?

[SEG]

13. Martin's monthly bank statement shows that he has an overdraft of £125·38.
He pays £200 into his bank account.
After this payment, what is the new balance on Martin's account?   [SEG]

14. Claire and Rob want to catch a ferry which leaves Dover at 7.15 pm.
The journey from their home to Dover takes 2 hours and 45 minutes.
They must arrive at the ferry terminal 20 minutes before the ferry leaves.

(a) What is the latest time at which they should leave home?

(b) Give your answer to part (a) in 24 hour clock mode.

The ferry leaves Dover at 7.15 pm and takes 75 minutes sailing from Dover to Calais.
French time is 1 hour in advance of British time.

(c) What is the French time when Claire and Rob arrive in France?   [SEG]

MODULE 3

N2 NUMBER 2

This unit will show you how to:

- Multiply numbers by 10, 100 or 1 000
- Divide numbers by 10, 100 or 1 000
- Multiply and divide numbers 'in your head'
- Multiply and divide without a calculator

Before you start:

You should know how to...	Check in N2
1. Read place value in numbers. For example: in 7 2 3 5 — 5 has value 5 units — 3 has value 3 tens — 2 has value 2 hundreds — 7 has value 7 thousands	**1.** What is the value of the underlined digit in each number? (a) 7<u>6</u>　(b) 7<u>6</u>0　(c) <u>7</u>600 (d) <u>7</u>900　(e) <u>7</u>90　(f) <u>7</u>9 (g) <u>4</u>50　(h) 101<u>1</u>　(i) 1<u>0</u>11

2.1 Multiplying numbers by 10

To multiply a number by 10, move all the digits one place to the
left and add a zero. A place value table will help.

Example

(a) $5 \times 10 = 50$

Th	H	T	U
			5
		5	0

$\times 10$

(b) $30 \times 10 = 300$

Th	H	T	U
		3	0
	3	0	0

$\times 10$

(c) $75 \times 10 = 750$

Th	H	T	U
		7	5
	7	5	0

$\times 10$

(d) $356 \times 10 = 3\,560$

Th	H	T	U
	3	5	6
3	5	6	0

$\times 10$

Exercise 2A

1. (a) 6×10 (b) 7×10 (c) 11×10 (d) 23×10
    (e) 32×10 (f) 45×10 (g) 80×10 (h) 61×10
    (i) 56×10 (j) 98×10 (k) 112×10 (l) 172×10
    (m) 451×10 (n) 390×10 (o) 916×10 (p) 206×10
    (q) 101×10 (r) 903×10 (s) 700×10 (t) 341×10

2. Pencils are sold in packs of 10.
    How many pencils are there in:

    (a) 8 packs
    (b) 24 packs
    (c) 33 packs
    (d) 72 packs
    (e) 100 packs
    (f) 144 packs?

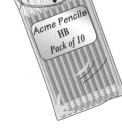

3. There are 10 millimetres in a centimetre.
    How many millimetres are there in:

    (a) 5 centimetres   (b) 13 centimetres
    (c) 22 centimetres   (d) 35 centimetres
    (e) 70 centimetres   (f) 100 centimetres?

MODULE 3

2.2 Multiplying numbers by 100

To multiply a number by 100, move all the digits two places to the left and add two zeros.

Example

(a) $5 \times 100 = 500$

TTh	Th	H	T	U
				5 $\times 100$
	5	0	0	

(b) $30 \times 100 = 3\,000$

TTh	Th	H	T	U
			3	0 $\times 100$
3	0	0	0	

(c) $75 \times 100 = 7\,500$

TTh	Th	H	T	U
		7	5 $\times 100$	
7	5	0	0	

(d) $365 \times 100 = 36\,500$

TTh	Th	H	T	U
	3	6	5 $\times 100$	
3	6	5	0	0

Exercise 2B

1. (a) 6×100 (b) 7×100 (c) 11×100
   (d) 23×100 (e) 32×100 (f) 45×100
   (g) 80×100 (h) 61×100 (i) 56×100
   (j) 98×100 (k) 112×100 (l) 172×100
   (m) 451×100 (n) 390×100 (o) 916×100
   (p) 206×100 (q) 101×100 (r) 903×100
   (s) 700×100 (t) 341×100

2. There are 100 pennies in a pound.
How many pennies are there in:

(a) £3   (b) £9
(c) £20   (d) £45
(e) £600   (f) £499?

3. There are 100 centimetres in a metre.
How many centimetres are there in:

(a) 2 metres   (b) 38 metres
(c) 27 metres   (d) 80 metres
(e) 76 metres   (f) 100 metres?

2.3 Multiplying numbers by 1 000

To multiply a number by 1 000, move all the digits three places to the left and add three zeros.

Example

(a) $5 \times 1\,000 = 5\,000$

HTh	TTh	Th	H	T	U
		5	0	0	0

(b) $30 \times 1\,000 = 30\,000$

HTh	TTh	Th	H	T	U
	3	0	0	0	0

(c) $75 \times 1\,000 = 75\,000$

HTh	TTh	Th	H	T	U
7	5	0	0	0	0

(d) $365 \times 1\,000 = 365\,000$

HTh	TTh	Th	H	T	U
3	6	5	0	0	0

Exercise 2C

1. (a) $6 \times 1\,000$ (b) $7 \times 1\,000$ (c) $11 \times 1\,000$
   (d) $23 \times 1\,000$ (e) $32 \times 1\,000$ (f) $45 \times 1\,000$
   (g) $80 \times 1\,000$ (h) $61 \times 1\,000$ (i) $56 \times 1\,000$
   (j) $98 \times 1\,000$ (k) $112 \times 1\,000$ (l) $172 \times 1\,000$
   (m) $451 \times 1\,000$ (n) $390 \times 1\,000$ (o) $916 \times 1\,000$
   (p) $206 \times 1\,000$ (q) $101 \times 1\,000$ (r) $903 \times 1\,000$
   (s) $700 \times 1\,000$ (t) $341 \times 1\,000$

2. There are 1 000 metres in a kilometre. How many metres are there in:

   (a) 4 kilometres   (b) 19 kilometres   (c) 27 kilometres
   (d) 83 kilometres   (e) 100 kilometres   (f) 153 kilometres?

3. There are 1 000 millilitres in a litre.
   How many millilitres are there in:

   (a) 5 litres
   (b) 13 litres
   (c) 22 litres
   (d) 35 litres
   (e) 70 litres
   (f) 100 litres?

MODULE 3

2.4 Dividing numbers by 10

To divide a number by 10, move all the digits one place to the right.

Example

(a) $50 \div 10 = 5$

Th	H	T	U	
	5	0		$\div 10$
		5		

(b) $300 \div 10 = 30$

Th	H	T	U	
	3	0	0	$\div 10$
		3	0	

(c) $750 \div 10 = 75$

Th	H	T	U	
	7	5	0	$\div 10$
		7	5	

(d) $3\,650 \div 10 = 365$

Th	H	T	U	
3	6	5	0	$\div 10$
	3	6	5	

Exercise 2D

1. (a) $70 \div 10$ (b) $80 \div 10$ (c) $120 \div 10$ (d) $320 \div 10$
    (e) $210 \div 10$ (f) $610 \div 10$ (g) $800 \div 10$ (h) $510 \div 10$
    (i) $650 \div 10$ (j) $890 \div 10$ (k) $1\,250 \div 10$ (l) $1\,270 \div 10$
    (m) $4\,510 \div 10$ (n) $2\,900 \div 10$ (o) $9\,030 \div 10$ (p) $1\,200 \div 10$
    (q) $3\,030 \div 10$ (r) $2\,000 \div 10$ (s) $5\,000 \div 10$ (t) $4\,100 \div 10$

2. A lottery syndicate has ten members. They share all winnings equally. What does each member receive if the syndicate wins a prize of:

(a) £10
(b) £900
(c) £10 000
(d) £45 000
(e) £267 800
(f) £1 878 340?

3. There are 10 millimetres in a centimetre.
Change these lengths into centimetres.

(a) 60 millimetres   (b) 170 millimetres   (c) 230 millimetres
(d) 300 millimetres   (e) 500 millimetres   (f) 750 millimetres

2.5 Dividing numbers by 100

To divide a number by 100, move all the digits two places to the right.

Example

(a) $500 \div 100 = 5$

(b) $3\,000 \div 100 = 30$

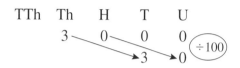

(c) $7\,500 \div 100 = 75$

(d) $36\,500 \div 100 = 365$

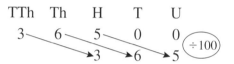

Exercise 2E

1. (a) $700 \div 100$
    (b) $600 \div 100$
    (c) $1\,200 \div 100$
    (d) $1\,300 \div 100$
    (e) $2\,500 \div 100$
    (f) $2\,600 \div 100$
    (g) $800 \div 100$
    (h) $3\,100 \div 100$
    (i) $7\,500 \div 100$
    (j) $1\,800 \div 100$
    (k) $1\,200 \div 100$
    (l) $12\,700 \div 100$
    (m) $8\,700 \div 100$
    (n) $2\,900 \div 100$
    (o) $19\,300 \div 100$
    (p) $12\,800 \div 100$
    (q) $13\,300 \div 100$
    (r) $20\,000 \div 100$
    (s) $55\,000 \div 100$
    (t) $241\,900 \div 100$

2. There are 100 centimetres in a metre.
    Change these lengths into metres.
    (a) 300 centimetres
    (b) 900 centimetres
    (c) 600 centimetres
    (d) 4 500 centimetres
    (e) 7 800 centimetres
    (f) 6 700 centimetres

3. There are 100 pennies in a pound.
    Change these amounts into pounds.
    (a) 200 pennies
    (b) 400 pennies
    (c) 1 000 pennies
    (d) 3 000 pennies
    (e) 2 500 pennies
    (f) 8 700 pennies

4. Change these amounts into pence.
    (a) £4·66
    (b) £5·80
    (c) £1·66
    (d) £4·77
    (e) £5·84
    (f) £2·94
    (g) £1·91
    (h) £0·36
    (i) £3·06
    (j) £3·82
    (k) £3·62
    (l) £0·14

MODULE 3

2.6 Dividing numbers by 1 000

To divide a number by 1 000, move all the digits three places to the right.

Example

(a) $5\,000 \div 1\,000 = 5$

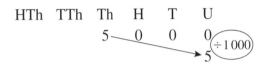

(b) $30\,000 \div 1\,000 = 30$

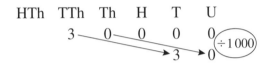

(c) $75\,000 \div 1\,000 = 75$

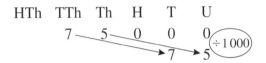

(d) $365\,000 \div 1\,000 = 365$

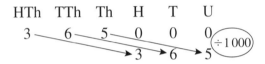

Exercise 2F

1. (a) $7\,000 \div 1\,000$
    (b) $4\,000 \div 1\,000$
    (c) $12\,000 \div 1\,000$
    (d) $32\,000 \div 1\,000$
    (e) $21\,000 \div 1\,000$
    (f) $49\,000 \div 1\,000$
    (g) $18\,000 \div 1\,000$
    (h) $512\,000 \div 1\,000$
    (i) $165\,000 \div 1\,000$
    (j) $890\,000 \div 1\,000$
    (k) $125\,000 \div 1\,000$
    (l) $270\,000 \div 1\,000$
    (m) $1\,450\,000 \div 1\,000$
    (n) $2\,900\,000 \div 1\,000$
    (o) $5\,030\,000 \div 1\,000$
    (p) $6\,200\,000 \div 1\,000$
    (q) $3\,435\,000 \div 1\,000$
    (r) $52\,430\,000 \div 1\,000$
    (s) $5\,367\,000 \div 1\,000$
    (t) $41\,321\,000 \div 1\,000$

2. There are 100 millilitres in a litre.
    Change these volumes into litres.
    (a) 1 000 millilitres
    (b) 9 000 millilitres
    (c) 10 000 millilitres
    (d) 5 000 millilitres
    (e) 27 000 millilitres
    (f) 78 000 millilitres

3. There are 1000 metres in a kilometre.
    Change these distances into kilometres.
    (a) 6 000 metres
    (b) 8 000 metres
    (c) 10 000 metres
    (d) 31 000 metres
    (e) 55 000 metres
    (f) 170 000 metres

MODULE 3

2.7 The multiplication table

This table shows all the multiplications from 1×1 to 10×10.

×	1	2	3	4	5	6	7	8	9	10
1	1	2	3	4	5	6	7	8	9	10
2	2	4	6	8	10	12	14	16	18	20
3	3	6	9	12	15	18	21	24	27	30
4	4	8	12	16	20	24	28	32	36	40
5	5	10	15	20	25	30	35	40	45	50
6	6	12	18	24	30	36	42	48	54	60
7	7	14	21	28	35	42	49	56	63	70
8	8	16	24	32	40	48	56	64	72	80
9	9	18	27	36	45	54	63	72	81	90
10	10	20	30	40	50	60	70	80	90	100

For example:
$5 \times 9 = 45$

MODULE 3

Exercise 2G

Answer all the questions without using a calculator or written calculations. Try to memorise the multiplication table but look up answers if you need to.

1. (a) 2×3 (b) 3×4 (c) 4×5 (d) 2×6 (e) 3×3
    (f) 4×4 (g) 5×3 (h) 2×5 (i) 6×4 (j) 3×7
    (k) 2×8 (l) 5×6 (m) 7×4 (n) 8×3 (o) 5×8
    (p) 4×8 (q) 7×2 (r) 4×2 (s) 10×3 (t) 2×10
    (u) 10×4 (v) 9×5 (w) 3×6 (x) 2×2 (y) 10×5

2. (a) 5×9 (b) 7×7 (c) 4×9 (d) 9×6 (e) 10×8
    (f) 9×7 (g) 8×8 (h) 9×9 (i) 7×10 (j) 10×10
    (k) 6×8 (l) 8×9 (m) 9×10 (n) 7×9 (o) 9×8
    (p) 10×6 (q) 8×7 (r) 7×6 (s) 9×2 (t) 3×9
    (u) 7×5 (v) 6×6 (w) 7×8 (x) 6×7 (y) 5×5

3. (a) $3 \times 5 \times 10$ (b) $4 \times 4 \times 10$ (c) $3 \times 6 \times 10$
    (d) $5 \times 4 \times 10$ (e) $2 \times 9 \times 10$ (f) $3 \times 8 \times 10$
    (g) $9 \times 3 \times 10$ (h) $6 \times 6 \times 10$ (i) $7 \times 3 \times 10$
    (j) $5 \times 5 \times 10$ (k) $3 \times 6 \times 10$ (l) $6 \times 8 \times 10$
    (m) $10 \times 6 \times 5$ (n) $10 \times 4 \times 8$ (o) $10 \times 8 \times 5$
    (p) $10 \times 2 \times 6$ (q) $4 \times 10 \times 6$ (r) $6 \times 10 \times 4$
    (s) $5 \times 10 \times 7$ (t) $7 \times 10 \times 7$ (u) $9 \times 10 \times 6$
    (v) $8 \times 10 \times 2$ (w) $3 \times 10 \times 3$ (x) $4 \times 10 \times 2$

4. (a) $4 \times 9 \times 100$ (b) $6 \times 5 \times 100$ (c) $9 \times 4 \times 100$
   (d) $9 \times 5 \times 100$ (e) $6 \times 7 \times 100$ (f) $7 \times 2 \times 100$
   (g) $4 \times 3 \times 100$ (h) $5 \times 3 \times 100$ (i) $3 \times 7 \times 100$
   (j) $6 \times 3 \times 10 \times 10$ (k) $5 \times 2 \times 10 \times 10$ (l) $9 \times 3 \times 10 \times 10$
  (m) $7 \times 10 \times 4 \times 10$ (n) $8 \times 10 \times 6 \times 10$ (o) $8 \times 10 \times 4 \times 10$
   (p) $9 \times 10 \times 6 \times 10$ (q) $4 \times 10 \times 9 \times 10$ (r) $7 \times 10 \times 5 \times 10$
   (s) $9 \times 10 \times 7 \times 10$ (t) $8 \times 10 \times 8 \times 10$ (u) $9 \times 10 \times 8 \times 10$
   (v) $9 \times 10 \times 9 \times 10$ (w) $8 \times 10 \times 7 \times 10$ (x) $6 \times 10 \times 7 \times 10$
   (y) $2 \times 10 \times 9 \times 10$

5. (a) $3 \times 9 \times 1\,000$ (b) $4 \times 6 \times 1\,000$ (c) $4 \times 5 \times 1\,000$
   (d) $6 \times 3 \times 1\,000$ (e) $2 \times 4 \times 1\,000$ (f) $7 \times 5 \times 1\,000$
   (g) $6 \times 6 \times 10 \times 100$ (h) $7 \times 7 \times 10 \times 100$ (i) $8 \times 4 \times 10 \times 100$
   (j) $9 \times 5 \times 100 \times 10$ (k) $5 \times 5 \times 100 \times 10$ (l) $4 \times 9 \times 100 \times 10$
  (m) $7 \times 10 \times 8 \times 100$ (n) $5 \times 10 \times 7 \times 100$ (o) $6 \times 10 \times 9 \times 100$
   (p) $3 \times 10 \times 3 \times 100$ (q) $4 \times 10 \times 4 \times 100$ (r) $5 \times 10 \times 2 \times 100$
   (s) $9 \times 100 \times 7 \times 10$ (t) $7 \times 100 \times 6 \times 10$ (u) $8 \times 100 \times 5 \times 10$
   (v) $3 \times 100 \times 4 \times 10$ (w) $8 \times 100 \times 8 \times 10$ (x) $7 \times 100 \times 8 \times 10$
   (y) $8 \times 100 \times 9 \times 10$

6. (a) 30×40 (b) 80×20 (c) 50×60 (d) 40×70 (e) 30×80
   (f) 20×60 (g) 60×30 (h) 90×20 (i) 40×20 (j) 70×20
   (k) 50×60 (l) 70×40 (m) 60×70 (n) 80×50 (o) 60×80
   (p) 30×700 (q) 300×20 (r) 800×30 (s) 600×80 (t) 700×90
   (u) 50×400 (v) 30×500 (w) 90×400 (x) 40×900 (y) 90×800

2.8 Multiplying numbers 'in your head'

A baker fills trays with 36 loaves of bread. How many loaves does he need to fill 7 trays?

To answer this question without a calculator or written calculation, think of 36 as 3 tens and 6 units:

$$36 \text{ is } 30 + 6$$
$$30 \times 7 = 10 \times 3 \times 7$$
$$= 10 \times 21$$
$$= 210$$
$$6 \times 7 = 42$$
$$\text{so } 36 \times 7 = 210 + 42$$
$$= 252$$

You may need to write down some steps but try to do as much of the calculation as you can 'in your head'.

Example

Peter Ashworth orders wood screws in packets of 25. How many wood screws will he receive if he orders 8 packets?

$$20 \times 8 = 160$$
$$5 \times 8 = 40$$
$$\text{so } 25 \times 8 = 200$$

He will receive 200 wood screws.

Exercise 2H

Answer all the questions without using a calculator.

1. (a) 12×5 (b) 14×3 (c) 13×6 (d) 16×2 (e) 17×3
   (f) 4×14 (g) 8×12 (h) 4×18 (i) 4×16 (j) 5×15
   (k) 25×4 (l) 24×5 (m) 26×6 (n) 27×2 (o) 35×8
   (p) 7×16 (q) 9×31 (r) 8×42 (s) 7×42 (t) 6×44
   (u) 27×8 (v) 26×9 (w) 86×7 (x) 5×66 (y) 35×9

2. A driver earns £9 an hour. How much will he earn if he works:
   (a) 12 hours   (b) 20 hours   (c) 23 hours   (d) 30 hours   (e) 36 hours?

3. A farmer expects to harvest 200 kilograms of oil seeds from every acre of a crop she plants.

   How many kilograms of seed will she harvest if she plants:
   (a) 3 acres   (b) 4 acres   (c) 70 acres   (d) 12 acres   (e) 28 acres?

4. Jade Nichols decides to save £8 pounds every week from her wages to pay for her holiday. How much will she have saved after:
   (a) 10 weeks   (b) 12 weeks   (c) 20 weeks
   (d) 27 weeks   (e) 51 weeks?

2.9 Dividing numbers 'in your head'

Most people work out divisions by thinking about the multiplication table. To work out $35 \div 7$, remember that $7 \times 5 = 35$ so $35 \div 7 = 5$

If there is not an exact answer from the multiplication tables you write a remainder.

Hint:
This triangle may help.

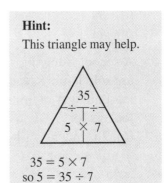

$35 = 5 \times 7$
so $5 = 35 \div 7$
or $7 = 35 \div 5$

Example

27 lollipops are shared by 4 children. How many lollipops does each child get and how many are left over?

Remembering that $4 \times 6 = 24$ gives you the answer:
$27 \div 4 = 6$ remainder 3

Exercise 21

Answer all the questions without using a calculator or written calculations.

1. (a) $28 \div 4$ (b) $24 \div 6$ (c) $18 \div 3$ (d) $36 \div 4$
   (e) $14 \div 2$ (f) $15 \div 5$ (g) $24 \div 8$ (h) $18 \div 9$
   (i) $16 \div 4$ (j) $27 \div 3$ (k) $40 \div 4$ (l) $35 \div 5$
   (m) $42 \div 6$ (n) $63 \div 7$ (o) $40 \div 8$ (p) $18 \div 2$
   (q) $36 \div 6$ (r) $54 \div 9$ (s) $48 \div 8$ (t) $49 \div 7$
   (u) $56 \div 8$ (v) $72 \div 9$ (w) $30 \div 5$ (x) $45 \div 9$
   (y) $81 \div 9$

2. (a) $11 \div 2$ (b) $14 \div 3$ (c) $23 \div 4$ (d) $21 \div 5$
   (e) $33 \div 6$ (f) $36 \div 7$ (g) $38 \div 7$ (h) $21 \div 8$
   (i) $15 \div 9$ (j) $8 \div 6$ (k) $21 \div 2$ (l) $26 \div 3$
   (m) $50 \div 6$ (n) $43 \div 5$ (o) $37 \div 8$ (p) $83 \div 9$
   (q) $25 \div 7$ (r) $25 \div 3$ (s) $75 \div 8$ (t) $44 \div 7$
   (u) $42 \div 9$ (v) $57 \div 6$ (w) $48 \div 5$ (x) $67 \div 8$
   (y) $98 \div 9$

3. On a school trip, up to four students will share each bedroom. What is the least number of bedrooms needed if the number of students going on the trip is:
   (a) 36
   (b) 38
   (c) 29
   (d) 39
   (e) 43?

4. A school is buying storage lockers for students. The lockers are sold in units, each unit having 9 lockers. What is the least number of units the school needs to buy to provide lockers for:
   (a) 36 students (b) 47 students (c) 53 students
   (d) 77 students (e) 89 students?

2.10 Using division by 10, 100 or 1 000 to divide numbers 'in your head'

Example 1

$350 \div 70$

If you divide both numbers by 10, this division is the same as $35 \div 7 = 5$

Example 2

$72\,000 \div 900$

If you divide both numbers by 100, this division is the same as $720 \div 9$

$720 \div 9 = 10 \times 72 \div 9 = 10 \times 8 = 80$

Example 3

$180\,000 \div 2\,000$

If you divide both numbers by 1 000, this division is the same as
$180 \div 2 = 10 \times 18 \div 2 = 10 \times 9 = 90$

Exercise 2J

Answer all the questions without using a calculator or written calculations.

1. (a) $160 \div 20$ (b) $140 \div 70$ (c) $300 \div 50$ (d) $160 \div 40$ (e) $150 \div 50$
    (f) $200 \div 20$ (g) $60 \div 30$ (h) $180 \div 60$ (i) $400 \div 50$ (j) $200 \div 40$
    (k) $150 \div 30$ (l) $160 \div 80$ (m) $360 \div 60$ (n) $490 \div 70$ (o) $400 \div 80$
    (p) $360 \div 90$ (q) $100 \div 20$ (r) $630 \div 70$ (s) $210 \div 30$ (t) $240 \div 80$
    (u) $180 \div 90$ (v) $300 \div 60$ (w) $140 \div 20$ (x) $320 \div 40$ (y) $480 \div 80$

2. (a) $800 \div 400$ (b) $900 \div 300$ (c) $2\,400 \div 400$
    (d) $2\,500 \div 500$ (e) $3\,200 \div 800$ (f) $4\,500 \div 500$
    (g) $1\,600 \div 800$ (h) $2\,700 \div 900$ (i) $2\,800 \div 700$
    (j) $4\,800 \div 600$ (k) $5\,600 \div 700$ (l) $4\,200 \div 700$
    (m) $6\,400 \div 800$ (n) $2\,700 \div 900$ (o) $2\,400 \div 600$
    (p) $3\,500 \div 500$ (q) $4\,200 \div 600$ (r) $1\,200 \div 400$
    (s) $2\,800 \div 400$ (t) $5\,400 \div 600$ (u) $7\,200 \div 800$
    (v) $1\,800 \div 300$ (w) $3\,600 \div 400$ (x) $1\,800 \div 300$

3. (a) $45\,000 \div 9\,000$ (b) $12\,000 \div 3\,000$ (c) $12\,000 \div 2\,000$
    (d) $27\,000 \div 3\,000$ (e) $10\,000 \div 5\,000$ (f) $20\,000 \div 5\,000$
    (g) $24\,000 \div 3\,000$ (h) $56\,000 \div 7\,000$ (i) $54\,000 \div 9\,000$
    (j) $6\,000 \div 2\,000$ (k) $64\,000 \div 8\,000$ (l) $63\,000 \div 9\,000$
    (m) $4\,000 \div 2\,000$ (n) $81\,000 \div 9\,000$ (o) $42\,000 \div 6\,000$
    (p) $25\,000 \div 5\,000$ (q) $12\,000 \div 2\,000$ (r) $12\,000 \div 3\,000$
    (s) $36\,000 \div 4\,000$ (t) $20\,000 \div 4\,000$ (u) $42\,000 \div 7\,000$

4. (a) $600 \div 20$ (b) $2\,400 \div 40$ (c) $35\,000 \div 500$
  (d) $2\,400 \div 20$ (e) $32\,000 \div 800$ (f) $72\,000 \div 900$
  (g) $48\,000 \div 80$ (h) $28\,000 \div 40$ (i) $28\,000 \div 70$
  (j) $320\,000 \div 800$ (k) $300\,000 \div 600$ (l) $350\,000 \div 700$
  (m) $24\,000 \div 60$ (n) $49\,000 \div 70$ (o) $27\,000 \div 30$
  (p) $20\,000 \div 50$ (q) $360\,000 \div 60$ (r) $54\,000 \div 90$
  (s) $630\,000 \div 90$ (t) $30\,000 \div 600$ (u) $720\,000 \div 8\,000$
  (v) $810\,000 \div 9\,000$ (w) $480\,000 \div 6\,000$ (x) $480\,000 \div 800$
  (y) $560\,000 \div 70$

2.11 Multiplying by single-digit numbers with written calculations

If multiplications by single-digit numbers are too difficult to do in your head, you do them on paper.

Example

Find   (a) 124×2 (b) 472×8 (c) 322×80

(a)
$$
\begin{array}{r}
124 \\
\times\ 2 \\
\hline
248 \\
\hline
\end{array}
$$

(b)
$$
\begin{array}{r}
472 \\
\times\ 8 \\
\hline
3\,776 \\
{}_{5\ 1} \\
\end{array}
$$

$8 \times 2 = 16$
16 is 6 units and 1 ten

$8 \times 70 = 560$
plus 10 carried
makes $570 = 7$ tens and 5 hundreds

$8 \times 400 = 3200$
plus 500 carried
makes $3\,700 = 7$ hundreds and 3 thousands

(c)
$$
\begin{array}{r}
322 \\
\times\ 80 \\
\hline
25\,760 \\
\hline
\end{array}
$$

Put down a zero. This multiplies the answer by 10. Then multiply by 8.

Exercise 2K

Answer all the questions without using a calculator.

1. (a) 234×2 (b) 232×3 (c) $2\,012 \times 4$ (d) 23×3 (e) $4\,302 \times 2$
  (f) 45×5 (g) 36×4 (h) 62×5 (i) 47×3 (j) 56×6
  (k) 64×8 (l) 47×5 (m) 84×7 (n) 87×9 (o) 43×8
  (p) 242×3 (q) 341×5 (r) 207×6 (s) 308×3 (t) 509×9
  (u) 345×6 (v) 563×8 (w) 547×6 (x) 324×9 (y) 649×8

MODULE 3

2. (a) 26×50 (b) 34×60 (c) 45×40 (d) 30×76 (e) 20×88
    (f) 40×72 (g) 67×30 (h) 73×50 (i) 80×88 (j) 39×40
    (k) 56×40 (l) 60×53 (m) 70×61 (n) 83×90 (o) 56×50
    (p) 30×57 (q) 231×40 (r) 567×50 (s) 344×60 (t) 202×90
    (u) 310×60 (v) 460×70 (w) 231×90 (x) 896×70 (y) 457×90

3. How many days are there in:
    (a) 12 weeks   (b) 23 weeks   (c) 40 weeks   (d) 38 weeks   (e) 52 weeks?

4. A politician has his office floors covered with hand-made ceramic tiles which cost £90 per square metre (m^2).

    Find the cost of using the tiles to cover an office with a floor area of:
    (a) $17 \, m^2$ (b) $23 \, m^2$ (c) $38 \, m^2$ (d) $72 \, m^2$ (e) $98 \, m^2$

2.12 Multiplying by two-digit numbers with written calculations

If multiplications by two-digit numbers are too difficult to do in your head, you do them on paper.

Example

Find $\quad 463 \times 85$

$$
\begin{array}{r}
463 \\
\times \, 85 \\
\hline
2\,315 \\
+ \, 37\,040 \\
\hline
39\,355 \\
\hline
\end{array}
$$

$2\,315 \longrightarrow \boxed{463 \times 5}$

$37\,040 \longrightarrow \boxed{463 \times 80}$

$39\,355 \longrightarrow \boxed{463 \times 85}$

Exercise 2L

1. (a) 26×34 (b) 64×45 (c) 53×24 (d) 47×32 (e) 56×43
    (f) 23×84 (g) 46×28 (h) 36×63 (i) 29×36 (j) 85×38
    (k) 59×23 (l) 76×22 (m) 34×56 (n) 85×55 (o) 78×39
    (p) 45×45 (q) 54×54 (r) 78×64 (s) 96×58 (t) 27×85
    (u) 67×39 (v) 38×54 (w) 85×58 (x) 96×75 (y) 58×65

2. (a) 234×41 (b) 563×22 (c) 781×51 (d) 607×45 (e) 730×36
    (f) 345×43 (g) 467×32 (h) 902×53 (i) 657×54 (j) 542×73
    (k) 709×85 (l) 560×74 (m) 355×67 (n) 902×55 (o) 983×24
    (p) 783×76 (q) 309×98 (r) 255×75 (s) 505×55 (t) 806×61
    (u) 788×61 (v) 592×47 (w) 775×84 (x) 957×86 (y) 692×78

3. The 123 students in Year 11 at Springfield High School are planning a leaving party. What will the total cost of the party be if each student pays:

    (a) £12   (b) £14   (c) £17   (d) £21   (e) £26?

4. A farmer expects to harvest 45 kilograms of apples from each tree he plants.
    How many kilograms will he harvest if he plants:

    (a) 45 trees   (b) 80 trees   (c) 144 trees
    (d) 586 trees   (e) 855 trees?

2.13 Dividing by single-digit numbers with written calculations

If divisions by single-digit numbers are too difficult to do in your head, you do them on paper.

Example

Find $318 \div 7$

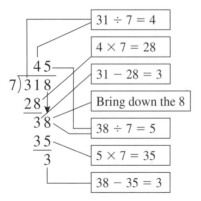

$318 \div 7 = 45$ remainder 3

Exercise 2M

1. (a) 255 ÷ 5   (b) 144 ÷ 2   (c) 138 ÷ 3
   (d) 208 ÷ 4   (e) 114 ÷ 2   (f) 365 ÷ 5
   (g) 352 ÷ 4   (h) 174 ÷ 3   (i) 240 ÷ 6
   (j) 192 ÷ 8   (k) 470 ÷ 5   (l) 198 ÷ 2
   (m) 294 ÷ 7   (n) 608 ÷ 8   (o) 396 ÷ 9
   (p) 522 ÷ 6   (q) 261 ÷ 3   (r) 384 ÷ 4
   (s) 455 ÷ 7   (t) 200 ÷ 8   (u) 261 ÷ 9
   (v) 492 ÷ 6   (w) 693 ÷ 9   (x) 520 ÷ 8
   (y) 576 ÷ 9

2. (a) 137 ÷ 2   (b) 200 ÷ 3   (c) 154 ÷ 5
   (d) 119 ÷ 4   (e) 306 ÷ 5   (f) 52 ÷ 3
   (g) 79 ÷ 2   (h) 114 ÷ 4   (i) 107 ÷ 6
   (j) 157 ÷ 8   (k) 140 ÷ 9   (l) 129 ÷ 7
   (m) 185 ÷ 9   (n) 227 ÷ 7   (o) 141 ÷ 6
   (p) 402 ÷ 8   (q) 195 ÷ 2   (r) 369 ÷ 4
   (s) 197 ÷ 5   (t) 242 ÷ 3   (u) 335 ÷ 6
   (v) 330 ÷ 8   (w) 232 ÷ 5   (x) 423 ÷ 7
   (y) 421 ÷ 9

3. Every day, from Monday to Friday, Michael puts a £1 coin in a jar in his bedroom. For how many weeks has Michael been saving when the amount in the jar is:

   (a) £65
   (b) £90
   (c) £125
   (d) £215
   (e) £260?

4. Each day, a farmer puts all the eggs his chickens have laid into boxes of six to sell.
How many boxes can be filled and how many eggs will be left over if the chickens have laid:

   (a) 271 eggs
   (b) 440 eggs
   (c) 305 eggs
   (d) 475 eggs
   (e) 502 eggs?

2.14 Dividing by two-digit numbers with written calculations

If divisions by two-digit numbers are too difficult to do in your head, you do them on paper.

Example

Find $500 \div 19$

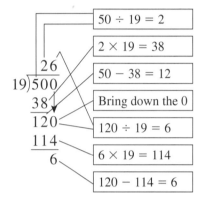

$$50 \div 19 = 2$$

$$2 \times 19 = 38$$

$$50 - 38 = 12$$

Bring down the 0

$$120 \div 19 = 6$$

$$6 \times 19 = 114$$

$$120 - 114 = 6$$

$$500 \div 19 = 26 \text{ remainder } 6$$

Exercise 2N

1. (a) $180 \div 12$ (b) $286 \div 11$ (c) $195 \div 13$ (d) $288 \div 12$
   (e) $704 \div 11$ (f) $350 \div 14$ (g) $304 \div 19$ (h) $270 \div 18$
   (i) $256 \div 16$ (j) $504 \div 12$ (k) $374 \div 17$ (l) $672 \div 21$
   (m) $360 \div 18$ (n) $225 \div 15$ (o) $572 \div 22$ (p) $609 \div 29$
   (q) $744 \div 31$ (r) $480 \div 32$ (s) $490 \div 35$ (t) $836 \div 38$
   (u) $897 \div 39$ (v) $492 \div 41$ (w) $882 \div 42$ (x) $900 \div 36$
   (y) $663 \div 51$

2. (a) $135 \div 12$ (b) $187 \div 13$ (c) $215 \div 14$ (d) $270 \div 12$
   (e) $222 \div 13$ (f) $230 \div 19$ (g) $317 \div 13$ (h) $311 \div 14$
   (i) $209 \div 13$ (j) $245 \div 12$ (k) $320 \div 19$ (l) $311 \div 18$
   (m) $320 \div 21$ (n) $472 \div 21$ (o) $600 \div 19$ (p) $426 \div 35$
   (q) $409 \div 25$ (r) $923 \div 23$ (s) $940 \div 31$ (t) $579 \div 14$
   (u) $680 \div 32$ (v) $986 \div 42$ (w) $946 \div 29$ (x) $827 \div 19$
   (y) $745 \div 51$

3. A baker sells bags of 12 bread rolls.
   How many bags can she fill if she bakes:

   (a) 408 rolls   (b) 396 rolls   (c) 492 rolls
   (d) 876 rolls   (e) 972 rolls?

4. Wizzochoc bars cost 49p each. Pria spends all her money on
Wizzochoc bars. How many bars can Pria buy and how
much change will she get if she has:

(a) £1·00
(b) £2·50
(c) £3·42
(d) £4·50
(e) £7·90?

2.15 Ratios

A **ratio** is used to compare numbers.

There are 12 patterned squares and 24 plain squares in this
picture.

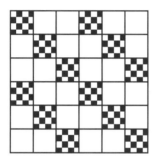

The ratio of patterned tiles to plain tiles is 12 to 24.
This is written as 12 : 24.

Both numbers divide by 12, so you can simplify the ratio:

$$12 : 24$$
$$= 12 \div 12 : 24 \div 12$$
$$= \qquad 1 : 2$$

> **Note**
> 12 is a **factor** of 12
> and 24.
> There is more about
> factors on page 210.

Example
Simplify these ratios:
(a) 6 : 4
(b) 25 : 40 : 60
(c) 64 centimetres : 1 metre

The simplified ratios are:
(a) 3 : 2   (divide by 2)
(b) 5 : 8 : 12   (divide by 5)
(c) 64 : 100 = 16 : 25   (divide by 4)

Exercise 20

1. Write down the ratio of shaded tiles to white tiles in each picture.

(a)

(b)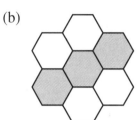

(c)

(d)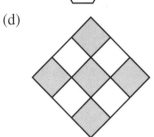

(e)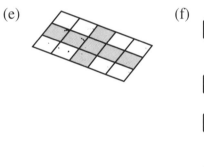

(f)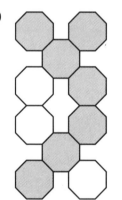

2. Simplify these ratios:

(a) 2 : 10   (b) 8 : 12   (c) 5 : 35   (d) 9 : 15   (e) 2 : 18

(f) 10 : 35   (g) 12 : 40   (h) 6 : 18   (i) 10 : 14   (j) 12 : 15

(k) 7 : 42   (l) 15 : 27   (m) 12 : 14   (n) 6 : 16   (o) 6 : 15

(p) 5 : 20   (q) 6 : 27   (r) 9 : 12   (s) 12 : 20   (t) 8 : 14

(u) 4 : 16 : 24   (v) 25 : 30 : 35   (w) 30 : 48 : 12   (x) 70 : 80 : 50   (y) 12 : 18 : 24

3. Simplify these ratios:

(a) 25 cm : 1 m   (b) 40 cm : 1 m

(c) 80 cm : 1 m   (d) 5 cm : 1 m

(e) 45 cm : 1 m   (f) 32 cm : 1 m

(g) 18 cm : 1 m   (h) 75 cm : 1 m

(i) 66 cm : 1 m   (j) 99 cm : 1 m

4. Simplify these ratios:

(a) 50p : £1·00 (b) 65p : £1·00
(c) 80p : £1·20 (d) £1·40 : £2·80
(e) £1.40 : £2·10 (f) £1·40 : £3·50
(g) £1.50 : £2·00 (h) £1·50 : £3·50
(i) £5.00 : £25·00 (j) £1·60 : £4·00

5. A farmer has a herd of 80 cows. 16 of the cows have calves. Find the ratio of cows with calves to cows without calves.

6. In a bag of 24 beads, 3 are red and the rest are green. Find the ratio of red beads to green beads.

7. Wayne owns 75 CDs, of which 25 are single CDs and the rest are long play. Find the ratio of single CDs to long play CDs.

8. Jo and Jillian have picked 16 kilograms of strawberries. Jo picked 6 kilograms. Find the ratio of the weight picked by Jo to the weight picked by Jillian.

9. On a bus there are 45 passengers. 20 of the passengers are male. Find the ratio of male passengers to female passengers.

10. A double-decker bus has 74 seats. 40 of these seats are on the top deck. Find the ratio of top deck seats to bottom deck seats.

2.16 Scaling up or down from a ratio

You can use ratios to work out quantities.

Example 1

A recipe for the pastry for an apple tart for 4 people requires 200 g of flour, 50 g of butter and 50 g of lard. How much flour, butter and lard are required to make an apple tart for 12 people?

The recipe is for 4 people.

You divide each quantity by 4 to find the amount needed for each person.

For one person: 50 g flour, 12·5 g butter, 12·5 g lard.

So for 12 people, you multiply these amounts by 12:

600 g flour, 150 g butter, 150 g lard.

MODULE 3

Example 2

Concrete is made by mixing sand, gravel and cement powder in the ratio 5 : 3 : 2. What quantities of sand and cement powder are needed to mix with 30 litres of gravel?

The gravel part of the ratio has been multiplied by 10. The quantities needed are:

> 50 litres of sand and 20 litres of cement powder.

Exercise 2P

1. A recipe for a pizza for 2 people requires 200 g of tomato sauce, 150 g of ham and 160 g of cheese. Find the quantities of tomato sauce, ham and cheese required for a pizza for:
   (a) 4 people   (b) 6 people   (c) 8 people   (d) 1 person   (e) 3 people

2. To make a fruit punch, Sandra Mina mixes apple juice, orange juice and lemonade in the ratio 1 : 3 : 2. Find the quantities of orange juice and lemonade needed to mix with the following quantities of apple juice.
   (a) 2 litres   (b) 4 litres   (c) 5 litres   (d) 10 litres   (e) 7 litres

3. The ratio of students staying for school lunch to students going home for lunch is 4 : 5. How many students stay for lunch if the number going home is:
   (a) 250   (b) 300   (c) 125   (d) 475   (e) 335?

4. If Marco works for 5 hours, he earns £12.
   How much does Marco earn if he works for:
   (a) 10 hours   (b) 20 hours   (c) 15 hours   (d) 1 hour   (e) 3 hours?

5. A car travels 120 miles and uses 20 litres of petrol.
   How many miles can the car travel using:
   (a) 40 litres   (b) 60 litres   (c) 1 litre   (d) 15 litres   (e) 12 litres?

6. A pile of 24 books is 12 cm high. How high is a pile of:
   (a) 48 books   (b) 72 books   (c) 36 books   (d) 1 book   (e) 10 books?

7. A machine produces 800 plastic buckets in 5 hours.
   How many buckets are produced in:
   (a) 10 hours   (b) 15 hours   (c) 1 hour   (d) 3 hours   (e) 14 hours?

8. A recipe for 4 people requires 8 eggs, 12 peaches and 400 g of cream. Find the quantities of eggs, peaches and cream required for a recipe for:
   (a) 8 people   (b) 12 people   (c) 1 person   (d) 3 people   (e) 7 people

MODULE 3

9. A recipe for 4 people requires 8 eggs, 12 peaches and 400 g
of cream.
Find the quantities of eggs and cream needed to mix with:

(a) 48 peaches (b) 3 peaches (c) 6 peaches (d) 24 peaches (e) 18 peaches

10. If she works for 4 hours, Nisha earns £32 but pays £8 of this
in tax. How much does Nisha earn and how much tax does
she pay if she works for:

(a) 12 hours (b) 1 hour (c) 3 hours (d) 6 hours (e) 9 hours?

2.17 Dividing quantities in a ratio

Example 1

Asaf and Afifa buy a packet of 24 sweets. Asaf pays 12p and
Afifa pays 36p. How many sweets should each receive?

The ratio of the amounts paid is 12 : 36 or 1 : 3.

To share 24 in the ratio 1 : 3 means dividing 24 into 4 parts.
If 24 is divided into 4 parts, each part is 6.

Asaf receives 1 part or $1 \times 6 = 6$ sweets.

Afifa receives 3 parts or $3 \times 6 = 18$ sweets.
Check: $6 + 18 = 24$

Example 2

Share 42 in the ratio 5 : 1

To share 42 in the ratio 5 : 1 means dividing 42 into 6 parts.
If 42 is divided into 6 parts, each part is 7.
First share is $5 \times 7 = 35$
Second share is $1 \times 7 = 7$
Check: $35 + 7 = 42$

$5 + 1 = 6$

Example 3

Share 99 in the ratio 1 : 3 : 7

To share 99 in the ratio 1 : 3 : 7 means dividing 99 into 11 parts.
If 99 is split into 11 parts, each part is 9.
First share is $1 \times 9 = 9$
Second share is $3 \times 9 = 27$
Third share is $7 \times 9 = 63$
Check: $9 + 27 + 63 = 99$

$1 + 3 + 7 = 11$

MODULE 3

Exercise 2Q

1. Share 24 in the ratios:
   (a) $1:7$ (b) $3:5$ (c) $3:1$ (d) $1:5$ (e) $5:7$

2. Share 72 in the ratios:
   (a) $2:1$ (b) $1:3$ (c) $5:3$ (d) $7:2$ (e) $4:5$

3. Share 70 in the ratios:
   (a) $9:1$ (b) $3:2$ (c) $1:6$ (d) $3:4$ (e) $3:7$

4. Share 120 in the ratios:
   (a) $2:1$ (b) $3:2$ (c) $1:5$ (d) $7:3$ (e) $9:1$

5. Share 99 in the ratios:
   (a) $8:1$ (b) $7:2$ (c) $10:1$ (d) $5:6$ (e) $1:2$

6. Share 42 in the ratios:
   (a) $5:1$ (b) $6:1$ (c) $3:1$ (d) $5:2$ (e) $4:3$

7. Share 128 in the ratios:
   (a) $7:1$ (b) $5:11$ (c) $15:17$ (d) $3:5$ (e) $31:33$

8. Share 40 in the ratios:
   (a) $1:2:5$ (b) $1:2:2$ (c) $2:3:5$ (d) $1:2:7$ (e) $1:1:2$

9. Share 360 in the ratios:
   (a) $3:5:7$ (b) $2:7:9$ (c) $1:3:5$ (d) $20:3:1$ (e) $4:5:11$

10. Share 630 in the ratios:
    (a) $2:5:8$ (b) $1:8:9$ (c) $1:2:18$ (d) $7:8:15$ (e) $15:12:8$

11. Davinder and Marianna share the 120 g of
    cereal left in a packet in the ratio $3:2$.
    How much cereal does Marianna receive?

12. A profit of £450 made on a market stall is shared between
    the stall holders in the ratio $4:5$.
    How much does each receive?

13. William and Shafiq contribute £3 and £4 to buy orange squash which they sell at a school fair. They make £21 in total. If they share the £21 in the ratio of their contributions, how much will William receive?

14. A recipe for pastry mixes flour, butter and lard in the ratio 4 : 1 : 1. What weight of flour, butter and lard are required to make 900 g of the pastry?

15. Concrete can be made by mixing sand, gravel and cement powder in the ratio 5 : 3 : 2. What volume of sand, gravel and cement powder will be needed to make 300 litres of concrete?

2.18 Squares and square roots

To make a **square** number you multiply a number by itself.
The first square number is $1 \times 1 = 1$
The fifth square number is $5 \times 5 = 25$.

You write 7^2, 'seven squared', to mean 7×7.

The area of this **square**
is $2 \text{ cm} \times 2 \text{ cm} = 4 \text{ cm}^2$

2 cm

2 cm

Example 1

Find the value of 20^2.
$$20^2 = 20 \times 20 = 400$$

Exercise 2R

1. What is the value of 6^2?

2. Calculate the value of 'ten squared'.

3. Calculate the value of each of these:

(a) 7^2 (b) 8^2 (c) 4^2 (d) 12^2 (e) 10^2

Finding a **square root** is the opposite of finding a **square**.

Example 2

Find the square root of 64.

$64 = 8 \times 8$ so **8** is the square root of 64.

You write **the square root of 25** like this $\sqrt{25}$.

You can find the square root of a number in three different ways:

1. **by inspection** when you can see the answer
   Example Find $\sqrt{36}$ Answer = 6

   > **Hint:**
   > You should remember
   > that $6 \times 6 = 36$.

2. **with a calculator**
   Example Find $\sqrt{3\,136}$
                Press
                so $\sqrt{3\,136} = 56$

3. **by trial and improvement**
   Example Find $\sqrt{256}$
                Try 10 $10 \times 10 = 100$ – too small
                Try 20 $20 \times 20 = 400$ – too large
                Try 15 $15 \times 15 = 225$ – a bit too small
                Try 16 $16 \times 16 = 256$ – just right   So $\sqrt{256} = \mathbf{16}$

Exercise 2S

1. Find each of these square roots by inspection.
   (a) $\sqrt{25}$ (b) $\sqrt{9}$ (c) $\sqrt{81}$ (d) $\sqrt{49}$ (e) $\sqrt{100}$

2. Use a calculator to find these square roots.
   (a) $\sqrt{289}$ (b) $\sqrt{1\,849}$ (c) $\sqrt{80\,656}$

3. Use trial and improvement to find $\sqrt{484}$.

Summary

Checkout N2

Summary	Checkout N2
1. To multiply a number by 10, move all the digits one place to the left and add a zero.	1. Multiply these numbers by 10. (a) 23 (b) 36
2. To multiply a number by 100, move all the digits two places to the left and add two zeros.	2. Multiply these numbers by 100. (a) 17 (b) 30
3. To multiply a number by 1 000, move all the digits three places to the left and add three zeros.	3. Multiply these numbers by 1 000. (a) 7 (b) 49
4. To divide a number by 10, move all the digits one place to the right.	4. Divide these numbers by 10. (a) 50 (b) 560
5. To divide a number by 100, move all the digits two places to the right.	5. Divide these numbers by 100. (a) 400 (b) 3 500
6. To divide a number by 1 000, move all the digits three places to the right.	6. Divide these numbers by 1 000. (a) 3 000 (b) 78 000

7. You should work out simple calculations in your head.

7. Work out:
   (a) 6×7 (b) 8×9
   (c) 40×5 (d) 90×700
   (e) 23×5 (f) 42×8
   (g) $36 \div 6$ (h) $63 \div 9$

8. Work out harder calculations on paper.

8. Work out:
   (a) $41 \div 8$ (b) $47 \div 5$
   (c) $160 \div 20$ (d) $540 \div 60$
   (e) 125×6 (f) 18×50
   (g) 237×5 (h) 846×49
   (i) $375 \div 3$ (j) $407 \div 5$
   (k) $324 \div 12$ (l) $951 \div 21$

9. Any number which divides exactly into 24 is called a **factor** of 24.

9. Find all the factors of:
   (a) 32   (b) 60

10 Ratios can be simplified by dividing both numbers by a common factor.

10. Simplify the ratios:
   (a) $4 : 16$ (b) $15 : 12 : 9$

11. You can scale up or down from a ratio.

11. If orange juice and water are mixed in the ratio of $2 : 7$, what quantity of water is needed to mix with 4 litres of orange juice?

12. You can divide amounts in a ratio.

12. Divide £24 in the ratios:
   (a) $1 : 5$ (b) $5 : 6 : 1$

MODULE 3

Revision exercise N2

1. Paul has five numbered discs.

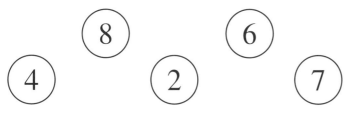

   (a) (i)   Which of Paul's numbers is a square number?
       (ii) Which of Paul's numbers is a multiple of 4, other than 4 itself?

Paul uses some of the discs to make a four figure number, 2684, as shown.

(b) (i) What is the value of the 6 in Paul's number?

   (ii) Paul multiplies his number by 10.
        What is the value of the 6 in his new number?

[SEG]

2. (a) What is the value of 5 in the number 3454?

   (b) The number 7923 is multiplied by 100.
       What is the value of the 2 in the answer?   [SEG]

3. (a) Write seven thousand three hundred and twenty nine in figures.

   (b) The number in part (a) is divided by 100.
       What is the value of the digit 2 in the answer?   [SEG]

4. Vicky buys 17 packs of oranges. Each pack contains 9 oranges.

   (a) How many oranges does she buy?

   (b) Give the number of oranges to the nearest 10.   [SEG]

5. Jeremy and Caroline find the following list of items for a buffet lunch for 20 people.

   40 chicken legs
   30 sausage rolls
   20 strawberry meringues
   5 one litre containers of orange juice.

   Jeremy and Caroline are organising a buffet lunch for 110 people.
   Re-write the list for a buffet lunch for these 110 people.

[SEG]

6. In a large restaurant, there are 19 waiters. Each waiter is paid £27 for an evening's work. Find the total amount paid by the restaurant to its waiters.   [SEG]

7. William is a cleaner at an hotel. Normally he cleans 8 bedrooms in a day and his pay is £34. On one day Emma helps William so that William only cleans 5 bedrooms. William agrees to divide his pay between them in the ratio of the number of bedrooms each has cleaned. How much does Emma receive?   [SEG]

8. (a) Write the number four thousand three hundred and sixty-seven in figures.
   (b) (i) Work out 2695 + 243.
       (ii) Work out 793 − 47.
   (c) Write the number 687 to the nearest 10.
   (d) The number 240 is divided by 10. What is the value of the 2 in the new number?   [SEG]

9. Yvonne makes 37 ties every day that she works. In one year, she works 239 days.

   Without using a calculator, work out how many ties Yvonne makes in that year.

   You **must** show all your working.   [SEG]

10. Tulips are being planted on a roundabout. For every 3 yellow tulips planted, there are 7 red tulips and 9 pink tulips. Altogether 1406 tulips are planted.

    How many red tulips are planted?   [SEG]

11. George has £80.50 to share between his two nieces. He decides to divide the money in the ratio of their ages. Ann is 8 years old and Joan is 15 years old.

    How much will Ann receive?

12. There are 200 tulips in a flower bed. Of these 64 are yellow. What fraction of the tulips are yellow?

13. A college party of 38 travel to London by minibus to watch an international hockey match. Each minibus can carry 15 passengers.

    How many minibuses travel to London?

14. At a theatre, 180 people are seated. There are 15 rows of seats.
Each row contains the same number of people.
How many are sitting in each row?

15. (a) 100 tennis balls are put into boxes.
Each box holds 3 tennis balls.

    (i) How many full boxes will there be?

    (ii) How many tennis balls will be left over?

  (b) (i) What is the remainder when 1000 is divided by 3?

    (ii) What is the remainder when 10 001 is divided by 3?

[NEAB]

16. Mrs. Preece is printing an examination for all year 11 students.
Each examination uses 14 sheets of paper.

  (a) There are 235 students in year 11.
How many sheets of paper does she need?

  (b) A ream contains 500 sheets of paper.
How many reams of paper does she need to print
all the examinations?   [NEAB]

17. Joe is making sandwiches for a meeting of the Women's Institute.
He bought 25 loaves of bread from the local supermarket.
The cost was £14.
How much was each loaf?   [NEAB]

N3 NUMBER 3

This unit will show you how to:

- Understand place value in decimal numbers
- Order decimal numbers
- Round decimal numbers
- Add and subtract decimal numbers

Before you start:

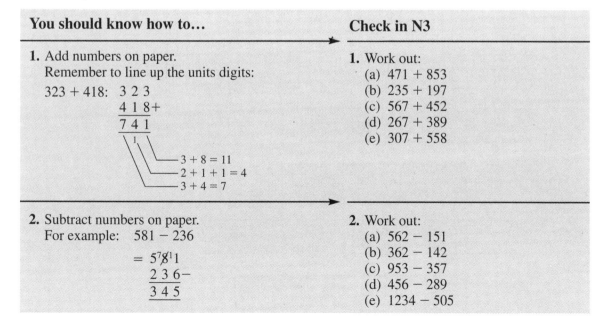

You should know how to...	Check in N3
1. Add numbers on paper. Remember to line up the units digits: $323 + 418$: see worked example	**1.** Work out: (a) $471 + 853$ (b) $235 + 197$ (c) $567 + 452$ (d) $267 + 389$ (e) $307 + 558$
2. Subtract numbers on paper. For example: $581 - 236$	**2.** Work out: (a) $562 - 151$ (b) $362 - 142$ (c) $953 - 357$ (d) $456 - 289$ (e) $1234 - 505$

MODULE 3

3.1 Place value in decimal numbers: Tenths

The number 3·8 has a **decimal point**.

The first digit which follows a decimal point is the **tenths** digit.

The number 3·8 means 3 and $\frac{8}{10}$.

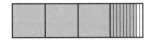

Example

Write the number represented by this picture as a decimal.

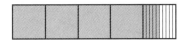

The number is 4·5.

Exercise 3A

You will need 2 millimetre graph paper for this exercise.

1. Write each number represented by the shaded part of each picture as a decimal.

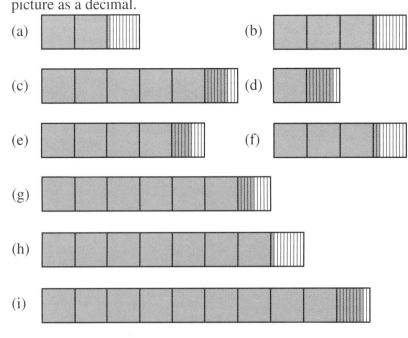

2. Draw pictures to represent these decimals.

(a) 2·7 (b) 6·1 (c) 4·9 (d) 1·2 (e) 7·6
(f) 6·7 (g) 5·5 (h) 9·3 (i) 3·4 (j) 8·7

3. Anita is measuring the length of a worm. This picture shows her ruler.

Anita can write down the length of the worm like this:

5 cm 7 mm

Or, Anita can use a decimal point and write the length like this:

5·7 cm

Write each of these worm lengths with a decimal point.

(a) 5 cm 8 mm (b) 6 cm 3 mm (c) 2 cm 9 mm (d) 4 cm 4 mm (e) 8 cm 1 mm
(f) 9 cm 7 mm (g) 7 cm 9 mm (h) 5 cm 2 mm (i) 10 cm 5 mm (j) 12 cm 6 mm

Write each of these worm lengths in centimetres and millimetres.

(k) 4·9 cm (l) 9·5 cm (m) 10·3 cm (n) 8·3 cm (o) 9·1 cm
(p) 1·9 cm (q) 3·8 cm (r) 8·6 cm (s) 12·4 cm (t) 13·3 cm

3.2 Ordering decimal numbers: Tenths

Nadia works on a farm which sells 'pick your own' fruit. One of her jobs is to weigh the boxes of strawberries that people have picked. She records these weights for ten boxes.

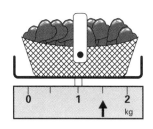

4·1 kg, 2·3 kg, 0·9 kg, 1·2 kg, 3·2 kg,
1·7 kg, 0·8 kg, 3·5 kg, 2·6 kg, 1·5 kg

These weights can be sorted into order, starting with the smallest, like this. Order the whole number part first:

0·9 kg 0·8 kg 1·2 kg 1·7 kg 1·5 kg 2·3 kg 2·6 kg 3·2 kg 3·5 kg

Now order the decimal part: 0·8 kg 0·9 kg 1·2 kg 1·5 kg 1·7 kg 2·3 kg 2·6 kg 3·2 kg 3·5 kg

Exercise 3B

Write a list of these numbers sorted into order, starting with the smallest.

1. 1·1, 2·3, 1·7, 2·4, 1·9
2. 3·1, 4·3, 3·8, 4·0, 2·7
3. 6·8, 8·6, 4·5, 5·4, 6·2, 2·6
4. 3·5, 5·3, 1·9, 9·1, 7·6, 6·7
5. 12·4, 13·3, 12·0, 13·7, 12·2, 12·8, 12·0, 13·5
6. 2·5, 3·6, 1·7, 4·3, 2·9, 3·0, 2·6, 1·1, 4·4, 6·2
7. 8·1, 5·6, 7·3, 2·6, 4·9, 4·6, 8·2, 8·0, 7·3, 9·1
8. 3·5, 3·4, 2·6, 0·7, 0·9, 2·1, 1·5, 3·0, 1·7, 2·2
9. 6·7, 7·6, 8·3, 3·8, 9·2, 2·9, 3·0, 0·3, 5·1, 1·5
10. 15·6, 14·3, 18·2, 14·6, 15·0, 13·3, 13·0, 14·5, 19·4, 18·0, 15·1, 13·2
11. 22·4, 23·6, 22·8, 23·6, 22·0, 23·0, 22·5, 22·9, 23·8, 23·0, 22·1, 23·8
12. 45·3, 43·5, 42·6, 46·2, 41·0, 40·1, 43·8, 48·3, 44·7, 47·4, 44·3, 43·4

3.3 Place value in decimal numbers: Hundredths

The number 3·87 has two digits after the decimal point.

The second digit which follows a decimal point is the **hundredths** digit.

The number 3·87 means 3 and $\frac{8}{10}$ and $\frac{7}{100}$.

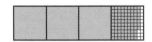

Example

Write the number represented by this picture as a decimal.

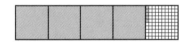

The number is 4·05.

Exercise 3C

You will need 2 millimetre graph paper for this exercise.

1. Write each number represented by the shaded part of each picture as a decimal.

(a)

(b)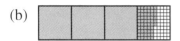

(c)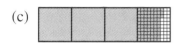

(d)

(e)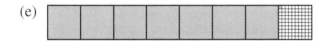

(f)

(g)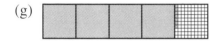

(h)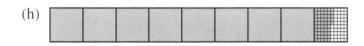

(i)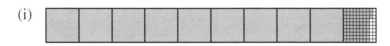

(j)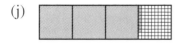

2. Draw pictures to represent these decimals.

    (a) 2·74   (b) 6·13

    (c) 4·99   (d) 1·02

    (e) 7·62   (f) 7·26

    (g) 5·05   (h) 9·37

    (i) 3·04   (j) 8·76

MODULE 3

3. Thomas is measuring the long jump on Sports Day. He is using a ruler marked in metres, tenths of a metre and centimetres. This picture shows him measuring a jump of 4 metres and 47 centimetres.

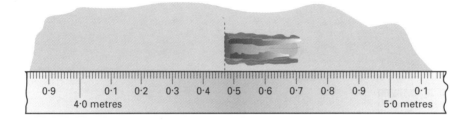

Thomas can write down the length of the jump like this:

4 m 47 cm

Or, he can use a decimal point and write the length like this:

4·47 m

> **Remember:**
> 100 cm = 1 m

Write each of these jump lengths with a decimal point.

(a) 3 m 38 cm (b) 2 m 30 cm (c) 2 m 3 cm (d) 2 m 9 cm (e) 4 m 1 cm
(f) 4 m 87 cm (g) 5 m 6 cm (h) 3 m 50 cm (i) 1 m 5 cm (j) 4 m 96 cm

Write each of these jumps lengths in metres and centimetres.

(k) 4·92 m (l) 3·51 m (m) 1·99 m (n) 2·60 m (o) 2·06 m
(p) 2·45 m (q) 4·09 m (r) 3·10 m (s) 3·01 m (t) 2·11 m

3.4 Ordering decimal numbers: Hundredths

These are the heights jumped by 10 students in a school high jump competition:

1·32 m, 0·89 m, 1·45 m, 1·06 m, 0·90 m,
1·22 m, 1·02 m, 1·20 m, 0·95 m, 1·34 m

These heights can be sorted into order, starting with the smallest.

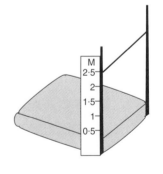

You order the whole number part first:

0·89 m   0·90 m   0·95 m   1·32 m   1·45 m   1·06 m   1·22 m   1·02 m   1·20 m   1·34 m

Now order the tenths:

0·89 m   0·90 m   0·95 m   1·06 m   1·02 m   1·22 m   1·20 m   1·32 m   1·34 m   1·45 m

Now order the hundredths:

0·89 m   0·90 m   0·95 m   1·02 m   1·06 m   1·20 m   1·22 m   1·32 m   1·34 m   1·45 m

To sort decimals with a mixture of decimal places it can help to add zeros.

Example

Sort these numbers into order, starting with the smallest.

> 2·31,   2·3,   2·6,   2·06,   2·53,   2·1

First make the number of decimal places the same by adding zeros:

The whole number parts are all 2, so sort using the tenths:

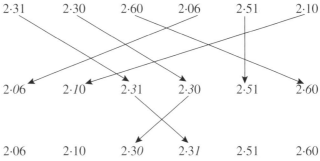

Now sort using the hundredths: 2·06   2·10   2·30   2·31   2·51   2·60

So the order is: 2·06,   2·1,   2·3,   2·31,   2·51,   2·6

Exercise 3D

Write a list of these numbers sorted into order, starting with the smallest.

1. 2·32, 2·23, 3·41, 3·14, 3·20, 3·02
2. 1·55, 1·21, 1·34, 1·43, 1·91, 1·84
3. 4·22, 4·12, 4·31, 4·13, 4·44, 4·04
4. 5·06, 5·63, 5·82, 5·02, 5·12, 5·21
5. 6·03, 7·25, 4·52, 4·02, 5·50, 6·21
6. 9·03, 9·01, 9·10, 9·04, 9·03, 9·33
7. 12·21, 12·35, 11·99, 10·68, 12·34, 13·52, 10·99, 10·09
8. 3·05, 4·5, 6·7, 6·34, 5·16, 5·2
9. 0·13, 0·3, 0·1, 0·09, 0·9, 0·01
10. 9·0, 9·3, 9·29, 9·03, 9·2, 9·19
11. 12·4, 12·37, 12·98, 12·89, 12·8, 12·9, 12·45, 12·4, 12·5, 12·37
12. 32·27, 32·72, 32·7, 32·2, 32·56, 32·65, 32·6, 32·06, 32·5, 32·05

3.5 Place value in decimal numbers: Thousandths

The number 3·875 has three digits after the decimal point.

The third digit which follows a decimal point is the **thousandths** digit.

The number 3·875 means 3 and $\frac{8}{10}$ and $\frac{7}{100}$ and $\frac{5}{1\,000}$.

MODULE 3

Example

Write each number as an addition of separate column values.

(a) 5·31

(b) 14·235

(a) $5·31 = 5 + \frac{3}{10} + \frac{1}{100}$

(b) $14·235 = 10 + 4 + \frac{2}{10} + \frac{3}{100} + \frac{5}{1\,000}$

Exercise 3E

1. Write each number as an addition of separate column values.

(a) 5·3	(b) 4·85	(c) 2·79	(d) 6·61	(e) 6·16
(f) 1·664	(g) 0·932	(h) 9·003	(i) 8·072	(j) 5·302
(k) 26·25	(l) 31·325	(m) 231·4	(n) 345·67	(o) 34·075
(p) 12·346	(q) 23·761	(r) 97·035	(s) 39·012	(t) 9·002
(u) 9·201	(v) 19·457	(w) 25·658	(x) 67·054	(y) 33·333

2. Write the decimal number represented by each addition.

(a) $3 + \frac{7}{10}$

(b) $7 + \frac{3}{10}$

(c) $6 + \frac{3}{10} + \frac{5}{100}$

(d) $7 + \frac{6}{100}$

(e) $20 + 7 + \frac{3}{10} + \frac{1}{100} + \frac{6}{1\,000}$

(f) $30 + 1 + \frac{5}{10} + \frac{1}{1\,000}$

(g) $40 + \frac{3}{10} + \frac{6}{100} + \frac{8}{1\,000}$

(h) $40 + 5 + \frac{7}{100} + \frac{9}{1\,000}$

(i) $60 + \frac{7}{1\,000}$

(j) $70 + 5 + \frac{4}{10} + \frac{3}{1\,000}$

(k) $100 + 40 + 8 + \frac{6}{10} + \frac{5}{100} + \frac{7}{1\,000}$

(l) $300 + 5 + \frac{7}{100}$

(m) $500 + 80 + \frac{5}{10} + \frac{1}{1\,000}$

(n) $100 + 10 + 1 + \frac{1}{10} + \frac{1}{100} + \frac{1}{1\,000}$

(o) $30 + 7 + \frac{2}{10} + \frac{3}{1\,000}$

(p) $600 + 50 + 7 + \frac{3}{100} + \frac{6}{1\,000}$

(q) $7\,000 + 200 + 50 + 7 + \frac{8}{10} + \frac{6}{100} + \frac{3}{1\,000}$

(r) $5\,000 + 200 + 3 + \frac{5}{10} + \frac{6}{1\,000}$

(s) $6\,000 + \frac{6}{1\,000}$

(t) $\frac{3}{10} + \frac{2}{1\,000} + 500$

(u) $80 + 9 + \frac{6}{100} + 100 + \frac{7}{1\,000}$

(v) $20 + \frac{2}{10} + 2\,000 + 200 + \frac{2}{100} + \frac{2}{1\,000}$

(w) $\frac{6}{100} + 3\,000 + \frac{2}{1\,000} + 100 + 5$

(x) $\frac{5}{1\,000} + 6 + 200 + \frac{7}{10} + 7\,000 + \frac{5}{100}$

3.6 Approximating decimal numbers: Nearest whole number

Susan weighs her dog Benji and finds she is 19·7 kg.
Susan might approximate and say Benji is about 20 kg.
This is because 19·7 is closer to 20 than to 19.

If Benji weighed 19·3 kg,
Susan would say Benji
is about 19 kg.

The number 19·5 is exactly half way
between 19 and 20. When a number
is in the middle we always round up.
If Benji weighed 19·5 kg, Susan would
say Benji is about 20 kg.

The word **correct** describes approximations. Susan would say
she had given Benji's weight **correct to the nearest kilogram**.

Example

In a maths lesson, Elia measured the hand spread of six friends.
These are her results:

   15·4 cm, 16·8 cm, 17·2 cm, 17·5 cm, 18·2 cm and 18·5 cm

Write Elia's measurements correct to the nearest centimetre.

The results are: 15 cm, 17 cm, 17 cm, 18 cm, 18 cm and 19 cm.

Exercise 3F

  1. Write the numbers in these lists correct to the nearest whole number.
  (a) 1·1, 2·3, 1·7, 2·4, 1·9
  (b) 3·1, 4·3, 3·8, 4·0, 2·7
  (c) 6·8, 8·6, 4·5, 5·4, 6·2, 2·6
  (d) 3·5, 5·3, 1·9, 9·1, 7·6, 6·7
  (e) 12·4, 13·3, 12·0, 13·7, 12·2, 12·8, 12·0, 13·5
  (f) 15·6, 14·3, 18·2, 14·6, 15·0, 13·3, 13·0, 14·5, 19·4, 18·0, 15·1, 13·2
  (g) 22·4, 23·6, 22·8, 23·6, 22·0, 23·0, 22·5, 22·9, 23·8, 23·0, 22·1, 23·8
  (h) 45·3, 43·5, 42·6, 46·2, 41·0, 40·1, 43·8, 48·3, 44·7, 47·4, 44·3, 43·4

2. Billy is measuring the height of some seedlings and writing the results down to the nearest centimetre. He records the height of one seedling as 9 cm. Which of these lengths could be Billy's accurate measurement:

A	9·0 cm	B	9·7 cm
C	9·5 cm	D	8·6 cm
E	8·4 cm	F	9·4 cm
G	8·5 cm	H	9·1 cm
I	9·8 cm	J	8·9 cm?

3.7 Approximating decimal numbers: Nearest tenth

Tariq jumped 4·37 m in the school long jump competition. Tariq approximates his jump and says, 'I jumped about 4·4 m.' This is because 4·37 is closer to 4·4 than to 4·3.

If Tariq had jumped 4·32 m he would say 'I jumped about 4·3 m.'

The number 4·35 is exactly in the middle between 4·3 and 4·4. When a number is in the middle you always round up. If Tariq had jumped 4·35 m, he would say, 'I jumped about 4·4 m.'

When you correct to the nearest tenth, you have written the number **correct to one decimal place**.

Example

Write these measurements correct to one decimal place.

(a) 15·24 cm	(b) 16·38 cm	(c) 17·25 cm
(d) 17·53 cm	(e) 18·29 cm	(f) 18·95 cm

The corrected measurements are:

(a) 15·2 cm	(b) 16·4 cm	(c) 17·3 cm
(d) 17·5 cm	(e) 18·3 cm	(f) 19·0 cm

Exercise 3G

1. Write out each list, giving each number correct to one decimal place.
   (a) 2·32, 2·28, 3·41, 3·14, 3·25, 3·09
   (b) 1·55, 1·20, 1·34, 1·43, 1·98, 1·85
   (c) 4·20, 4·95, 4·36, 4·13, 4·44, 4·08
   (d) 5·06, 5·63, 5·82, 5·97, 5·19, 5·21
   (e) 6·08, 7·25, 4·52, 4·19, 5·56, 6·98
   (f) 9·03, 9·75, 9·10, 9·06, 9·07, 9·35
   (g) 12·21, 12·35, 11·99, 10·68, 12·34, 13·52, 10·99, 10·09
   (h) 3·05, 4·50, 6·73, 6·34, 5·17, 5·95

2. Jody has calculated the average amount he spends each day on his school dinner. He writes down:

   'I spend £1·40, correct to the nearest 10p, on my school dinner each day.'

   Which of these amounts could be the exact answer to Jody's calculation:
   A £1·42   B £1·45   C £1·37   D £1·44
   E £1·34   F £1·39   G £1·36   H £1·35
   I £1·43   J £1·40?

3.8 Approximating decimal numbers: Nearest hundredth

Samantha and three friends decide to share the £13·79 cost of a taxi ride home from a disco. She uses a calculator to work out 13·79 ÷ 4 and gets the answer 3·4475. Samantha knows that £3·4475 is not an actual amount of money so she rounds the answer to £3·45. This is because 3·4475 is closer to 3·45 than to 3·44.

If the fare had been £13·77, Samantha's answer would have been £3·4425. Samantha would round this to £3·44.

If the fare had been £13·78, Samantha's answer would have been £3·445. When a number is in the middle we always round up. Samantha would round this to £3·45.

When we correct to the nearest hundredth, we say we have written the number **correct to two decimal places**.

Example

Write these measurements correct to two decimal places.

(a) 15·246 m   (b) 16·381 m   (c) 17·255 m
(d) 17·532 m   (e) 18·996 m   (f) 18·550 m

The corrected numbers are:

(a) 15·25 m   (b) 16·38 m   (c) 17·26 m
(d) 17·53 m   (e) 19·00 m   (f) 18·55 m

Exercise 3H

1. Write out each list, giving each number correct to two
   decimal places.
   (a) 2·325, 2·237, 3·401, 3·104, 3·236, 3·502
   (b) 1·505, 1·281, 1·334, 1·493, 1·916, 1·845
   (c) 4·225, 4·128, 4·371, 4·153, 4·349, 4·404
   (d) 5·016, 5·163, 5·196, 5·105, 5·997, 5·121
   (e) 6·403, 7·525, 4·659, 4·602, 5·550, 6·528
   (f) 9·935, 9·395, 9·104, 9·996, 9·308, 9·138
   (g) 12·005, 12·315, 11·904, 10·607, 12·314, 13·059, 10·926, 10·394
   (h) 3·056, 4·523, 6·995, 6·994, 5·106, 5·218, 7·999, 4·456

2. Arup and some friends shared the cost of a meal in an
   Indian restaurant. Arup used a calculator to work out that
   each person needed to pay £8·78, correct to the nearest
   penny. Which of these amounts could be the exact answer to
   Arup's calculation:
   A £8·784   B £8·776   C £8·774   D £8·784
   E £8·785   F £8·7866   G £8·7845   H £8·7891
   I £8·78   J £8·78333?

3.9 Adding decimal numbers 'in your head'

Simple decimal additions can be completed without a calculator
or written calculations.

Examples

(a) $0·4 + 0·5 = 0·9$
(b) $0·7 + 0·6 = 1·3$
(c) $3·1 + 4·5 = 3 + 4 + 0·1 + 0·5 = 7·6$
(d) $8·2 + 2·9 = 8 + 2 + 0·2 + 0·9 = 10 + 1·1 = 11·1$
(e) $7·25 + 1·3 = 7 + 1 + 0·2 + 0·3 + 0·05 = 8·55$

Exercise 3I

Do these in your head.

1. (a) $0.4 + 0.3$ (b) $0.3 + 0.5$ (c) $0.8 + 0.1$ (d) $0.4 + 0.4$
(e) $0.5 + 0.2$ (f) $0.3 + 0.3$ (g) $0.4 + 0.2$ (h) $0.5 + 0.1$
(i) $0.2 + 0.2$ (j) $0.5 + 0.4$ (k) $0.6 + 0.3$ (l) $0.7 + 0.1$
(m) $0.8 + 0.2$ (n) $0.9 + 0.1$ (o) $0.6 + 0.2$ (p) $1.2 + 0.1$
(q) $1.3 + 0.2$ (r) $2.4 + 0.1$ (s) $2.1 + 0.3$ (t) $3.2 + 0.7$
(u) $2.1 + 0.6$ (v) $3.3 + 0.7$ (w) $1.5 + 0.5$ (x) $5.4 + 0.6$
(y) $3.1 + 0.1$

2. (a) $0.5 + 0.6$ (b) $0.7 + 0.6$ (c) $0.8 + 0.8$ (d) $0.8 + 0.5$
(e) $0.9 + 0.2$ (f) $0.3 + 0.9$ (g) $0.4 + 0.8$ (h) $0.9 + 0.5$
(i) $0.8 + 0.3$ (j) $0.7 + 0.4$ (k) $0.9 + 0.4$ (l) $0.8 + 0.8$
(m) $0.9 + 0.9$ (n) $0.6 + 0.9$ (o) $0.9 + 0.7$ (p) $1.5 + 0.7$
(q) $2.6 + 0.8$ (r) $1.6 + 0.6$ (s) $3.7 + 0.7$ (t) $4.8 + 0.9$
(u) $2.2 + 0.8$ (v) $6.5 + 0.5$ (w) $2.4 + 0.7$ (x) $3.8 + 0.9$
(y) $4.7 + 0.5$

3. (a) $3.1 + 5.1$ (b) $4.2 + 6.4$ (c) $1.6 + 2.3$ (d) $7.2 + 6.3$
(e) $1.3 + 2.3$ (f) $5.2 + 1.7$ (g) $1.6 + 2.2$ (h) $1.5 + 3.3$
(i) $7.2 + 3.2$ (j) $6.5 + 6.1$ (k) $7.6 + 2.4$ (l) $8.6 + 1.1$
(m) $4.4 + 3.3$ (n) $6.3 + 8.1$ (o) $7.4 + 6.1$ (p) $5.4 + 7.1$
(q) $1.1 + 5.2$ (r) $8.1 + 8.1$ (s) $2.9 + 3.1$ (t) $5.8 + 2.2$
(u) $6.5 + 9.4$ (v) $5.2 + 6.5$ (w) $3.4 + 5.4$ (x) $9.7 + 8.3$
(y) $6.8 + 9.1$

4. (a) $7.5 + 3.5$ (b) $7.9 + 6.3$ (c) $5.4 + 2.9$ (d) $6.7 + 2.4$
(e) $2.6 + 3.6$ (f) $1.8 + 1.5$ (g) $3.9 + 7.2$ (h) $1.7 + 1.8$
(i) $3.7 + 2.6$ (j) $1.8 + 5.4$ (k) $1.9 + 3.6$ (l) $3.8 + 2.3$
(m) $4.6 + 3.5$ (n) $4.9 + 3.5$ (o) $3.8 + 1.9$ (p) $1.8 + 4.6$
(q) $3.7 + 2.3$ (r) $4.9 + 5.7$ (s) $4.8 + 4.8$ (t) $6.9 + 7.9$
(u) $3.7 + 5.7$ (v) $8.6 + 6.8$ (w) $7.7 + 3.9$ (x) $8.3 + 9.8$
(y) $7.2 + 9.9$

5. (a) $0.3 + 0.04$ (b) $2.05 + 0.6$ (c) $1.06 + 0.7$ (d) $0.9 + 1.04$
(e) $2.8 + 1.02$ (f) $0.6 + 0.34$ (g) $1.7 + 0.15$ (h) $2.45 + 3.4$
(i) $6.56 + 1.2$ (j) $1.3 + 2.64$ (k) $1.62 + 0.03$ (l) $0.51 + 2.08$
(m) $1.85 + 0.04$ (n) $0.73 + 3.06$ (o) $1.05 + 1.94$ (p) $1.43 + 0.08$
(q) $3.56 + 0.08$ (r) $0.76 + 5.08$ (s) $2.06 + 2.76$ (t) $3.07 + 5.89$
(u) $0.78 + 0.6$ (v) $1.84 + 0.2$ (w) $0.8 + 3.76$ (x) $2.95 + 6.05$
(y) $3.99 + 1.09$

MODULE 3

3.10 Adding decimal numbers with written calculations

If decimal additions are too difficult to do in your head, you do them on paper.

Example

(a) $3\cdot4 + 7\cdot8 + 2\cdot6$ (b) $13\cdot75 + 14\cdot86$ (c) $4\cdot45 + 7 + 6\cdot3$

(a) $\begin{array}{r} 3\cdot4 \\ 7\cdot8 \\ +\ 2\cdot6 \\ \hline 13\cdot8 \\ \small{1} \end{array}$

Line up the decimal points.

(b) $\begin{array}{r} 13\cdot75 \\ +\ 14\cdot86 \\ \hline 28\cdot61 \\ \small{1\ 1} \end{array}$

Line up the decimal points.

(c) $\begin{array}{r} 4\cdot45 \\ 7\cdot00 \\ +\ 6\cdot30 \\ \hline 17\cdot75 \end{array}$

Add zeros so that all the numbers have the same number of decimal places.

Line up the decimal points.

Exercise 3J

Do these on paper.

1. (a) $3\cdot6 + 2\cdot7 + 4\cdot6$ (b) $5\cdot3 + 6\cdot7 + 8\cdot1$ (c) $6\cdot6 + 7\cdot6 + 0\cdot9$
(d) $3\cdot7 + 8\cdot4 + 9\cdot2$ (e) $8\cdot6 + 6\cdot4 + 2\cdot5$ (f) $5\cdot7 + 8\cdot7 + 9\cdot7$
(g) $2\cdot2 + 6\cdot1 + 9\cdot0$ (h) $7\cdot8 + 0\cdot6 + 1\cdot9$ (i) $2\cdot5 + 3\cdot5 + 6\cdot5$
(j) $6\cdot4 + 4\cdot6 + 7\cdot8$ (k) $15\cdot3 + 6\cdot4 + 0\cdot8$ (l) $0\cdot7 + 6\cdot5 + 2\cdot3$
(m) $7\cdot8 + 5\cdot4 + 0\cdot1$ (n) $6\cdot7 + 8\cdot4 + 9\cdot3$ (o) $0\cdot6 + 3\cdot8 + 5\cdot9$
(p) $9\cdot6 + 0\cdot9 + 0\cdot7$ (q) $9\cdot0 + 0\cdot7 + 1\cdot8$ (r) $4\cdot5 + 6\cdot0 + 0\cdot8$
(s) $5\cdot5 + 6\cdot6 + 7\cdot7$ (t) $6\cdot3 + 0\cdot9 + 0\cdot5$ (u) $0\cdot7 + 1\cdot7 + 9\cdot6$
(v) $0\cdot8 + 0\cdot6 + 9\cdot1$ (w) $8\cdot9 + 13\cdot2 + 34\cdot0$ (x) $19\cdot7 + 0\cdot9 + 8\cdot6$
(y) $11\cdot5 + 15\cdot8 + 0\cdot9$

2. (a) $3\cdot67 + 4\cdot32$ (b) $7\cdot22 + 6\cdot35$ (c) $9\cdot05 + 8\cdot74$
(d) $4\cdot75 + 0\cdot24$ (e) $8\cdot62 + 9\cdot27$ (f) $7\cdot66 + 3\cdot25$
(g) $8\cdot07 + 6\cdot66$ (h) $3\cdot56 + 5\cdot29$ (i) $7\cdot09 + 3\cdot76$
(j) $6\cdot43 + 5\cdot39$ (k) $7\cdot45 + 6\cdot62$ (l) $8\cdot73 + 0\cdot95$
(m) $10\cdot56 + 7\cdot51$ (n) $9\cdot81 + 11\cdot27$ (o) $15\cdot93 + 7\cdot25$
(p) $1\cdot24 + 1\cdot86$ (q) $5\cdot65 + 1\cdot58$ (r) $3\cdot67 + 2\cdot89$
(s) $5\cdot76 + 0\cdot84$ (t) $9\cdot98 + 0\cdot09$ (u) $13\cdot45 + 6\cdot87$
(v) $7\cdot89 + 18\cdot11$ (w) $16\cdot87 + 9\cdot63$ (x) $56\cdot45 + 34\cdot66$
(y) $89\cdot56 + 76\cdot27$

3. (a) $5 + 6\cdot3 + 0\cdot2$ (b) $7\cdot3 + 15 + 2\cdot8$ (c) $9\cdot7 + 6\cdot3 + 9$
     (d) $17\cdot5 + 8 + 2\cdot3$ (e) $6\cdot7 + 6\cdot5 + 18$ (f) $20 + 7\cdot6 + 9\cdot4$
     (g) $7\cdot5 + 9 + 11\cdot2$ (h) $8 + 4\cdot6 + 6$ (i) $4 + 2\cdot5 + 4\cdot09$
     (j) $9 + 1\cdot23 + 4\cdot45$ (k) $4\cdot65 + 7 + 0\cdot9$ (l) $17 + 1\cdot7 + 0\cdot17$
     (m) $10\cdot05 + 5\cdot63 + 2\cdot1$ (n) $5\cdot04 + 4\cdot5 + 5$ (o) $9\cdot9 + 8 + 6\cdot74$
     (p) $34\cdot4 + 76\cdot015$ (q) $54\cdot8 + 9\cdot237$ (r) $8\cdot999 + 0\cdot001$
     (s) $34 + 3\cdot4 + 0\cdot34$ (t) $56\cdot71 + 8\cdot34 + 5$ (u) $0\cdot99 + 9\cdot9 + 19$
     (v) $78\cdot6 + 7\cdot86 + 0\cdot786$ (w) $67\cdot45 + 8\cdot9 + 0\cdot51 + 13$
     (x) $34\cdot506 + 4\cdot891 + 6\cdot05$ (y) $54\cdot5 + 67\cdot32 + 17 + 0\cdot992$

4. A group of 8 friends want to buy a CD which costs £9·50.
When they check their pockets, these are the amounts of
money each has:

     £2·38,   £3·75,   £2·73,   £2·60,
     £2·89,   £3·09,   £2·86,   £2·65

Which three of these amounts add up to exactly £9·50?

3.11 Subtracting decimal numbers 'in your head'

You need to be able to do simple decimal subtractions without a
calculator or written calculations.

Examples

(a) $0\cdot8 - 0\cdot3 = 0\cdot5$
(b) $7\cdot6 - 1\cdot4 = 6\cdot2$
(c) $1\cdot6 - 0\cdot9 = 0\cdot7$
(d) $8\cdot2 - 2\cdot9 = 8\cdot2 - 2 - 0\cdot9 = 6\cdot2 - 0\cdot9 = 5\cdot3$

Exercise 3K

Do these in your head.

1. (a) $0\cdot9 - 0\cdot2$ (b) $0\cdot8 - 0\cdot1$ (c) $0\cdot5 - 0\cdot4$ (d) $0\cdot7 - 0\cdot7$ (e) $0\cdot5 - 0\cdot3$
     (f) $0\cdot8 - 0\cdot4$ (g) $0\cdot3 - 0\cdot2$ (h) $0\cdot2 - 0\cdot1$ (i) $0\cdot7 - 0\cdot4$ (j) $0\cdot9 - 0\cdot5$
     (k) $2\cdot9 - 0\cdot4$ (l) $4\cdot8 - 0\cdot7$ (m) $3\cdot6 - 0\cdot4$ (n) $2\cdot8 - 0\cdot5$ (o) $5\cdot7 - 0\cdot3$
     (p) $2\cdot6 - 1\cdot4$ (q) $5\cdot6 - 2\cdot2$ (r) $6\cdot9 - 2\cdot7$ (s) $5\cdot6 - 1\cdot6$ (t) $7\cdot9 - 2\cdot7$
     (u) $8\cdot7 - 3\cdot4$ (v) $7\cdot8 - 4\cdot6$ (w) $9\cdot9 - 6\cdot3$ (x) $2\cdot8 - 0\cdot8$ (y) $9\cdot9 - 5\cdot1$

2. (a) $1\cdot7 - 0\cdot8$ (b) $1\cdot4 - 0\cdot6$ (c) $1\cdot3 - 0\cdot5$ (d) $1\cdot2 - 0\cdot4$ (e) $1\cdot6 - 0\cdot8$
     (f) $1\cdot7 - 0\cdot9$ (g) $1\cdot3 - 0\cdot6$ (h) $1\cdot5 - 0\cdot8$ (i) $1\cdot1 - 0\cdot4$ (j) $1\cdot2 - 0\cdot6$
     (k) $1\cdot1 - 0\cdot5$ (l) $1\cdot3 - 0\cdot8$ (m) $1\cdot2 - 0\cdot3$ (n) $1\cdot1 - 0\cdot6$ (o) $1\cdot2 - 0\cdot5$
     (p) $1\cdot5 - 0\cdot6$ (q) $1\cdot6 - 0\cdot9$ (r) $1\cdot3 - 0\cdot7$ (s) $1\cdot1 - 0\cdot8$ (t) $1\cdot4 - 0\cdot7$
     (u) $1\cdot3 - 0\cdot9$ (v) $1\cdot4 - 0\cdot8$ (w) $1\cdot1 - 0\cdot9$ (x) $1\cdot3 - 0\cdot9$ (y) $1\cdot5 - 0\cdot7$

MODULE 3

3. (a) 8·2 − 1·6   (b) 7·3 − 2·7   (c) 6·4 − 5·9
   (d) 7·2 − 1·8   (e) 4·5 − 6·7   (f) 6·7 − 2·7
   (g) 9·3 − 2·9   (h) 9·4 − 8·6   (i) 6·7 − 4·6
   (j) 9·3 − 5·7   (k) 7·5 − 3·8   (l) 5·6 − 3·7
   (m) 6·1 − 4·6   (n) 3·4 − 1·7   (o) 4·5 − 2·8
   (p) 6·7 − 2·8   (q) 4·5 − 2·9   (r) 7·3 − 4·9
   (s) 9·3 − 7·4   (t) 8·7 − 3·9   (u) 6·5 − 3·8
   (v) 7·6 − 5·8   (w) 3·2 − 1·8   (x) 2·8 − 1·9
   (y) 5·6 − 4·8

3.12 Subtracting decimal numbers with written calculations

If decimal subtractions are too difficult to do in your head, you do them on paper.

Example

(a) 35·7 − 24·9   (b) 65·47 − 28·23   (c) 124·5 − 6·38

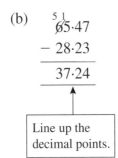 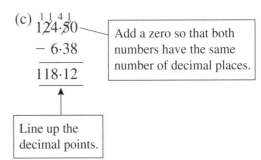

(a)
$$\begin{array}{r} 3\overset{4}{\cancel{5}}\overset{1}{\cdot}7 \\ -\ 24\cdot9 \\ \hline 10\cdot8 \end{array}$$

Line up the decimal points.

(b)
$$\begin{array}{r} \overset{5}{\cancel{6}}\overset{1}{5}\cdot47 \\ -\ 28\cdot23 \\ \hline 37\cdot24 \end{array}$$

Line up the decimal points.

(c)
$$\begin{array}{r} 1\overset{1}{2}\overset{1}{4}\cdot\overset{4}{\cancel{5}}\overset{1}{0} \\ -\ 6\cdot38 \\ \hline 118\cdot12 \end{array}$$

Add a zero so that both numbers have the same number of decimal places.

Line up the decimal points.

Exercise 3L

Do these on paper.

1. (a) 23·8 − 12·7   (b) 34·6 − 11·5   (c) 48·9 − 26·2
   (d) 56·3 − 32·1   (e) 29·5 − 15·5   (f) 32·8 − 11·9
   (g) 67·3 − 24·6   (h) 56·8 − 21·9   (i) 35·7 − 24·9
   (j) 87·3 − 24·7   (k) 64·9 − 35·7   (l) 43·7 − 28·2
   (m) 81·6 − 45·4   (n) 93·4 − 58·3   (o) 26·7 − 18·5
   (p) 12·5 − 8·6   (q) 34·6 − 7·8   (r) 58·4 − 9·5
   (s) 67·5 − 9·9   (t) 27·4 − 8·6   (u) 45·6 − 18·7
   (v) 93·7 − 28·9   (w) 84·5 − 17·8   (x) 56·2 − 28·4
   (y) 95·1 − 45·3

MODULE 3

2. (a) 45·34 − 24·12   (b) 56·77 − 11·35   (c) 67·45 − 32·21
(d) 89·07 − 56·05   (e) 34·56 − 12·34   (f) 45·64 − 22·47
(g) 78·23 − 67·18   (h) 43·62 − 31·35   (i) 67·54 − 16·49
(j) 43·26 − 31·08   (k) 56·35 − 43·84   (l) 89·32 − 46·51
(m) 78·19 − 31·91   (n) 45·67 − 24·76   (o) 85·02 − 12·51
(p) 34·56 − 29·21   (q) 67·94 − 59·22   (r) 83·65 − 78·43
(s) 43·55 − 27·24   (t) 84·27 − 78·03   (u) 80·16 − 31·54
(v) 70·35 − 67·52   (w) 50·22 − 17·56   (x) 50·03 − 21·78
(y) 60·04 − 11·57

3. (a) 67·32 − 4·7   (b) 70·45 − 12·7   (c) 56·39 − 31·6
(d) 74·21 − 7·4   (e) 87·31 − 45·4   (f) 16·7 − 3·45
(g) 36·9 − 11·36   (h) 56·3 − 22·25   (i) 89·2 − 17·07
(j) 16·4 − 5·27   (k) 4·5 − 3·72   (l) 7·6 − 0·85
(m) 13·6 − 2·77   (n) 78·2 − 31·93   (o) 56·7 − 42·82
(p) 42·7 − 6·85   (q) 34·2 − 8·56   (r) 27·3 − 18·92
(s) 67·3 − 28·54   (t) 34·31 − 18·55   (u) 27 − 19·53
(v) 34 − 25·81   (w) 67 − 0·56   (x) 89 − 3·67
(y) 78 − 49·47

4. Sammy-Jo works in a clothes shop. She is preparing this poster for display in a sale.

OLD PRICE	SALE PRICE	SAVING
£56·99	£35·50	£21·49
£45·50	£32·80	
£58·00	£25·99	
£62·55	£49·89	
£56·30	£45·79	
£69·00	£45·99	
£56·20	£45·59	
£37·90	£23·99	
£60·00	£39·99	
£80·00	£65·69	

Copy and complete the poster for Sammy-Jo.

Summary

1. The first digit after a decimal point is the **tenths** digit.

2. The second digit after a decimal point is the **hundredths** digit.

3. It will help to add a zero in the hundredths column when sorting numbers with two decimal places.

4. The third digit after a decimal point is the **thousandths** digit.

5. It will help to add a zero in the thousandths column when sorting numbers with three decimal places.

Checkout N3

1. (a) What place value does the underlined digit have?
   (i) 3·$\underline{7}$ (ii) 1$\underline{4}$·8   (iii) 67·$\underline{3}$
   (b) Write these lengths with a decimal point:
   (i) 3 cm 5 mm   (ii) 6 cm 8 mm
   (c) Write these lengths in millimetres and centimetres:
   (i) 4·3 cm   (ii) 6·9 cm
   (d) Write this list in order, starting with the smallest number:
   3·4, 3·2, 3·0, 4·2, 2·4, 2·9, 3·8, 3·5

2. (a) What place value does the underlined digit have?
   (i) 3·7$\underline{9}$ (ii) 14·$\underline{8}$6   (iii) 67·3$\underline{7}$
   (b) Write these lengths with a decimal point:
   (i) 3 m 54 cm   (ii) 6 m 83 cm
   (c) Write these lengths in metres and centimetres:
   (i) 4·78 m   (ii) 13·65 m

3. Write the list in order, starting with the smallest number:
   (a) 6·42, 6·28, 6·09, 6·31, 6·25, 6·30, 6·80, 6·08
   (b) 5·7, 5·65, 5·04, 5·6, 5·55, 5·5, 5·05, 5·4

4. (a) What place value does the underlined digit have?
   (i) 3·79$\underline{2}$ (ii) 14·80$\underline{6}$ (iii) 67·3$\underline{7}$5
   (b) Write as a decimal:

   (i) $3 + \frac{2}{10} + \frac{3}{100} + \frac{7}{1\,000}$

   (ii) $20 + \frac{7}{10} + \frac{6}{1\,000} + 5 + \frac{3}{100}$

5. Write the list in order, starting with the smallest number:
   (a) 7·427, 7·423, 7·401, 7·435, 7·048, 7·421
   (b) 8·76, 8·653, 8·049, 8·63, 8·55, 8·5, 8·059, 8·488

6. Correct to the nearest whole number, 17·3, 18·5 and 9·7 are 17, 19 and 10.

———————————————►

7. Correct to one decimal places, 12·25, 3·42 and 5·78 are 12·3, 3·4 and 5·8.

———————————————►

8. Correct to two decimal places, 3·456, 8·795 and 4·064 are 3·46, 8·80 and 4·06.

———————————————►

9. Simple decimal numbers can be added or subtracted in your head.

———————————————►

10. For more difficult calculations, add zeros so that all numbers have the same number of decimal places. Then line up the decimal points and use normal written methods for addition or subtraction. Don't forget to carry the point down into the answer.

6. Write correct to the nearest whole number:
   (a) 12·7   (b) 13·5   (c) 4·3

7. Write correct to one decimal place:
   (a) 5·63   (b) 8·79   (c) 6·95

8. Write correct to two decimal places:
   (a) 6·783   (b) 7·049   (c) 12·996

9. Do these in your head.
   (a) $0·6 + 0·5$ (b) $1·6 + 2·3$
   (c) $0·75 + 0·4$ (d) $0·75 + 0·04$
   (e) $5 + 2·9$ (f) $3·25 + 1·13$
   (g) $0·9 - 0·3$ (h) $1·7 - 0·6$
   (i) $6·7 - 2·2$ (j) $4·6 - 3·8$

10. Do these on paper.
   (a) $4·7 + 5·6 + 2·1$ (b) $3·4 + 17 + 2·96$
   (c) $34·78 + 49·56$ (d) $13·7 + 34·56 + 4·9$
   (e) $23·9 - 12·7$ (f) $56·2 - 27·4$
   (g) $70·45 - 4·8$ (h) $67 - 13·45$

MODULE 3

Revision exercise N3

1. (a) Write in figures three thousand and forty-seven.

    (b) Put these numbers in order, smallest first.

        5·32   5·1   5·09   5·8

    (c) Copy this diagram and mark the position of the number 7·4 on the scale.

    (d) What number is 0·3 more than 5·34?   [SEG]

2. (a) 6·08 m of carpet is cut from a 7·50 m length.
      How much is left?
      Give your answers in centimetres.

(b) A bookcase is 1·65 m long.
How many bookcases can be put along a wall
which is 6·08 m long?   [SEG]

3. Chocolate bars cost 23p each.

   (a) How many chocolate bars can be bought for £5?

   (b) How much change will there be?   [NEAB]

4. Tina wants to calculate: $\dfrac{42{\cdot}15}{8{\cdot}7 - 3{\cdot}9}$

   (a) Write each of the numbers in Tina's calculation to
   the nearest whole number.

   (b) Hence find an estimate of the answer for Tina.   [SEG]

5. Claire buys a train ticket which costs £8·36.
   She pays with a £10 note.

   (a) How much change does she receive?

   This change is given in the smallest number of coins.

   (b) How is the change given?   [SEG]

6. Thomas takes his family out to lunch. The lunch costs
   £4·90 for each adult.
   His son, Luke, has a child's meal for half price.

   (a) What is the cost of Luke's meal?

   Thomas pays the bill for his wife, his mother, himself
   and Luke.

   (b) How much does Thomas pay?   [SEG]

7. Barbara wants to calculate: $\dfrac{39{\cdot}57}{1{\cdot}92 + 3{\cdot}15}$

   (a) Write each of the numbers in Barbara's calculation to
   the nearest whole number.

   (b) Hence, find an estimate of the answer for Barbara.
                                                         [SEG]

8. A snack bar sells coffee at 48 pence per cup. In one day 838
   cups are sold. By rounding each number to one significant
   figure, estimate the total amount received from the sale of
   coffee, giving your answer in pounds.

9. A theatre manager is considering a new promotion.
   He considers giving away ice-creams at the interval of the
   production.
   The ice-creams cost 31 pence each and there are 792 seats
   in the theatre.
   By rounding each number to one significant figure,
   estimate the total cost of this promotion in pounds.   [SEG]

10. A lecturer takes a college art group of 56 students to a
    modern art exhibition.
    The trip costs each student £18·70.
    By rounding each number to one significant figure,
    estimate the total amount of money that the lecturer
    will collect.   [SEG]

11. (a) Write 37·478 correct to 1 decimal place.
    (b) Calculate $2 \times 3^2 + \sqrt{5 \cdot 76}$.   [SEG]

12. A wholesaler pays £51·84 for a case containing 576 eggs.
    (a) Calculate the cost of one egg.

    He sells 180 eggs to Julie at this price.

    (b) How much does he charge Julie?
        Give your answer in £'s.   [SEG]

MODULE 3

N4 NUMBER 4

Money, length and weight all use the metric system.

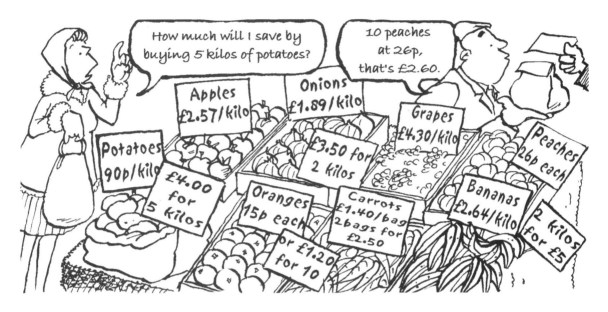

This unit will show you how to:

- Multiply and divide decimal numbers by 10, 100 or 1 000
- Multiply and divide decimal numbers without a calculator
- Understand recurring decimals
- Multiply and divide decimal numbers with a calculator

Before you start:

You should know how to…	Check in N4
1. Multiply numbers together. Look back at the methods on pages 126 and 131.	**1.** Calculate: (a) 34 × 7 (b) 23 × 5 (c) 48 × 17 (d) 234 × 6 (e) 217 × 23 (f) 345 × 72
2. Divide numbers. Look back at pages 127 and 134 to remind yourself of the methods you can use.	**2.** Work out: (a) 120 ÷ 5 (b) 261 ÷ 3 (c) 576 ÷ 8 (d) 450 ÷ 18 (e) 714 ÷ 14 (f) 260 ÷ 20

4.1 Multiplying decimal numbers by 10

When a decimal number is multiplied by 10, all the digits move one place to the left, while the decimal point remains fixed.

Example

(a) $35 \times 10 = 350$

(b) $3{\cdot}5 \times 10 = 35$

(c) $0{\cdot}35 \times 10 = 3{\cdot}5$

(d) $0{\cdot}035 \times 10 = 0{\cdot}35$

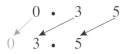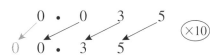

There are 10 millimetres (mm) in one centimetre (cm).
To convert a length in centimetres to a length in millimetres, you multiply by 10.

Example

The length of the worm is $8{\cdot}7$ cm.

The length of the worm is also $8{\cdot}7 \times 10 = 87$ mm.

Exercise 4A

1. Multiply each number by 10.

(a) 56	(b) 453	(c) 273	(d) 703	(e) 102
(f) 4·5	(g) 8·7	(h) 19·3	(i) 54·1	(j) 78·9
(k) 7·23	(l) 5·27	(m) 23·21	(n) 30·56	(o) 21·67
(p) 0·67	(q) 0·345	(r) 0·205	(s) 0·528	(t) 0·223
(u) 0·02	(v) 0·034 5	(w) 0·052	(x) 0·067 4	(y) 0·005 42

2. Change each length into millimetres.

(a) 2 cm	(b) 6 cm	(c) 8 cm	(d) 1 cm	(e) 2·0 cm
(f) 2·6 cm	(g) 7·4 cm	(h) 5·9 cm	(i) 4·3 cm	(j) 3·5 cm
(k) 15·8 cm	(l) 24·9 cm	(m) 35·5 cm	(n) 89·6 cm	(o) 28·9 cm
(p) 2·56 cm	(q) 5·37 cm	(r) 7·05 cm	(s) 9·08 cm	(t) 6·75 cm
(u) 0·9 cm	(v) 0·7 cm	(w) 0·1 cm	(x) 0·2 cm	(y) 0·35 cm

4.2 Multiplying decimal numbers by 100

When a decimal number is multiplied by 100, all the digits move
two places to the left, while the decimal point remains fixed.

Example

(a) 3·5 × 100 = 350

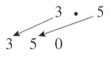

(b) 0·35 × 100 = 35

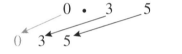

(c) 0·035 × 100 = 3·5

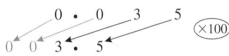

There are 100 centimetres (cm) in one metre (m).
To convert a length in metres to a length in centimetres, you
multiply by 100.

Example

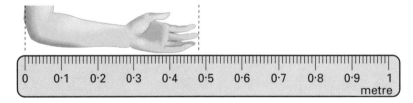

The length of the arm is 0·48 m.

The length of the arm is also 0·48 × 100 = 48 cm.

Exercise 4B

1. Multiply each number by 100.

(a) 7	(b) 6	(c) 57	(d) 123	(e) 347
(f) 4·5	(g) 7·8	(h) 3·4	(i) 18·7	(j) 27·3
(k) 5·67	(l) 7·31	(m) 19·56	(n) 0·83	(o) 34·51
(p) 0·537	(q) 0·347	(r) 0·524	(s) 0·564	(t) 0·231
(u) 0·032	(v) 0·076 1	(w) 0·093 2	(x) 0·072 5	(y) 0·001 5

2. Change all these lengths into centimetres.

(a) 2 m	(b) 5 m	(c) 3 m	(d) 4 m	(e) 1·0 m
(f) 1·5 m	(g) 1·7 m	(h) 2·5 m	(i) 8·9 m	(j) 7·6 m
(k) 15·3 m	(l) 29·5 m	(m) 32·8 m	(n) 27·5 m	(o) 34·1 m
(p) 5·64 m	(q) 9·25 m	(r) 8·63 m	(s) 9·34 m	(t) 7·31 m
(u) 0·25 m	(v) 0·37 m	(w) 0·83 m	(x) 0·62 m	(y) 0·77 m

4.3 Multiplying decimal numbers by 1 000

When a decimal number is multiplied by 1 000, all the digits move three places to the left, while the decimal point remains fixed.

Examples

(a) $358 \times 1\,000 = 358\,000$
(b) $35·8 \times 1\,000 = 35\,800$
(c) $3·58 \times 1\,000 = 3\,580$
(d) $0·358 \times 1\,000 = 358$

Hint:
Use a place value table like this one:

TTh   Th   H   T   U   •   tths   hths   thths

There are 1 000 millilitres (ml) in one litre (ℓ).
To convert a volume in litres to a volume in millilitres, you multiply by 1 000.

Example

The volume of the cola is $0·330\ \ell$.
The volume of the cola is also $0·330 \times 1\,000 = 330$ ml.

Exercise 4C

1. Multiply each number by 1 000.

   (a) 5
   (b) 9
   (c) 67
   (d) 453
   (e) 217·0

   (f) 3·5
   (g) 9·8
   (h) 5·4
   (i) 17·7
   (j) 47·3

   (k) 5·68
   (l) 7·51
   (m) 19·76
   (n) 0·93
   (o) 38·51

   (p) 0·437
   (q) 0·347
   (r) 0·724
   (s) 0·594
   (t) 0·271

   (u) 0·052 3
   (v) 0·096 1
   (w) 0·097 2
   (x) 0·081 5
   (y) 0·000 5

2. Change all these volumes into millilitres.

   (a) 4 ℓ
   (b) 1·5 ℓ
   (c) 1·7 ℓ
   (d) 15·3 ℓ
   (e) 27·5 ℓ

   (f) 9·34 ℓ
   (g) 7·31 ℓ
   (h) 0·250 ℓ
   (i) 0·373 ℓ
   (j) 6·258 ℓ

3. There are 1 000 metres (m) in one kilometre (km).
   Change all these lengths into metres.

   (a) 5 km
   (b) 2·4 km
   (c) 4·5 km
   (d) 12·5 km
   (e) 18·4 km

   (f) 45·9 km
   (g) 7·45 km
   (h) 0·526 km
   (i) 0·573 km
   (j) 9·456 km

4. There are 1 000 grams (g) in one kilogram (kg).
   Change all these weights into grams.

   (a) 9 kg
   (b) 6·4 kg
   (c) 3·2 kg
   (d) 14·7 kg
   (e) 14·8 kg

   (f) 32·8 kg
   (g) 6·33 kg
   (h) 0·585 kg
   (i) 0·843 kg
   (j) 7·540 kg

4.4 Dividing decimal numbers by 10

When a decimal number is divided by 10, all the digits move
one place to the right, while the decimal point remains fixed.

Examples

(a) 3 580 ÷ 10 = 358
(b)   358 ÷ 10 = 35·8
(c)   35·8 ÷ 10 = 3·58
(d)   3·58 ÷ 10 = 0·358

There are 10 millimetres (mm) in one
centimetre (cm).
To convert a length in millimetres to a length
in centimetres, you divide by 10.

Hint:

Use a place value table like this one:

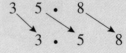

Example

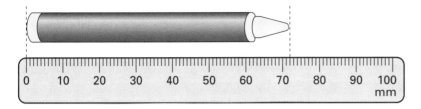

The length of the crayon is 72 mm.

The length of the crayon is also $72 \div 10 = 7 \cdot 2$ cm.

Exercise 4D

1. Divide each number by 10.

(a) 70	(b) 250	(c) 340	(d) 250	(e) 4 560
(f) 23	(g) 67	(h) 123	(i) 456	(j) 271
(k) 45·6	(l) 34·7	(m) 65·9	(n) 99·9	(o) 56·2
(p) 4·7	(q) 9·03	(r) 6·17	(s) 8·1	(t) 7·6
(u) 0·32	(v) 0·9	(w) 0·09	(x) 0·53	(y) 0·053

2. Change all these lengths into centimetres.

(a) 200 mm	(b) 600 mm	(c) 500 mm	(d) 100 mm	(e) 60 mm
(f) 260 mm	(g) 740 mm	(h) 590 mm	(i) 430 mm	(j) 350 mm
(k) 158 mm	(l) 249 mm	(m) 355 mm	(n) 896 mm	(o) 289 mm
(p) 25.6 mm	(q) 53·7 mm	(r) 70·5 mm	(s) 90·8 mm	(t) 67·5 mm

4.5 Dividing decimal numbers by 100

When a decimal number is divided by 100, all the digits move two places to the right, while the decimal point remains fixed.

Examples

(a) $3\,580 \div 100 = 35 \cdot 8$
(b) $358 \div 100 = 3 \cdot 58$
(c) $35 \cdot 8 \div 100 = 0 \cdot 358$

There are 100 centimetres (cm) in one metre (m). To convert a length in centimetres to a length in metres, you divide by 100.

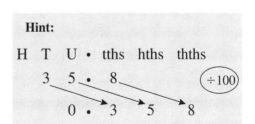

MODULE 3

Example

The length of the banner is 89 cm.

The length of the banner is also $89 \div 100 = 0.89$ m.

Exercise 4E

1. Divide each number by 100.

(a) 700	(b) 2 500	(c) 3 400	(d) 2 500	(e) 45 600
(f) 230	(g) 670	(h) 1 230	(i) 4 560	(j) 2 710
(k) 456	(l) 347	(m) 659	(n) 999	(o) 562
(p) 24·7	(q) 19·3	(r) 26·17	(s) 8·1	(t) 7·6
(u) 0·32	(v) 0·9	(w) 0·09	(x) 0·53	(y) 0·053

2. Change all these lengths into metres.

(a) 200 cm	(b) 600 cm	(c) 500 cm	(d) 100 cm	(e) 60 cm
(f) 260 cm	(g) 740 cm	(h) 590 cm	(i) 430 cm	(j) 350 cm
(k) 158 cm	(l) 249 cm	(m) 355 cm	(n) 896 cm	(o) 289 cm
(p) 25·6 cm	(q) 53·7 cm	(r) 70·5 cm	(s) 90·8 cm	(t) 67·5 cm

4.6 Dividing decimal numbers by 1 000

When a decimal number is divided by 1 000, all the digits move
three places to the right, while the decimal point remains fixed.

Examples

(a) $358\,000 \div 1\,000 = 358$
(b) $35\,800 \div 1\,000 = 35.8$
(c) $3\,580 \div 1\,000 = 3.58$
(d) $358 \div 1\,000 = 0.358$

There are 1 000 millilitres (ml) in one litre (ℓ).
To convert a volume in millilitres to a volume in
litres, you divide by 1 000.

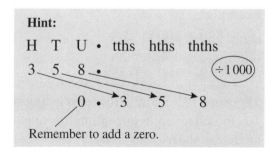

Example

The volume of the cough medicine is 1 300 ml.

The volume of the cough medicine is also $1\,300 \div 1\,000 = 1{\cdot}3\,\ell$.

Exercise 4F

1. Divide each number by 1 000.

(a) 5 000	(b) 9 000	(c) 3 500	(d) 9 800	(e) 5 400
(f) 17 700	(g) 47 300	(h) 5 680	(i) 7 550	(j) 9 374
(k) 3 856	(l) 437	(m) 271	(n) 52·3	(o) 96·1
(p) 9·72	(q) 8·1	(r) 5·7	(s) 9	(t) 11
(u) 0·5	(v) 1·9	(w) 0·17	(x) 0·05	(y) 3·142

2. Change all these volumes into litres.

(a) 400 ml	(b) 150 ml	(c) 170 ml	(d) 53 ml	(e) 25 ml
(f) 75 ml	(g) 750 ml	(h) 250 ml	(i) 500 ml	(j) 1 250 ml

3. There are 1 000 metres (m) in one kilometre (km).
Change all these lengths into kilometres.

(a) 500 m	(b) 240 m	(c) 3 500 m	(d) 12 700 m	(e) 18 450 m
(f) 45 900 m	(g) 7 457 m	(h) 5 269 m	(i) 573·5 m	(j) 1 456·8 m

4. There are 1 000 grams (g) in one kilogram (kg).
Change all these weights into kilograms.

(a) 900 g	(b) 640 g	(c) 320 g	(d) 147 g	(e) 148 g
(f) 1 328 g	(g) 1 633 g	(h) 2 585 g	(i) 3 843 g	(j) 7 500 g

4.7 Multiplying decimal numbers 'in your head'

Look at this calculation:

$$0.3 \times 4$$

You can use these rules to find the answer:

- Ignore any decimal points and multiply normally.   → $3 \times 4 = 12$
- Count the number of digits after the decimal point(s)   →   There is 1 d.p. in 0.3
  in the calculation.
- Put the same number of digits after the decimal point   → $12 \rightarrow 1.2$
  in the answer.

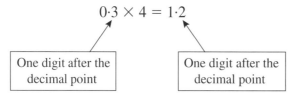

In the same way:

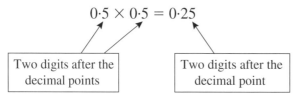

Examples

(a) $0.8 \times 2 = 1.\underline{6}$ (b) $0.4 \times 0.5 = 0.\underline{20}$ (c) $0.\underline{03} \times 7 = 0.\underline{21}$

(d) $0.\underline{03} \times 0.\underline{7} = 0.\underline{021}$ (e) $2.\underline{3} \times 2 = 4.\underline{6}$ (f) $1.\underline{2} \times 0.\underline{4} = 0.\underline{48}$

Exercise 4G

Do these in your head.

1. (a) 0.5×2 (b) 0.8×1 (c) 0.3×3 (d) 5×0.6 (e) 7×0.2

     (f) 8×0.5 (g) 0.9×2 (h) 0.6×2 (i) 0.2×5 (j) 0.1×6

     (k) 8×0.4 (l) 4×0.4 (m) 9×0.5 (n) 8×0.6 (o) 6×0.4

     (p) 0.7×9 (q) 0.4×2 (r) 0.1×1 (s) 0.1×9 (t) 0.5×3

2. (a) 0.6×0.3 (b) 0.5×0.1 (c) 0.7×0.6 (d) 0.8×0.3 (e) 0.9×0.4

     (f) 0.7×0.5 (g) 0.3×0.9 (h) 0.8×0.8 (i) 0.7×0.7 (j) 0.4×0.1

     (k) 0.1×0.3 (l) 0.6×0.6 (m) 0.9×0.8 (n) 0.4×0.7 (o) 0.7×0.8

     (p) 0.9×0.9 (q) 0.2×0.1 (r) 0.3×0.2 (s) 0.9×0.6 (t) 0.1×0.7

3. (a) 0.05×5 (b) 0.04×3 (c) 0.06×4 (d) 0.08×2 (e) 0.09×2

     (f) 3×0.09 (g) 7×0.04 (h) 5×0.08 (i) 2×0.07 (j) 5×0.03

     (k) 0.02×6 (l) 0.03×3 (m) 0.02×2 (n) 0.01×5 (o) 0.03×2

     (p) 5×0.06 (q) 7×0.01 (r) 4×0.02 (s) 8×0.01 (t) 5×0.04

4. (a) 0.04×0.4 (b) 0.06×0.3 (c) 0.04×0.1 (d) 0.08×0.4 (e) 0.06×0.6
    (f) 0.03×0.1 (g) 0.6×0.01 (h) 0.7×0.6 (i) 0.8×0.08 (j) 0.9×0.06
    (k) 0.8×0.07 (l) 0.1×0.09 (m) 0.08×0.6 (n) 0.05×0.2 (o) 0.09×0.5
    (p) 0.07×0.9 (q) 0.08×0.9 (r) 0.07×0.7 (s) 0.7×0.03 (t) 0.8×0.03

5. (a) 1.2×3 (b) 1.1×4 (c) 2.2×2 (d) 1.5×3 (e) 1.3×3
    (f) 1.2×0.2 (g) 1.1×0.5 (h) 3.2×0.2 (i) 2.1×0.3 (j) 4.1×0.2
    (k) 0.32×2 (l) 0.22×4 (m) 5×0.11 (n) 2×0.42 (o) 3×0.33
    (p) 0.12×0.2 (q) 0.11×0.5 (r) 0.31×0.6 (s) 0.42×0.4 (t) 0.15×0.4

6. This board shows the prices at Runnigan's
    travelling fair.

Find the cost of:
(a) 3 rides on the Dodgems
(b) 4 rides on the Big Wheel
(c) 6 rides on the Tea Cups
(d) 4 rides on the Waltzer
(e) 8 rides on the Swing Boats
(f) 5 rides on the Rockets

MODULE 3

4.8 Multiplying decimal numbers with written calculations

If written calculations are needed, the same rules are used to
place the point in the answer.

Examples

(a) 12.4×2

One digit after the point

(b) 4.72×8

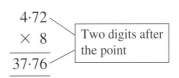

Two digits after the point

(c) 3.22×80

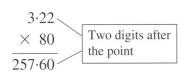

Two digits after the point

(d) 4.63×8.5

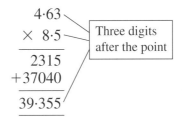

Three digits after the point

Exercise 4H

Do these on paper.

1. (a) 4.5×7 (b) 5.6×8 (c) 3.9×5 (d) 8.2×5 (e) 4.7×6
   (f) 16.5×6 (g) 16.3×4 (h) 29.1×7 (i) 34.5×6 (j) 32.6×6

2. (a) 3.25×8 (b) 7.03×5 (c) 9.06×7 (d) 4.25×6 (e) 5.36×8
   (f) 7.08×6 (g) 6.24×5 (h) 8.77×3 (i) 4.65×9 (j) 2.45×6

3. (a) 5.7×40 (b) 7.2×80 (c) 5.4×90 (d) 2.7×50 (e) 3.8×90
   (f) 7.22×20 (g) 6.45×40 (h) 9.34×30 (i) 8.64×70 (j) 7.31×50

4. (a) 1.6×1.7 (b) 1.5×1.5 (c) 1.8×2.2 (d) 1.3×4.5 (e) 2.5×3.8
   (f) 4.51×7.6 (g) 6.03×1.4 (h) 8.25×1.7 (i) 1.25×1.8 (j) 4.26×7.2

5. A carpet used for hallways costs £8·56 per metre.
   Find the cost of carpeting hallways of length:
   (a) 3 m   (b) 5 m   (c) 20 m   (d) 7·8 m   (e) 14·2 m

6.
   ## ASSISTANT COOK
   ### £4·65 per hour
   *To work 28 hours per week at
   John Mansfield School, Peterborough*

   (a) How much will the assistant cook earn each week?
   (b) How much will the assistant cook earn if she works 38
       weeks each year?

7. During November, a central heating boiler was used for 4.6
   hours each day. During December, the same boiler was used
   for 5·4 hours each day.
   (a) Calculate the total time for which the boiler was used
       during November and December.
   (b) The boiler costs £0.52 per hour to run. Calculate the
       total cost of using the boiler during November and
       December.

8. Find the total cost of:
   (a) 24 paving slabs
   (b) 1·5 cubic metres of sand
   (c) 144 paving slabs
   (d) 3·2 cubic metres of sand
   (e) 30 paving slabs and 2·5 cubic
       metres of sand

SPECIAL OFFER

**PAVING SLABS £1·45 each
SAND £5·68 per cubic metre**

4.9 Dividing decimal numbers without a calculator

In this example, the number you are dividing into has a decimal point.

Example 1

$3.15 \div 7$

$$
\begin{array}{r}
0.45 \\
7\overline{)3.15} \\
2\,8 \\
\hline
35 \\
35 \\
\hline
0
\end{array}
$$

The decimal point is directly above the decimal point in the calculation.

In this example, the number you are dividing into has no decimal point.

Example 2

$17 \div 4$

$$
\begin{array}{r}
4.25 \\
4\overline{)17.00} \\
16 \\
\hline
1\,0 \\
8 \\
\hline
20 \\
20 \\
\hline
0
\end{array}
$$

A decimal point and zeros are added to the 17 so that division can continue past the decimal point. The decimal point is directly above the decimal point in the calculation.

Exercise 4I

Do these on paper.

1. (a) $19.2 \div 6$ (b) $6.5 \div 5$ (c) $10.8 \div 4$ (d) $24.3 \div 3$ (e) $12.8 \div 8$
    (f) $13.5 \div 5$ (g) $23.2 \div 4$ (h) $10.6 \div 2$ (i) $17.1 \div 3$ (j) $28.8 \div 6$
    (k) $2.24 \div 4$ (l) $1.74 \div 3$ (m) $7.44 \div 6$ (n) $0.45 \div 3$ (o) $5.04 \div 6$
    (p) $3.75 \div 3$ (q) $21.64 \div 4$ (r) $21.35 \div 7$ (s) $20.16 \div 9$ (t) $6.85 \div 5$

MODULE 3

2. (a) $7 \div 2$ (b) $15 \div 4$ (c) $13 \div 4$ (d) $22 \div 5$ (e) $21 \div 2$
   (f) $67 \div 4$ (g) $18 \div 5$ (h) $37 \div 2$ (i) $33 \div 4$ (j) $18 \div 4$
   (k) $69 \div 2$ (l) $126 \div 5$ (m) $226 \div 4$ (n) $3 \div 4$ (o) $4 \div 5$
   (p) $1 \div 2$ (q) $1 \div 4$ (r) $9 \div 8$ (s) $7 \div 8$ (t) $13 \div 8$

3. A syndicate wins a lottery prize of £12 367. How much will each person get, correct to the nearest penny, if the number in the syndicate is:
   (a) 4 people   (b) 8 people   (c) 5 people   (d) 2 people   (e) 10 people?

4.10 Recurring decimals

Sometimes, no matter how many zeros you add, the answer repeats the same pattern over and over again. This is called a **recurring decimal**. The answer is written with dots over the recurring digits.

Examples

(a) $10 \cdot 3 \div 3$

(b) $13 \cdot 6 \div 6$

$$\begin{array}{r} 3 \cdot 33 \\ 3\overline{)10 \cdot 00} \\ \underline{9} \\ 1\,0 \\ \underline{9} \\ 10 \end{array}$$

$$\begin{array}{r} 2 \cdot 266 \\ 6\overline{)13 \cdot 6000} \\ \underline{12} \\ 1\,6 \\ \underline{1\,2} \\ 40 \\ \underline{36} \\ 40 \\ \underline{36} \\ 40 \end{array}$$

$10 \div 3 = 3 \cdot \dot{3}$

$13 \cdot 6 \div 6 = 2 \cdot 2\dot{6}$

Exercise 4J

1. Do these on paper.
   (a) $16 \div 3$ (b) $14 \div 6$ (c) $25 \div 9$ (d) $136 \div 3$ (e) $137 \div 3$
   (f) $23 \div 6$ (g) $25 \div 6$ (h) $41 \div 3$ (i) $12 \div 9$ (j) $31 \div 9$
   (k) $4 \cdot 9 \div 9$ (l) $7 \cdot 1 \div 9$ (m) $12 \cdot 5 \div 3$ (n) $6 \cdot 2 \div 6$ (o) $1 \cdot 21 \div 3$
   (p) $0 \cdot 7 \div 6$ (q) $0 \cdot 22 \div 3$ (r) $0 \cdot 28 \div 9$ (s) $0 \cdot 4 \div 6$ (t) $0 \cdot 4 \div 3$

2. Chantal, Jo and Laura always share equally the taxi fare home on Friday night. How much does each pay, correct to the nearest penny, if the fare is:
   (a) £14   (b) £17   (c) £18·50   (d) £15·40   (e) £14·80?

4.11 Multiplying decimal numbers with a calculator

To complete the calculation 3·56 × 1·2, you press the keys:

| 3 | · | 5 | 6 | × | 1 | · | 2 | = |

The answer is 4·272

You often need to round the answer given by a calculator.

Suppose the calculation was to solve the problem,
'Find the cost of 1·2 kg of cheese at £3·56 a kg'.
The answer will be £4·27 to the nearest penny.

Exercise 4K

Use a calculator to solve these.

1. Give the full answer to each calculation and also the answer
   correct to one decimal place.
   (a) 1·5 × 3·7   (b) 56·1 × 24·3   (c) 17·3 × 5·7   (d) 1·85 × 0·7
   (e) 26·5 × 9·6   (f) 7·5 × 9·1   (g) 67·3 × 24·2   (h) 3·14 × 13·1
   (i) 34·7 × 6·4   (j) 74·5 × 16·3   (k) 9·2 × 30·7   (l) 45·3 × 9·8
   (m) 12·9 × 8·4   (n) 3·14 × 8·32   (o) 51·6 × 8·67   (p) 3·14 × 13·6
   (q) 7·5 × 56·33   (r) 67·8 × 19·1   (s) 85·4 × 40·3   (t) 56·7 × 89·39

2.

   CHEDDAR
   £4·48 a kg

   LEICESTER
   £4·59 a kg

   CHESHIRE
   £5·42 a kg

   BRIE
   £6·38 a kg

   Find the cost, to the nearest penny, of:
   (a) 1·3 kg of Cheddar   (b) 0·8 kg of Leicester
   (c) 0·5 kg of Cheshire   (d) 1·1 kg of Brie
   (e) 0·7 kg of Cheddar   (f) 0·25 kg of Cheshire
   (g) 0·3 kg of Brie   (h) 1·25 kg of Leicester
   (i) 0·45 kg of Cheshire   (j) 0·36 kg of Brie
   (k) 0·28 kg of Cheddar   (l) 0·54 kg of Leicester

MODULE 3

3. A television can be bought for £234 cash or with a £23·40 deposit and 12 monthly payments of £22·80.
   (a) How much does it cost to buy the television by monthly payments?
   (b) How much cheaper is it to pay cash for the television?

4. A roll of cloth is sold at £4·58 per metre. Find the cost of the following lengths of the cloth:
   (a) 5 m   (b) 3·8 m   (c) 2·5 m   (d) 0·9 m   (e) 4·7 m

4.12 Dividing decimal numbers with a calculator

To complete the calculation 3·56 ÷ 1·2, you press the keys:

| 3 | · | 5 | 6 | ÷ | 1 | · | 2 | = |

The answer is 2·9666667 (on an eight-digit calculator).

You often need to round the answer given by a calculator.

Suppose the calculation was to solve the problem,

> 'A piece of cheese weighing 1·2 kg costs £3·56, find the cost per kg'.

The answer will be £2·97 to the nearest penny.

Exercise 4L

Solve these using a calculator.

1. Give the answer to each calculation correct to one decimal place.
   (a) 35 ÷ 11   (b) 45 ÷ 8   (c) 137 ÷ 9   (d) 458 ÷ 12   (e) 311 ÷ 15
   (f) 13·5 ÷ 7   (g) 8·9 ÷ 17   (h) 56·7 ÷ 16   (i) 68·9 ÷ 46   (j) 234·56 ÷ 53
   (k) 15 ÷ 0·9   (l) 64 ÷ 1·1   (m) 125 ÷ 4·6   (n) 364 ÷ 5·8   (o) 100 ÷ 1·3
   (p) 16·7 ÷ 8·6   (q) 1·23 ÷ 6·7   (r) 8·19 ÷ 1·13   (s) 33·28 ÷ 3·1   (t) 0·452 ÷ 1·9

2. The total cost of a school trip to London will be £463·80. Find the cost per student (to the nearest penny) if the number going on the trip is:
   (a) 32   (b) 38   (c) 43   (d) 41   (e) 47

MODULE 3

3. A teacher buys a box of 60 sweatshirts for £280.
   (a) How much does each sweatshirt cost?
   (b) How much must the teacher sell each sweatshirt for if she wants to make a £200 profit for the school?

4. A car is travelling at 95 kilometres per hour.
   (a) How many metres will the car travel in one hour at this speed?
   (b) How many metres will the car travel in one minute at this speed?
   (c) How many metres will the car travel in one second at this speed?

4.13 Metric and Imperial measure

Most of the measurements we use are metric, that is they are based on the decimal system.

There are still some imperial measures in use such as miles, feet and pints.

You need to know approximate conversions between metric and imperial units.

This table shows the conversions you need to know.

	Approximate conversions
Length	1 inch ≈ 2·54 cm 1 mile ≈ 1·61 km
Mass	1 pound ≈ 454 g 1 kilogram ≈ 2·21 pounds
Capacity	1 gallon ≈ 4·55 litres 1 litre ≈ 1·76 pints

The symbol ≈ stands for 'is approximately equal to'. The measurement given is a good working estimate.

Example

Natalie drives a distance of 12 miles.
Roughly how many kilometres (km) has she driven?
Give your answer to 1 decimal place.

$$1 \text{ mile} \approx 1\cdot61 \text{ km}$$
$$12 \times 1\cdot61 = 19\cdot32$$
Natalie has driven roughly 19·3 km.

Exercise 4M

1. Convert these distances to kilometres. Give your answer to 1 dp.
   (a) 10 miles   (b) 4 miles   (c) 25 miles   (d) 8·5 miles

2. A jam making plant uses 420 lb of sugar an hour.
   Roughly how many kilograms is this?

3. A watering can holds 3 Imperial gallons.
   Approximately how many litres of water will the watering can hold?

4. The length of a carpet is measured as 4′ 8″.
   (a) Roughly what is this in centimetres?
   (b) Roughly how long is the carpet in metres?

   > 4′ stands for 4 feet and
   > 8″ stands for 8 inches.
   >
   > 12 inches = 1 foot

5. For a flight an aircraft has 3 850 litres of fuel.
   (a) Roughly how many gallons is this?
   (b) Jim estimates that the aircraft has about 2 200 pints of fuel.
       Is this a good estimate? Explain your answer.

6. A man gives his weight as 168 lb.
   What is his weight in kilograms?

Summary

Checkout N4

1. When a decimal number is multiplied by 10, all the digits move one place to the left, while the decimal point remains fixed.

   1. Multiply each number by 10:
      (a) 13·45   (b) 0·25
      (c) 1·034

2. There are 10 millimetres (mm) in one centimetre (cm).

   2. Change each length into milllimetres:
      (a) 3·4 cm   (b) 13·8 cm
      (c) 9·6 cm

3. When a decimal number is multiplied by 100, all the digits move two places to the left, while the decimal point remains fixed.

   3. Multiply each number by 100:
      (a) 13·45   (b) 0·253
      (c) 1·034

4. There are 100 centimetres (cm) in one metre (m).

   4. Change each length into centimetres:
      (a) 3·42 m   (b) 13·08 m
      (c) 9·67 m

5. When a decimal number is multiplied by 1 000, all the digits move three places to the left, while the decimal point remains fixed.

   5. Multiply each number by 1 000:
      (a) 13·45   (b) 0·253
      (c) 1·532 4

6. There are 1 000 millilitres (ml) in one litre (ℓ).

   6. Change each volume into millilitres:
      (a) 3·42 ℓ (b) 3·108 ℓ
      (c) 0·35 ℓ

MODULE 3

7. When a decimal number is divided by 10, all the digits move one place to the right, while the decimal point remains fixed.

7. (a) Divide each number by 10:
(i) 13·4   (ii) 25   (iii) 1·34
(b) Change each length into centimetres:
(i) 45 mm (ii) 127 mm (iii) 6 mm

---

8. When a decimal number is divided by 100, all the digits move two places to the right, while the decimal point remains fixed.

8. (a) Divide each number by 100:
(i) 134·8   (ii) 25·3   (iii) 1·4
(b) Change each length into metres:
(i) 342 cm   (ii) 35 cm
(iii) 196 cm

---

9. When a decimal number is divided by 1 000, all the digits move three places to the right, while the decimal point remains fixed.

9. (a) Divide each number by 1 000:
(i) 1 345   (ii) 253   (iii) 1.5
(b) Change each volume into litres:
(i) 1 342 ml   (ii) 310 ml
(iii) 35 ml

---

10. To find the answer to a decimal multiplication:
• Ignore any decimal points and multiply normally.
• Count the number of digits after the decimal point(s) in the calculation.
• Put the same number of digits after the decimal point in the answer.

10. (a) Do these in your head.
(i) $0·5 \times 3$
(ii) $6 \times 0·2$
(iii) $0·3 \times 0·4$
(iv) $0·6 \times 0·05$
(v) $1·2 \times 4$
(vi) $0·9 \times 11$
(vii) $1·2 \times 0·3$
(viii) $2·4 \times 0·04$
(b) Do these on paper.
(i) $4·8 \times 7$
(ii) $2·35 \times 9$
(iii) $1·25 \times 1·8$
(iv) $4·26 \times 3·2$

---

11. When dividing decimals, zeros are added so that division can continue past the decimal point. The decimal point in the answer is directly above the decimal point in the calculation.

11. Do these on paper.
(a) $4·5 \div 5$ (b) $5·04 \div 6$
(c) $21·42 \div 7$ (d) $0·48 \div 3$
(e) $23 \div 4$ (f) $15 \div 8$

---

12. A **recurring decimal** repeats the same pattern over and over again. The answer is written with dots over the recurring digits.

12. Do these on paper.
(a) $17 \div 3$ (b) $0·4 \div 6$
(c) $12·5 \div 9$ (d) $1·21 \div 6$

MODULE 3

13. Calculator answers often need to be rounded.

13. (a) Calculate correct to 1 decimal place:
   (i)   13 × 16·89
   (ii) 2·7 × 1·05
   (iii) 85·3 × 17·4
   (iv) 4·58 × 16
   (v)   13 ÷ 16·89
   (vi) 2·7 ÷ 1·05
   (vii) 85·3 ÷ 17·4
   (viii) 4·58 ÷ 16

(b) Calculate correct to 2 decimal places:
   (i)   3·45 × 1·31
   (ii) 3·207 × 17
   (iii) 6·83 × 1·2
   (iv) 3·5 × 3·08
   (v)   3·45 ÷ 1·31
   (vi) 3·207 ÷ 17
   (vii) 6·83 ÷ 1·2
   (viii) 3·5 ÷ 3·08

Revision exercise N4

1. Complete the following shopping bill:

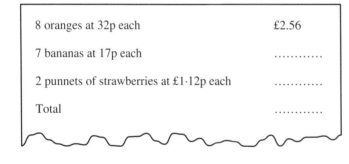

8 oranges at 32p each	£2.56
7 bananas at 17p each	....
2 punnets of strawberries at £1·12p each	....
Total	....

[NEAB]

2. Use your calculator to find the value of $\dfrac{38\cdot21 + 7\cdot84}{15\cdot34 - 6\cdot58}$

Give your answer to an appropriate degree of accuracy.   [SEG]

3. A market trader pays £8·84 for 26 cauliflowers. How much does he pay, in pence, for one cauliflower?   [SEG]

4. Alice buys gold braid to decorate her dress.
She buys a length of 2·89 metres. The shop charges Alice £7·24 per metre for the exact length which she buys.
How much does Alice pay for the gold braid?   [SEG]

5. Use your calculator to find the value of

$$\frac{8\cdot27^2}{9\cdot41 + 2\cdot84}$$

Give your answer to an appropriate degree of accuracy.

[SEG]

6. Use your calculator to find the value of

$$\frac{2\cdot987 + 7\cdot82}{18\cdot41 - 4\cdot68}$$

Give your answer to an appropriate degree of accuracy.

[SEG]

7. Rachel buys 8 pounds of potatoes for £2·56.
How much does Wasim pay for 11 pounds of potatoes
sold at the same price per pound? [SEG]

8. This marker shows the flood levels in various years.

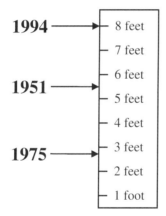

(a) This is the year 2001. How many years ago did the
flood level reach about $5\frac{1}{2}$ feet?

(b) 1 foot is about 30 centimetres.
How many **metres** was the flood level in 1994?

[NEAB]

9. (a) One litre is equal to 1·75 pints. A motorist buys 40 litres
of petrol. How many pints of petrol is this?

(b) Eight pints are equal to one gallon. How many gallons
of petrol did the motorist buy?

(c) Forty litres of petrol cost £18. What is the price of
twenty five litres? [SEG]

10. (a) John is 8·4 kg heavier than Alan.
    The sum of their weights is 133.2 kg.
    How heavy is Alan?

  (b) Before starting a diet Derek weighed 80 kg.
    He now weighs 8 kg less.
    Calculate his weight loss as a percentage of his
    previous weight.

  (c) Sarah weighs 54 kg.
    What is Sarah's weight in pounds?   [SEG]

11. Petrol costs 71·5p per litre.
  Judith puts £20 worth of petrol into her car.
  How many litres has Judith bought?
  Give your answers correct to one decimal place.   [SEG]

12. Packs of wrapping paper cost 68 pence.
  Shelley buys as many packs as she can for £10.

  (a) How many packs does she buy?

  Shelley pays with a £10 note.

  (b) How much change is she given?

  The change is given using the smallest number of coins.

  (c) How is the change given?   [SEG]

13. Bob buys some presents for Easter.

  (a) Copy and complete his bill.

Chocolot plc	
	Cost (£)
4 large eggs at £2·99 each	....
2 luxury eggs at £4·99 each	....
3 small eggs at 29 pence each	....
1 bunch of flowers at £11·22	_____
Total	£ _____

                                                          [SEG]

14. (a) Convert 2·4 kilograms to grams.

(b) A pack of writing paper weighs 2·4 kg. There are 500
sheets of paper in the pack. Calculate the weight,
in grams, of one sheet of paper.

(c) A sheet of paper has a thickness of 0·9 mm.
Calculate the thickness of a pack of 500 sheets of
paper.   [SEG]

15. The cost of a ticket from Heathrow airport to central London
is £4·40 single and £6·90 return. Children under the age of
16 pay half price.

(a) How much does a return ticket cost for a child?

Max buys return tickets for himself, his wife and his three
daughters aged 18, 17 and 13.

(b) How much does Max pay in total?

Max pays with a £50 note.

(c) How much change does Max receive?

Max is given this change in the least number of notes and
coins possible.

(d) List the notes and coins Max is given.   [SEG]

MODULE 3

N5 NUMBER 5

This unit will show you how to:

● Calculate with fractions, decimals and percentages
● Understand the equivalence of fractions, decimals and percentages

Before you start:

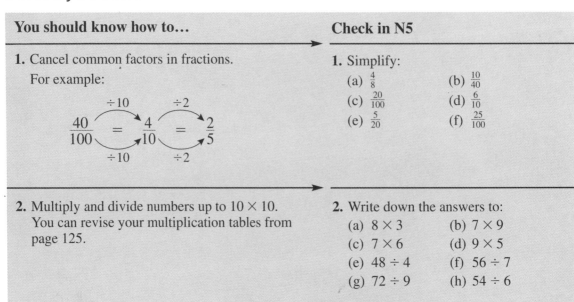

You should know how to...	Check in N5
1. Cancel common factors in fractions. For example: $$\frac{40}{100} \xrightarrow[\div 10]{\div 10} \frac{4}{10} \xrightarrow[\div 2]{\div 2} \frac{2}{5}$$	**1.** Simplify: (a) $\frac{4}{8}$ (b) $\frac{10}{40}$ (c) $\frac{20}{100}$ (d) $\frac{6}{10}$ (e) $\frac{5}{20}$ (f) $\frac{25}{100}$
2. Multiply and divide numbers up to 10×10. You can revise your multiplication tables from page 125.	**2.** Write down the answers to: (a) 8×3 (b) 7×9 (c) 7×6 (d) 9×5 (e) $48 \div 4$ (f) $56 \div 7$ (g) $72 \div 9$ (h) $54 \div 6$

5.1 Understanding fractions

This pie chart shows the pets owned by the student in a class.
You can use **fractions** to describe the chart. The chart shows that:

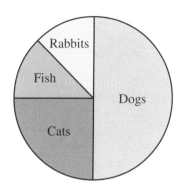

- $\frac{1}{2}$ of the students own dogs
- $\frac{1}{4}$ of the students own cats
- $\frac{1}{8}$ of the students own fish
- $\frac{1}{8}$ of the students own rabbits.

You can use fractions to describe the ways things are divided.

$\frac{4}{5}$ of this shape is coloured.

$\frac{2}{3}$ of the faces are smiling.

Exercise 5A

1. What fraction of each shape is coloured?

(a)

(b)

(c)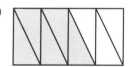

(d)

(e)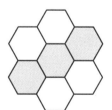

(f)

(g)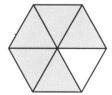

(h)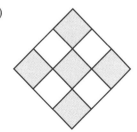

MODULE 3

(i) 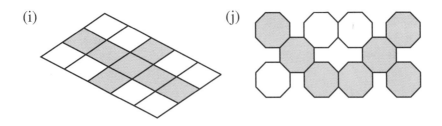 (j)

2.

What fraction of these ice-creams:
(a) have a flake
(b) have raspberry sauce
(c) do not have a flake
(d) have a flake and raspberry sauce
(e) have neither a flake nor raspberry sauce
(f) have raspberry sauce but not a flake
(g) do not have raspberry sauce?

3. (a) What fraction of the days of the week start with the letter T?
(b) What fraction of the months of the year have exactly 30 days?
(c) What fraction of an hour is 15 minutes?
(d) What fraction of £1·00 is 75p?
(e) What fraction of one minute is 30 seconds?

4. The letters a, e, i, o and u are called vowels.
What fraction of the letters in these words are vowels?
(a) Manchester
(b) apple
(c) piglets
(d) umbrella
(e) octopus

5.2 Improper fractions and mixed numbers

A fraction like $\frac{12}{7}$ is called an **improper** fraction because it is greater than one.

$\frac{12}{7}$ can be written as $1\frac{5}{7}$

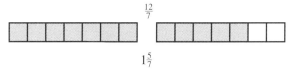

A quantity like $1\frac{5}{7}$ is called a **mixed number**.

Examples

(a) $\frac{3}{2} = 1\frac{1}{2}$ (b) $\frac{13}{4} = 3\frac{1}{4}$ (c) $\frac{8}{3} = 2\frac{2}{3}$

Exercise 5B

1. Change each improper fraction into a mixed number.

(a) $\frac{12}{5}$ (b) $\frac{7}{4}$ (c) $\frac{9}{5}$ (d) $\frac{4}{3}$ (e) $\frac{5}{2}$

(f) $\frac{6}{3}$ (g) $\frac{7}{6}$ (h) $\frac{8}{7}$ (i) $\frac{5}{3}$ (j) $\frac{9}{7}$

(k) $\frac{13}{12}$ (l) $\frac{19}{3}$ (m) $\frac{18}{6}$ (n) $\frac{29}{4}$ (o) $\frac{9}{1}$

(p) $\frac{33}{5}$ (q) $\frac{11}{2}$ (r) $\frac{9}{4}$ (s) $\frac{15}{13}$ (t) $\frac{100}{99}$

(u) $\frac{6}{5}$ (v) $\frac{21}{17}$ (w) $\frac{11}{4}$ (x) $\frac{19}{2}$ (y) $\frac{17}{4}$

2. Change each mixed number into an improper fraction.

(a) $1\frac{1}{2}$ (b) $2\frac{1}{3}$ (c) $1\frac{1}{4}$ (d) $1\frac{2}{5}$ (e) $2\frac{1}{6}$

(f) $1\frac{4}{7}$ (g) $1\frac{1}{8}$ (h) $1\frac{5}{12}$ (i) $1\frac{5}{13}$ (j) $7\frac{1}{4}$

(k) $6\frac{1}{2}$ (l) $3\frac{2}{3}$ (m) $2\frac{3}{4}$ (n) $2\frac{1}{5}$ (o) $2\frac{5}{6}$

(p) $2\frac{1}{7}$ (q) $1\frac{5}{8}$ (r) $3\frac{7}{12}$ (s) $2\frac{1}{17}$ (t) $3\frac{5}{7}$

(u) $9\frac{1}{2}$ (v) $7\frac{1}{3}$ (w) $6\frac{3}{4}$ (x) $1\frac{4}{5}$ (y) $3\frac{5}{6}$

Simplifying fractions

You can simplify fractions by dividing the numerator and denominator by the same number. This is known as cancelling.

Example

Simplify:

(a) $\frac{5}{10}$ (b) $\frac{20}{100}$ (c) $\frac{12}{18}$ (d) $\frac{48}{100}$

(a) 5 and 10 both divide by 5:

(b) 20 and 100 both divide by 20

Note you can do this in stages:

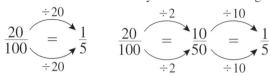

$$\frac{20}{100} \xrightarrow{\div 20} = \xrightarrow{\div 20} \frac{1}{5} \qquad \frac{20}{100} \xrightarrow{\div 2} = \xrightarrow{\div 2} \frac{10}{50} \xrightarrow{\div 10} = \xrightarrow{\div 10} \frac{1}{5}$$

(c)

$$\frac{12}{18} \xrightarrow{\div 2} = \xrightarrow{\div 2} \frac{6}{9} \xrightarrow{\div 3} = \xrightarrow{\div 3} \frac{2}{3}$$

(d)

$$\frac{48}{100} \xrightarrow{\div 2} = \xrightarrow{\div 2} \frac{24}{50} \xrightarrow{\div 2} = \xrightarrow{\div 2} \frac{12}{25}$$

5.3 Percentages and fractions

Percentages are fractions with a denominator of 100.
% means 'out of 100'.

$$10\% \text{ is the same as } \frac{10}{100} = \frac{1}{10}$$

$$50\% \text{ is the same as } \frac{50}{100} = \frac{1}{2}$$

$$40\% \text{ is the same as } \frac{40}{100} = \frac{2}{5}$$

Example

Change these percentages into fractions.

(a) 11% (b) 25% (c) 64%

(a) $11\% = \frac{11}{10}$

(b) $25\% = \frac{25}{100} \xrightarrow{\div 25} = \xrightarrow{\div 25} \frac{1}{4}$

(c) $64\% = \frac{64}{100} \xrightarrow{\div 4} = \xrightarrow{\div 4} \frac{16}{25}$

Exercise 5C

Change these percentages into fractions. Simplify your fractions
where possible.

1. 30%	**2.** 20%	**3.** 75%	**4.** 90%	**5.** 80%
6. 5%	**7.** 45%	**8.** 4%	**9.** 12%	**10.** 24%
11. 60%	**12.** 2%	**13.** 22%	**14.** 98%	**15.** 35%
16. 72%	**17.** 95%	**18.** 65%	**19.** 17%	**20.** 42%
21. 12%	**22.** 14%	**23.** 16%	**24.** 99%	**25.** 15%

MODULE 3

5.4 Percentages of quantities

If calculations are simple they can be done in your head or on paper. With more difficult numbers use a calculator.

How much can you save if you book this holiday before the end of June?

14 nights in Ibiza

Half board, two-star hotel.
Flight to and from Gatwick.

£340 per person

Save <u>20%</u> *if you book by the end of June*

The saving will be 20% of £340.

10% of £340 is £34
so 20% of £340 is £68.

Example 1

Calculate 45% of 80
$$45\% \text{ of } 80 = \frac{45}{100} \times 80 = 80 \div 100 \times 45 = 36$$

Example 2

A plumber charges £62·40 for a repair but adds 17·5% V.A.T. to the bill. Find the total charge.

$$17\cdot5\% \text{ of } 62\cdot40 = 62\cdot4 \div 100 \times 17\cdot5 = 10\cdot92$$
$$\text{Total charge} = £62\cdot40 + £10\cdot92 = £73\cdot32$$

Exercise 5D

1. Calculate.
   (a) 10% of 700   (b) 25% of 800   (c) 50% of 600
   (d) 75% of 400   (e) 20% of 80   (f) 15% of 120
   (g) 40% of 95   (h) 4% of 125   (i) 80% of 150
   (j) 30% of 60   (k) 60% of 45   (l) 70% of 200
   (m) 45% of 400   (n) 12% of 150   (o) 34% of 300
   (p) 65% of 240   (q) 16% of 25   (r) 25% of 16
   (s) 8% of 250   (t) 90% of 90   (u) 24% of 75
   (v) 64% of 275   (w) 78% of 350   (x) 55% of 60
   (y) 60% of 55

MODULE 3

2. Calculate.

(a) 5% of 62	(b) 17% of 80	(c) 11% of 92	(d) 56% of 127
(e) 23% of 267	(f) 42% of 384	(g) 3% of 1 200	(h) 7% of 95
(i) 45% of 508	(j) 98% of 580	(k) 18% of 670	(l) 9% of 15
(m) 17·5% of 80	(n) 17·5% of 240	(o) 17·5% of 140	(p) 17·5% of 99
(q) 12·5% of 56	(r) 3·1% of 250	(s) 24% of 67·8	(t) 50% of 34·8
(u) 75% of 44·8	(v) 7·5% of 160	(w) 7·5% of 48	(x) 12·5% of 16·8
(y) 14·3% of 34·2			

3.

15% Off GRAND SALE

FOR EXAMPLE

Coat £98 reduced by £14·70 to £83·30

Find the amount the following items will be reduced by and the new cost:

(a) A dress costing £80   (b) A pair of trousers costing £60

(c) A top costing £30   (d) A pair of shoes costing £70

(e) A shirt costing £45   (f) A jacket costing £48

(g) A belt costing £18   (h) A pair of socks costing £4·80

4.

CLASSIC COMPUTERS

Computer systems from £400 to £4 000

Example. Home System 3 000

£550 + 17·5% V.A.T.

£550 + £96·25 = **£646·25**

These are the prices of computer systems before V.A.T. is added. Calculate the amount of V.A.T. to add and the full price.

(a) Home System 4 000, £640   (b) Office System 2 000, £800

(c) Game Player 5 000, £1 200   (d) Home Office 4 000, £500

(e) Game Player 2 000, £750   (f) Home System 1 000, £320

(g) Office System 5 000, £3 250   (h) Home Office 2 000, £390

5.5 Fractions, percentages and decimals

To change a fraction to a decimal, you divide the top number by the bottom number.

To change a decimal to a percentage, you multiply by 100.

Example

Change $\frac{3}{4}$ to a decimal and a percentage.

$$
\begin{array}{r}
0{\cdot}75 \\
4\overline{)3{\cdot}00} \\
\underline{2\ 8} \\
20 \\
\underline{20} \\
0
\end{array}
$$

$\frac{3}{4} = 0{\cdot}75 = 75\%$

When the numbers are more difficult, use a calculator.

Example

Change $\frac{23}{25}$ to a decimal and a percentage.

$\frac{23}{25} = 23 \div 25 = 0{\cdot}92 = 92\%$

Exercise 5E

1. Change each fraction to a decimal and a percentage.

   (a) $\frac{1}{2}$ (b) $\frac{1}{4}$ (c) $\frac{3}{4}$ (d) $\frac{3}{5}$ (e) $\frac{7}{10}$ (f) $\frac{11}{20}$ (g) $\frac{3}{25}$

   (h) $\frac{27}{50}$ (i) $\frac{1}{5}$ (j) $\frac{9}{10}$ (k) $\frac{3}{20}$ (l) $\frac{18}{25}$ (m) $\frac{1}{50}$ (n) $\frac{2}{5}$

   (o) $\frac{1}{10}$ (p) $\frac{9}{20}$ (q) $\frac{17}{25}$ (r) $\frac{43}{50}$ (s) $\frac{7}{20}$ (t) $\frac{21}{25}$ (u) $\frac{11}{50}$

   (v) $\frac{13}{20}$ (w) $\frac{11}{25}$ (x) $\frac{49}{50}$ (y) $\frac{24}{25}$

2.

HEEL'S SHOES	SOLE'S SHOES	SHOO'S SHOES
SPECIAL OFFER	*SPECIAL OFFER*	*SPECIAL OFFER*
LE BOC TRAINERS	**LE BOC TRAINERS**	**LE BOC TRAINERS**
Normal price £120	Normal price £120	Normal price £120
$\frac{1}{3}$ OFF	30% OFF	$\frac{5}{12}$ OFF

   (a) What is the cash reduction in Heel's shop?
   (b) What is the cash reduction in Sole's shop?
   (c) What is the cash reduction in Shoo's shop?
   (d) What is the percentage reduction in Heel's shop?
   (e) What is the percentage reduction in Shoo's shop?

5.6 Writing one number as a percentage of another

To write one number as a percentage of another:

- form a fraction with the two numbers
- convert the fraction to a decimal
- convert the decimal to a percentage.

Example 1

Write 48 as a percentage of 64.

$$48 \text{ as a fraction of } 64 = \frac{48}{64}$$
$$48 \text{ as a percentage of } 64 = 48 \div 64 \times 100 = 75\%$$

Example 2

Siloben scores 126 out of 144 in an English test.
What is her percentage mark?

$$\text{Siloben's mark as a fraction} = \frac{126}{144}$$
$$\text{Siloben's mark as a percentage} = 126 \div 144 \times 100 = 87\cdot5\%$$

Example 3

A coat is reduced from £76 to £57 in a sale.
What is the percentage reduction?

$$\text{Cash reduction} = £76 - £57 = £19$$
$$\text{Reduction as a fraction} = \frac{19}{76}$$
$$\text{Reduction as a percentage} = 19 \div 76 \times 100 = 25\%$$

Exercise 5F

1. Write:

(a) 40 as a percentage of 80
(b) 36 as a percentage of 48
(c) 6 as a percentage of 24
(d) 10 as a percentage of 25
(e) 27 as a percentage of 45
(f) 9 as a percentage of 60
(g) 35 as a percentage of 125
(h) 64 as a percentage of 80
(i) 78 as a percentage of 156
(j) 15 as a percentage of 50
(k) 56 as a percentage of 80
(l) 300 as a percentage of 400
(m) 39 as a percentage of 156
(n) 132 as a percentage of 240
(o) 484 as a percentage of 605
(p) 221 as a percentage of 425
(q) 39 as a percentage of 65
(r) 63 as a percentage of 90
(s) 76 as a percentage of 80
(t) 51 as a percentage of 150
(u) 360 as a percentage of 800
(v) 35 as a percentage of 500
(w) 44 as a percentage of 275
(x) 126 as a percentage of 150
(y) 412 as a percentage of 515

2.

HISTORY TEST (marks out of 80)

Janice	12
Jo	24
Rob	48
Elizabeth	60
Mike	32
Fozia	56
Kaleek	40
Nicky	50
Ruth	70
Yvette	76

This list was pinned up after a History test. Copy out the list, giving each mark as a percentage of 80.

3. Write each of these times as a percentage of one hour:

(a) 15 minutes (b) 30 minutes (c) 12 minutes (d) 27 minutes (e) 36 minutes
(f) 45 minutes (g) 48 minutes (h) 51 minutes (i) 39 minutes (j) 57 minutes

4. Andrew is the manager of a record shop. He decides to hold a sale of Abba items. Before the sale he starts to prepare this list for the staff.

Sale items only	Old price	Sale price	Cash saving	% saving
CDs	£12·50	£10·00	£2·50	20%
Single CDs	£3·60	£3·06	£0·54	
Tapes	£11·60	£8·70		
Posters	£4·80	£4·20		
Books	£5·40	£2·97		

Copy and complete Andrew's list.

5. Oranges can be bought for 12p each or £1·62 for a bag of 15.
(a) How much does it cost to buy 15 oranges at 12p each?
(b) What is the saving by buying a bag of 15 oranges?
(c) What is the percentage saving by buying a bag of 15 oranges?
(d) Special offer bags of the oranges are marked '20% extra free'. How many oranges do these bags contain?
(e) What fraction of the oranges in special offer bags are free?

SUPER SAVER
20%
extra FREE

5.7 Increasing and decreasing an amount by a given percentage

Example 1

If an Inter City season ticket costs £2 632 now, how much will it cost after a 21% rise?

Method 1
To find the new cost of a ticket you
find 21% of £2 632 and then add this to
the original:

$$21\% \text{ of } £2\,632 = \frac{21}{100} \times £2\,632$$

Increase in fare = £552·72
New cost of fare = £2 632 + £552·72
= £3 184·72

Method 2
Consider the original amount of £2 632
as 100%. Increasing it by 21% is the same
as finding 121% of the original cost.

$$121\% = \frac{121}{100} = 1·21$$

Therefore the quickest way of increasing the
original fare by 21% is to multiply it by 1·21.

$$121\% \text{ of } £2\,632 = 1·21 \times £2\,632$$
New cost of fare = £3 184·72

Example 2

The marked price of a sweater is £24·90.
What is its sale price?

Method 1
The reduction = 20% of £24·90

$$= \frac{20}{100} \times £24·90$$

$$= £4·98$$
The sale price = £24·90 − £4·98
= £19·92

Method 2
£24·90 is the equivalent of 100% and so
decreasing the price by 20% is equivalent to
finding 80% of the original price.

$$\frac{80}{100} \times £24·90 \qquad = 0·80 \times £24·90$$

Sale price   = £19·92

Exercise 5G

Give all answers to the nearest 1p.

1. Increase the following rail fares by 10%.
   (a) £9·20   (b) £3·70   (c) £5·00   (d) £9·81   (e) £9·13

2. Increase the given amount by the required percentage:

    (a) £72·12 by 50%   (b) 95p by 10%   (c) £360 by 120%

    (d) £220 by 30%   (e) £124·80 by 25%   (f) £19·99 by 90%

3. Reduce the following marked prices by 20% to find the sale prices:

    (a) £30·00   (b) £10·50   (c) £17·60   (d) 45p   (e) £12·99

4. Increase the given amount by the required percentage:

    (a) £54·10 by 8%   (b) 84p by 30%   (c) £128 by 60%

    (d) £27·15 by $17\frac{1}{2}$%   (e) £99·05 by 40%   (f) £1·62 by 33%

Summary

1. You can use fractions to describe the way things are divided.

2. $\frac{12}{5}$ is an **improper fraction** and can be written as a **mixed number** like this: $2\frac{2}{5}$
The mixed number $4\frac{2}{3}$ can be written as the improper fraction $\frac{14}{3}$

3. Percentages are fractions with 100 as their bottom number.
$$64\% = \frac{64}{100}$$

4. To work out a percentage of a quantity, change the percentage to a fraction.
$$45\% \text{ of } 80 = \frac{45}{100} \times 80 = 80 \div 100 \times 45 = 36$$

5. To change a fraction to a decimal, divide the top number by the bottom number.
To change a decimal to a percentage, multiply by 100

6. To write one number as a percentage of another:
- form a fraction with the two numbers
- convert the fraction to a decimal
- convert the decimal to a percentage.

Checkout N5

1. What fraction of each shape is coloured?

    (a)

    (b)

2. (a) Write as mixed numbers:
        (i) $\frac{17}{2}$ (ii) $\frac{16}{3}$ (iii) $\frac{9}{4}$

    (b) Write as improper fractions:
        (i) $3\frac{1}{2}$ (ii) $2\frac{3}{4}$ (iii) $7\frac{2}{3}$

3. Change these percentages to fractions:
    (a) 20%   (b) 75%   (c) 36%

4. Calculate:
    (a) 50% of 400   (b) 25% of 16

    (c) 12% of 175   (d) 85% of 260

    (e) 17·5% of £20 (f) 17·5% of £36

5. Change each fraction to a decimal and a percentage.
    (a) $\frac{3}{4}$ (b) $\frac{4}{5}$ (c) $\frac{3}{20}$ (d) $\frac{23}{25}$

6. (a) Write:
        (i)   60 as a percentage of 120
        (ii) 24 as a percentage of 50
        (iii) 150 as a percentage of 250

    (b) A coat is reduced from £80 to £56. Find the percentage reduction.

Revision exercise N5

1. (a) Copy and shade $\frac{1}{4}$ of this shape.

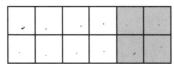

(b) Copy and shade 10% of this shape.

(c) What fraction of this shape is shaded?
Give your answer in its simplest form.

[NEAB]

2. Eric receives his gas bill.
It is for £120 plus VAT at 5%.

(a) Calculate the VAT.

(b) Hence find the total amount Eric has to pay. [SEG]

3. There are 250 people on a beach and $\frac{1}{5}$ of them are children.

(a) How many children are on the beach?

(b) Express $\frac{1}{5}$ as a percentage. [SEG]

4. James wants to buy a surf board and finds the following
advertisement.

> **_Sun'n'Sea Sports_**
>
> Our Price
> $\frac{1}{3}$ Off Recommended price
> of
> £276

Calculate the final cost of the surf board. [SEG]

5. Louise has a bill for repairs to her car.
The bill is for £343 plus VAT at 17·5%.

 (a) Calculate the VAT charged.

 (b) Hence find the total amount Louise has to pay.   [SEG]

6. There are 150 people staying in an hotel.
Of the 150 people, 60 are children.

 (a) Express the number of children as a fraction of the
  total number of people.
  Give your answer in its simplest form.

 Of the 150 people, 90 are male.

 (b) Express the number who are male as a percentage of
  the total number of people.   [SEG]

7. There are 300 cars in a multi-storey car park.
Of the 300 cars, 40% are on the ground floor.

 (a) How many cars are on the ground floor?

 Of these 300 cars, $\frac{1}{5}$ are on the top floor.

 (b) How many cars are on the top floor?

 (c) Express $\frac{1}{5}$ as a percentage.   [SEG]

8. (a) A shopkeeper has 12 bags of nails.
  In each bag there are 150 nails.
  How many nails are there altogether?

 (b) David buys 150 nails.
  He uses 80% of the nails.
  How many nails does he use?

 (c) The shopkeeper has 45 boxes of bolts.
  In one week the shopkeeper sells $\frac{2}{5}$ of the boxes.
  How many boxes does he sell?   [SEG]

9. There are 340 people watching a tennis match and 40% of
them are male.

 (a) (i) How many are male?

  (ii) Express 40% as a fraction, giving your answer in
   its simplest form.

 There are 151 adults watching and the rest are children.
 Forty-two of the children are under 12 years old.

 (b) What fraction of the children are under 12 years old?
  Give your answer in its simplest form.   [SEG]

10. Every day, Ron drives a bus between Cambridge and Oxford. His bus can carry 40 passengers.

On Monday, $\frac{5}{8}$ of the seats for passengers are used.

(a) How many passengers are on the bus on Monday?

On Tuesday, 30 passengers are on the bus.

(b) What percentage of the seats are used? [SEG]

11. Two friends want to book a summer holiday. They see two different advertisements for special offers from local travel agents.

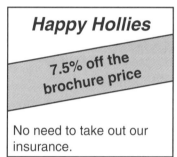

The brochure price of their holiday is the same from each travel agent, £524 per person.
Calculate the cost of the holiday package, for each of the two friends, booked at

(a) Priceless Packages,

(b) Happy Hollies. [SEG]

12. Brian buys 1000 Christmas trees. He sells $\frac{3}{5}$ of them at £8 each. He then reduces the price by 40%.

(a) What is the new selling price?

Brian sells all the remaining trees at this reduced price.

(b) How much money does Brian receive **altogether** from selling the trees? [SEG]

13. Jason bought an old bicycle for £36. He repaired it and resold it for £52.

What was his percentage profit? [NEAB]

14. Steve receives his electricity bill. The charge for the electricity he has used is £70 plus VAT at 5%.

(a) Calculate the VAT charged.

(b) Hence find the total amount Steve has to pay. [SEG]

MODULE 3

Module 3   Practice Calculator Test

1. Harry is paid £4·20 per hour for the basic 38 hour week he works.
Overtime in the evenings is paid at £6·50 per hour.
On Sundays Harry is paid £8·90 per hour.
Complete the pay sheet given below:

	Total Pay	
Harry Reilly	£	p
38 hours at £4·20 per hour		
2 hours at £6·50 per hour		
4 hours at £8·90 per hour		
TOTAL (for week)		

(4 marks)

2. (a) Nisha buys 28 chocolate bars which are priced at 23p each.
She is given a reduction of £1 because she is buying so many.
How much does Nisha pay for the chocolate?

Nisha pays with a £20 note.

(b) How much change is Nisha given?

This change is given in the smallest number of notes and coins.

(c) How is the change given?   **(7 marks)**

3. Write 30·247 correct to 1 decimal place.   **(1 mark)**

4. The cost of entry to a theme park is £38·50 for an adult.

(a) Give this cost to the nearest £10.

A child's ticket costs 60% of the cost of an adult ticket.

(b) Using your answer to part (a), calculate the cost of a child's ticket.   **(3 marks)**   [SEG]

5. Barry buys 300 mountain bikes for £15 000 and he starts to sell them at £110 each.

After he has sold $\frac{3}{4}$ of the bikes, Barry reduces the price by 20%.

(a) What is the new selling price of the bike?

Barry sells $\frac{3}{4}$ of the bikes at £110 each. He then sells all the remaining bikes at the reduced price.

(b) What is the total amount which Barry receives from selling the 300 bikes? **(6 marks)** [SEG]

6. Lilin travelled by train to London Waterloo.
She left work at 5·20 pm and arrived at Pinhoe station 20 minutes later.
From Pinhoe station she caught the next train to Salisbury.
At Salisbury she got on the first train going to London Waterloo.
The times of the times are shown on this timetable.

Exeter St. Davids ....dp	1330	–	1450	1545	1620	1700	1741	1822	2029
Exeter Central ....dp	1334	–	1459	1549	1624	1704	1745	1826	2033
Pinhoe	1339	–	–	–	1629	1709	1750	–	2038
Whimple	1346	–	1508	–	1636	1716	1757	1835	2045
Feniton	1351	–	1514	–	1641	1721	1802	1841	2050
....ar	1358	–	1521	1605	1648	1729	1809	1847	2057
Honiton ....dp	1358	–	1521	1605	1648	1729	1809	1851	2057
Axminster	1409	–	1532	1616	1659	1740	1820	1902	2108
Crewkerne.............................	1422	–	1545	1629	1713	1753	1842	1923	2133
....ar	1431	–	1554	1638	1722	1802	1851	1932	2142
Yeovil Junction ....dp	1432	–	1556	1639	1723	1803	1903	1938	2143
Sherborne	1439	–	1603	1646	1730	1810	1910	1944	2150
Templecombe.......................	1446	–	1610	1653	1737	1817	1917	1952	2157
....ar	1454	1553	1617	1701	1745	1824	1924	1959	2205
Gillingham ....dp	1454	1553	1624	1701	1745	1829	1931	1959	2205
Tisbury..................................	1504	1603	1634	–	1755	1839	1941	2010	2215
Salisbury ....ar	1519	1625	1649	1723	1809	1853	1955	2036	2235
Southampton Central .....ar	*1559*	*1659*	*1736*	*1759*	*1907*	*2004*	*2104*	*2202*	*2322v*
Portsmouth & S'sea........ar	*1643*	*1743*	–	*1843*	*1948*	*2048*	*2147*	*2243*	*0004v*
Salisbury ....dp	1523	1636	–	1725	1815	1915	–	2045	2240
Grateley................................	–	1648	–	–	1827	1927	–	2057	2252
Andover.................................	1541	1655	–	1743	1834	1934	–	2104	2259
Whitchurch (Hants)	–	1703	–	–	1842	1942	–	2112	2307
Overton	–	1709	–	–	1848	1948	–	2118	2313
Basingstoke ....ar	1557	1717	–	1801	1856	1956	–	2126	2321
Reading........................ar	*1628*	*1747*	–	*1846*	*1928*	*2028*	–	*2203*	*0003*
Woking...............................ar	*1617*	*1741*	–	*1820*	*1916*	*2017*	–	*2146*	*0007*
Clapham Junction ....ar	*1642*	*1802*	–	*1844*	*1936*	*2037*	–	*2211*	*0046*
London Waterloo..............ar	*1650*	*1810*	–	*1852*	*1944*	*2051*	–	*2219*	*0005*

Calculate how long it took Lilin to reach London Waterloo from the time she left work.
Give your answer in hours and minutes.

(4 marks) [SEG]

7. Mark wants to send his mother a box of chocolates which normally cost £9·99.
He sees a special offer in a local shop.

Chocolate and Candy Unlimited

save one third

off normal price

(a) How much would the chocolates cost from Chocolate and Candy Unlimited?

Mark knows he can get 24% off the normal price of £9·99 if he buys the chocolates with his credit card at another shop, Chocolate Box.

(b) How much would the chocolates cost from Chocolate Box if Mark pays by credit card?   **(6 marks)**

Module 3   Practice Non-calculator Test

1. Liz wants to calculate the approximate value of

$$\frac{3\cdot84}{18\cdot3 + 21\cdot9}$$

(a) Write down each of the numbers in Liz's calculation to the nearest whole number.

(b) Hence find an estimate of the answer to the calculation.
     (5 marks)

2. Kim receives £74·82 for a week's work. There are three £20 notes in her pay packet.
(a) How much does Kim receive which is not in £20 notes? This money is given in the smallest number of notes and coins.
(b) How is this money given?   **(4 marks)**

3. (a) Write 0·3 as a fraction.
   (b) Write $\frac{3}{4}$ as a decimal.
   (c) Find the square of 5.
   (d) Find the square root of 49.
   (e) Evaluate $0\cdot04^2$.   **(6 marks)**   [SEG]

4. There are 600 passengers on a ship.
Of these 600 passengers, $\frac{3}{5}$ eat in the restaurant.

   (a) (i) How many passengers eat in the restaurant?
   (ii) Write $\frac{3}{5}$ as a percentage.

   (b) Of the 600 passengers, there are 48 who have travelled
   as a group. What percentage of the passengers are in
   this group?

   (c) Of the 600 passengers, 210 are children.
   Express the number of children as a fraction of the total
   number of passengers.
   Give your fraction in its simplest form.

   (7 marks)   [SEG]

5. Work out 31×247 **(3 marks)**

6. Karen receives her gas bill.
The charge for gas is £72 plus VAT at 5%.

   (a) Calculate the VAT charged.

   (b) Hence find the total price which Karen has
   to pay.   **(3 marks)**

7. A family decorate their home with 300 lights coloured red
and blue.
The number of red lights to blue lights is in the ratio of 5 : 1.
How many lights are blue?   **(2 marks)**

8. A hire company hires out steam cleaners.
The cost of hire is £8 plus £11·50 per day.
Calculate the cost of 4 days hire of a steam cleaner.

   (2 marks)

AS1 MORE NUMBER

You use fractions when you share equally.

This unit will show you how to:

- Split numbers into factors and prime factors
- Use factors to simplify fractions and ratios
- Find the highest common factor and least common multiple
- Add and subtract fractions
- Find fractions of a quantity

Before you start

You should know how to...	Check in AS1
1. Multiply and divide integers. For example, $9 \times 7 = 63$	**1.** Work out: (a) 7×8 (b) 9×12 (c) 21×5 (d) $88 \div 11$ (e) $51 \div 3$ (f) $95 \div 5$
2. Convert improper fractions to mixed numbers. For example, $\frac{25}{6} = 4\frac{1}{6}$	**2.** Write as mixed numbers: (a) $\frac{3}{2}$ (b) $\frac{5}{3}$ (c) $\frac{12}{11}$ (d) $\frac{22}{7}$ (e) $\frac{31}{5}$ (f) $\frac{19}{4}$

1.1 Factors, even numbers, odd numbers, prime numbers and multiples

- Any number which divides exactly into 24 is called a **factor** of 24.
  The factors of 24 are 1, 2, 3, 4, 6, 8, 12 and 24.
  To find the factors of any number, start by dividing by 1, then 2, then 3, and so on.

Example

Find the factors of 15.

Try	$15 \div 1 = 15$	so 1 and 15 are factors
	$15 \div 2 = 7\cdot5$	so 2 is not a factor
	$15 \div 3 = 5$	so 3 and 5 are factors
	$15 \div 4 = 3\cdot75$	so 4 is not a factor
	$15 \div 5 = 3$	which you've already had so you've now found all the factors:

1, 3, 5 and 15.

Remember:
1 and the number itself are **always** factors.

- An **even number** has 2 as a factor, so 24 is an even number.
  The even numbers are 2, 4, 6, 8, 10, 12, 14, ...
- An **odd number** does not have 2 as a factor, so 15 is an odd number.
  The odd numbers are 1, 3, 5, 7, 9, 11, 13, ...
- A **prime number** has **only two factors**, itself and 1, so 11 is a prime number.
  The prime numbers are 2, 3, 5, 7, 11, 13, 17, ...

Hint:
1 is **not** a prime number.

- A **multiple** of 3 is any number in the 3 times table.

The first five multiples of 3 and 3, 6, 9, 12 and 15.
The first seven multiples of 9 are 9, 18, 27, 36, 45, 54 and 63.

Exercise 1A

1. Write down all the factors of:
   (a) 8   (b) 18   (c) 10   (d) 12   (e) 27
   (f) 28   (g) 23   (h) 36   (i) 35   (j) 31
   (k) 40   (l) 48   (m) 50   (n) 51   (o) 64

2. Write down the next five even numbers after:
   (a) 14   (b) 22   (c) 36   (d) 108   (e) 200

3. Write down the next five odd numbers after:
   (a) 17   (b) 21   (c) 53   (d) 71   (e) 311

4. (a) Explain why 9 is not a prime number.
   (b) Explain why 15 is not a prime number.
   (c) Write down the first 15 prime numbers.

5. Write down the first six multiples of:
   (a) 4   (b) 5   (c) 6   (d) 7   (e) 8
   (f) 10   (g) 12   (h) 15   (i) 20   (j) 50

6. Look at this list of numbers: 9, 12, 15, 17, 18.
   Using each number only once, write down:
   (a) an even number (b) an odd number (c) a multiple of 5
   (d) a factor of 24 (e) a prime number

7. Look at this list of numbers: 1, 2, 5, 9, 14.
   Using each number only once, write down:
   (a) an even number (b) an odd number (c) a multiple of 3
   (d) a factor of 21 (e) a prime number

8. Look at this list of numbers: 3, 11, 20, 24, 25.
   Using each number only once, write down:
   (a) an even number (b) an odd number (c) a multiple of 5
   (d) a factor of 27 (e) a prime number

9. The factors of 12 are **1**, **2**, 3, **4**, 6, 12.
   The factors of 8 are **1**, **2**, **4**, 8.

   The **common factors** of 8 and 12 are 1, 2, 4.

   Find all the common factors of:
   (a) 10 and 25   (b) 28 and 49   (c) 12 and 36
   (d) 18 and 24   (e) 35 and 45   (f) 16 and 40

1.2 Highest common factor (HCF)

The **highest common factor (HCF)** of two or more numbers is:

  the common factor with the highest value.

Example 1
Find the HCF of 18, 24 and 42.
- List all the factors of all the numbers: 18 factors: **1, 2, 3, 6**, 9, 18
                                             24 factors: **1, 2, 3**, 4, **6**, 8, 12, 24
                                             42 factors: **1, 2, 3, 6**, 7, 14, 21, 42
- List the common factors: common factors: 1, 2, 3, 6

The HCF of 18, 24 and 42 is: 6.

Exercise 1B
1. Find the HCF of:
   (a) 24 and 40   (b) 50 and 75   (c) 63 and 81
   (d) 49 and 91   (e) 45 and 60   (f) 132 and 55
   (g) 168 and 60   (h) 10 and 150   (i) 750 and 50
   (j) 240 and 150   (k) 242 and 176   (l) 144 and 360

2. Find the HCF of:
   (a) 24, 36 and 60
   (b) 45, 75 and 15
   (c) 49, 126 and 91
   (d) 26, 182 and 65
   (e) 126, 28 and 70
   (f) 60, 37 and 113
   (g) 175, 50 and 1 250
   (h) 99, 9 and 409
   (i) 154, 98 and 84
   (j) 234, 66 and 102
   (k) 104, 128 and 76
   (l) 72, 144 and 540

1.3 Least common multiple (LCM)

The **least common multiple (LCM)** of two or more numbers is:

the smallest number into which they will all divide exactly.

Example 1

Find the LCM of 6, 8 and 12.

List the multiples: 6, 12, 18, **24**, …
                       8, 16, **24**, 32, …
                       12, **24**, 36, …

The LCM of 6, 8 and 12 is: **24**.

Exercise 1C

1. Find the LCM of:
   (a) 2, 3 and 5
   (b) 3, 4 and 5
   (c) 5, 6 and 7
   (d) 4, 5 and 7
   (e) 5, 7 and 9
   (f) 2, 7 and 10
   (g) 2, 3, 5 and 7
   (h) 2, 6 and 10
   (i) 2, 5, 8 and 10

2. Find the LCM of:
   (a) 3, 5 and 8
   (b) 6, 7 and 9
   (c) 6, 7 and 8
   (d) 4, 5, 7 and 8
   (e) 4, 6, 7 and 12
   (f) 3, 5, 7 and 9
   (g) 2, 5, 7 and 11
   (h) 2, 6, 9 and 15
   (i) 3, 5, 8 and 12

1.4 Equivalent fractions

$\frac{1}{2}$ and $\frac{2}{4}$ are different ways of writing the same fraction.

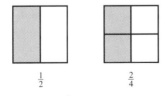

$\frac{1}{2}$ $\frac{2}{4}$

$\frac{1}{2}$ and $\frac{2}{4}$ are **equivalent** fractions.

$\frac{2}{3}$ and $\frac{6}{9}$ are also equivalent fractions.

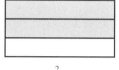

$$\frac{2}{3} \qquad\qquad\qquad \frac{6}{9}$$

Exercise 1D

What equivalent fractions are shown in these diagrams?

1.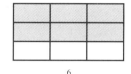

2.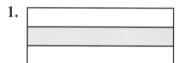

3.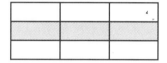

4. 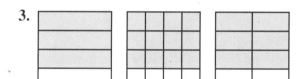   **5.**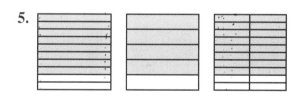

6.    **7.**

8.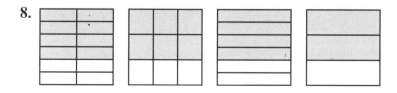

1.5 Making pairs of equivalent fractions

Look at this pair of equivalent fractions:

$$\frac{2}{3} \qquad \frac{8}{12}$$

$\frac{2}{3}$ can be turned into $\frac{8}{12}$ by multiplying both the 2 and the 3 by 4.

A similar multiplication exists for all pairs of equivalent fractions.

Example

Complete the missing number in this pair of equivalent fractions.

$$\frac{3}{4} \quad = \quad \frac{}{20}$$

The 4 has been multiplied by 5. The 3 must also be multiplied by 5 to fill in the missing number.

$$\frac{3}{4} \quad = \quad \frac{15}{20}$$

Exercise 1E

Copy and complete the following pairs of equivalent fractions.

1. $\frac{3}{4} = \frac{}{12}$
2. $\frac{2}{3} = \frac{}{6}$
3. $\frac{4}{5} = \frac{}{25}$
4. $\frac{1}{2} = \frac{}{8}$

5. $\frac{1}{2} = \frac{}{12}$
6. $\frac{2}{3} = \frac{}{15}$
7. $\frac{3}{5} = \frac{}{15}$
8. $\frac{3}{4} = \frac{}{20}$

9. $\frac{4}{5} = \frac{}{20}$
10. $\frac{1}{6} = \frac{}{42}$
11. $\frac{3}{7} = \frac{}{42}$
12. $\frac{1}{2} = \frac{}{14}$

13. $\frac{4}{7} = \frac{}{14}$
14. $\frac{3}{8} = \frac{}{40}$
15. $\frac{7}{10} = \frac{}{40}$
16. $\frac{1}{4} = \frac{}{12}$

17. $\frac{2}{3} = \frac{}{12}$
18. $\frac{3}{5} = \frac{}{35}$
19. $\frac{6}{7} = \frac{}{35}$
20. $\frac{7}{12} = \frac{}{24}$

21. $\frac{5}{8} = \frac{}{24}$
22. $\frac{5}{9} = \frac{}{90}$
23. $\frac{3}{5} = \frac{}{30}$
24. $\frac{2}{5} = \frac{}{45}$

25. $\frac{3}{8} = \frac{}{24}$

1.6 Simplifying fractions

Look at this fraction:

$$\frac{6}{15}$$

Both 6 and 15 divide by 3, so this fraction can be simplified.

$$\frac{6}{15} = \frac{2}{5}$$ $\div 3$

Example

Simplify the fractions:

(a) $\frac{4}{16}$ (b) $\frac{27}{30}$ (c) $\frac{40}{25}$

The simplified fractions are:

(a) $\frac{4}{16} = \frac{1}{4}$ ÷4 (b) $\frac{27}{30} = \frac{9}{10}$ ÷3 (c) $\frac{40}{25} = \frac{8}{5} = 1\frac{3}{5}$ ÷5

Exercise 1F

1. Simplify each of the following fractions.

(a) $\frac{2}{4}$ (b) $\frac{8}{32}$ (c) $\frac{9}{12}$ (d) $\frac{4}{6}$ (e) $\frac{20}{25}$

(f) $\frac{15}{25}$ (g) $\frac{50}{70}$ (h) $\frac{24}{27}$ (i) $\frac{54}{60}$ (j) $\frac{70}{110}$

(k) $\frac{9}{27}$ (l) $\frac{12}{14}$ (m) $\frac{3}{6}$ (n) $\frac{16}{4}$ (o) $\frac{20}{15}$

(p) $\frac{20}{30}$ (q) $\frac{40}{32}$ (r) $\frac{18}{30}$ (s) $\frac{105}{75}$ (t) $\frac{18}{18}$

(u) $\frac{45}{50}$ (v) $\frac{3}{9}$ (w) $\frac{54}{63}$ (x) $\frac{22}{33}$ (y) $\frac{44}{50}$

2. What fraction of 1 hour is:
   (a) 30 minutes (b) 10 minutes (c) 15 minutes
   (d) 20 minutes (e) 5 minutes?

3. What fraction of 1 minute is:
   (a) 25 seconds (b) 40 seconds (c) 36 seconds
   (d) 55 seconds (e) 24 seconds?

4. What fraction of £1·00 is:
   (a) 25p (b) 50p (c) 75p (d) 80p (e) 45p?

Remember:
There are
● 60 minutes in 1 hour
● 60 seconds in 1 minute

MODULE 5

1.7 Adding fractions from the same family

$\frac{3}{4}$ means 3 out of 4 parts.

$\frac{3}{4}$ of this shape is shaded.

3 parts are shaded — 3 — 3 is the **numerator**

There are 4 parts — 4 — 4 is the **denominator**
in total

The **denominator** of a fraction is the family it belongs to.

$\frac{3}{4}$ belongs to 'quarters'. $\frac{1}{5}$ belongs to 'fifths'.

You can add fractions from the same family.
You just add the numerators.

Example

(a) $\frac{2}{7} + \frac{1}{7} = \frac{3}{7}$ (b) $\frac{3}{5} + \frac{3}{5} = \frac{6}{5} = 1\frac{1}{5}$

(c) $1\frac{3}{4} + \frac{3}{4} = 1\frac{6}{4} = 2\frac{2}{4} = 2\frac{1}{2}$ (d) $2\frac{3}{8} + 3\frac{7}{8} = 5\frac{10}{8} = 6\frac{2}{8} = 6\frac{1}{4}$

Exercise 1G

1. Add $\frac{3}{5}$ to:

   (a) $\frac{1}{5}$ (b) $\frac{2}{5}$ (c) $\frac{3}{5}$ (d) $\frac{4}{5}$ (e) $1\frac{4}{5}$

2. Add $\frac{3}{4}$ to:

   (a) $\frac{1}{4}$ (b) $\frac{3}{4}$ (c) $1\frac{1}{4}$ (d) $2\frac{3}{4}$ (e) $5\frac{1}{4}$

3. Add $\frac{2}{7}$ to:

   (a) $\frac{1}{7}$ (b) $\frac{3}{7}$ (c) $\frac{5}{7}$ (d) $\frac{6}{7}$ (e) $1\frac{5}{7}$

4. Add $1\frac{2}{3}$ to:

   (a) $\frac{1}{3}$ (b) $\frac{2}{3}$ (c) $1\frac{1}{3}$ (d) $2\frac{2}{3}$ (e) $3\frac{1}{3}$

5. Add $1\frac{3}{4}$ to:

   (a) $\frac{3}{4}$ (b) $2\frac{1}{4}$ (c) $5\frac{3}{4}$ (d) $1\frac{1}{2}$ (e) $5\frac{1}{2}$

6. Add $\frac{3}{11}$ to:

   (a) $\frac{3}{11}$ (b) $\frac{5}{11}$ (c) $\frac{7}{11}$ (d) $11\frac{5}{11}$ (e) $4\frac{10}{11}$

7. Add $1\frac{5}{6}$ to:

   (a) $\frac{5}{6}$ (b) $\frac{1}{6}$ (c) $1\frac{5}{6}$ (d) $5\frac{1}{6}$ (e) $11\frac{5}{6}$

8. Add $3\frac{8}{9}$ to:

   (a) $\frac{7}{9}$ (b) $\frac{1}{9}$ (c) $\frac{5}{9}$ (d) $7\frac{1}{9}$ (e) $\frac{4}{9}$

9. Add $1\frac{5}{8}$ to:

   (a) $\frac{5}{8}$ (b) $\frac{7}{8}$ (c) $1\frac{3}{8}$ (d) $4\frac{7}{8}$ (e) $5\frac{1}{8}$

10. Add $3\frac{5}{12}$ to:

   (a) $\frac{3}{12}$ (b) $\frac{7}{12}$ (c) $\frac{5}{12}$ (d) $\frac{11}{12}$ (e) $3\frac{7}{12}$

1.8 Subtracting fractions with the same denominator

Example

(a) $\frac{7}{8} - \frac{3}{8} = \frac{4}{8} = \frac{1}{2}$ 　　　　(b) $1\frac{6}{7} - \frac{2}{7} = 1\frac{4}{7}$

(c) $8\frac{4}{11} - \frac{7}{11} = 8 - \frac{3}{11} = 7\frac{8}{11}$ 　　(d) $6\frac{4}{7} - 3\frac{3}{7} = 3\frac{4}{7} - \frac{3}{7} = 3\frac{1}{7}$

Exercise 1H

1. Subtract $\frac{2}{5}$ from:

   (a) $\frac{4}{5}$ (b) $\frac{3}{5}$ (c) $3\frac{4}{5}$ (d) $6\frac{2}{5}$ (e) $1\frac{3}{5}$

2. Subtract $\frac{1}{4}$ from:

   (a) $\frac{3}{4}$ (b) $\frac{1}{2}$ (c) $3\frac{3}{4}$ (d) $8\frac{1}{4}$ (e) $9\frac{1}{2}$

3. Subtract $\frac{3}{7}$ from:

   (a) $\frac{4}{7}$ (b) $\frac{5}{7}$ (c) $1\frac{4}{7}$ (d) $4\frac{6}{7}$ (e) $7\frac{3}{7}$

4. Subtract $5\frac{2}{9}$ from:

   (a) $8\frac{4}{9}$ (b) $6\frac{7}{9}$ (c) $5\frac{5}{9}$ (d) $9\frac{8}{9}$ (e) $5\frac{1}{3}$

5. Subtract $2\frac{1}{4}$ from:

   (a) $3\frac{3}{4}$ (b) $5\frac{1}{4}$ (c) $7\frac{3}{4}$ (d) $3\frac{1}{2}$ (e) $2\frac{1}{2}$

6. Subtract $2\frac{3}{11}$ from:

   (a) $3\frac{4}{11}$ (b) $2\frac{8}{11}$ (c) $5\frac{9}{11}$ (d) $7\frac{7}{11}$ (e) 3

7. Subtract $\frac{4}{9}$ from:

   (a) $6\frac{5}{9}$ (b) $1\frac{4}{9}$ (c) $1\frac{3}{9}$ (d) $1\frac{2}{9}$ (e) 1

8. Subtract $\frac{5}{8}$ from:

   (a) $4\frac{7}{8}$ (b) $4\frac{5}{8}$ (c) $4\frac{3}{8}$ (d) $4\frac{1}{8}$ (e) 4

9. Subtract $3\frac{3}{4}$ from:

   (a) $5\frac{1}{4}$ (b) $6\frac{1}{4}$ (c) $7\frac{1}{2}$ (d) 14 (e) $2\frac{1}{4}$

10. Subtract $2\frac{5}{8}$ from:

   (a) 5 (b) $4\frac{3}{8}$ (c) $6\frac{1}{8}$ (d) 7 (e) $7\frac{1}{2}$

MODULE 5

1.9 Adding and subtracting fractions with different denominators

Look at this addition problem:

$$\tfrac{2}{3} + \tfrac{1}{2}$$

The denominators of both fractions are turned into 6. The addition becomes:

$$\tfrac{4}{6} + \tfrac{3}{6} = \tfrac{7}{6} = 1\tfrac{1}{6}$$

> To do a sum like this, the fractions must be from the same family so you must make the denominators the same.

The denominator of 6 was chosen because both 2 and 3 divide exactly into 6. 2 and 3 are factors of 6. (See page 86.)

Example

(a) $\tfrac{3}{4} + \tfrac{2}{3} = \tfrac{9}{12} + \tfrac{8}{12} = \tfrac{17}{12} = 1\tfrac{5}{12}$

(b) $\tfrac{7}{8} - \tfrac{3}{4} = \tfrac{7}{8} - \tfrac{6}{8} = \tfrac{1}{8}$

(c) $1\tfrac{2}{3} + 2\tfrac{4}{7} = 3\tfrac{14}{21} + \tfrac{12}{21} = 3\tfrac{26}{21} = 4\tfrac{5}{21}$

(d) $2\tfrac{1}{2} - 1\tfrac{4}{5} = 1\tfrac{5}{10} - \tfrac{8}{10} = 1 - \tfrac{3}{10} = \tfrac{7}{10}$

Exercise 1I

1. (a) $\tfrac{3}{4} + \tfrac{1}{5}$ (b) $\tfrac{3}{4} + \tfrac{1}{2}$ (c) $\tfrac{1}{5} + \tfrac{2}{3}$

    (d) $\tfrac{1}{2} + \tfrac{2}{3}$ (e) $\tfrac{1}{2} + \tfrac{5}{7}$ (f) $\tfrac{4}{5} + \tfrac{2}{3}$

    (g) $\tfrac{3}{4} + \tfrac{5}{7}$ (h) $\tfrac{7}{10} + \tfrac{5}{7}$ (i) $\tfrac{5}{6} + \tfrac{3}{5}$

    (j) $\tfrac{5}{12} + \tfrac{5}{6}$ (k) $2\tfrac{1}{2} + \tfrac{1}{3}$ (l) $3\tfrac{1}{4} + \tfrac{2}{5}$

    (m) $1\tfrac{1}{2} + \tfrac{5}{6}$ (n) $2\tfrac{3}{10} + \tfrac{4}{5}$ (o) $3\tfrac{1}{2} + \tfrac{3}{10}$

    (p) $2\tfrac{3}{4} + 1\tfrac{5}{6}$ (q) $1\tfrac{4}{5} + 2\tfrac{2}{3}$ (r) $3\tfrac{3}{4} + 2\tfrac{3}{5}$

    (s) $1\tfrac{4}{5} + 3\tfrac{3}{4}$ (t) $1\tfrac{5}{6} + 3\tfrac{2}{9}$ (u) $3\tfrac{2}{3} + 1\tfrac{4}{9}$

    (v) $2\tfrac{5}{8} + 5\tfrac{3}{4}$ (w) $4\tfrac{1}{2} + 3\tfrac{5}{11}$ (x) $2\tfrac{5}{12} + 3\tfrac{1}{3}$

    (y) $2\tfrac{5}{12} + 3\tfrac{3}{4}$

2. (a) $\tfrac{3}{5} - \tfrac{1}{2}$ (b) $\tfrac{5}{8} - \tfrac{1}{2}$ (c) $\tfrac{11}{12} - \tfrac{2}{3}$

    (d) $\tfrac{7}{9} - \tfrac{2}{3}$ (e) $\tfrac{11}{16} - \tfrac{5}{8}$ (f) $\tfrac{13}{24} - \tfrac{3}{8}$

    (g) $\tfrac{11}{15} - \tfrac{2}{5}$ (h) $\tfrac{3}{4} - \tfrac{2}{5}$ (i) $\tfrac{4}{5} - \tfrac{3}{4}$

    (j) $\tfrac{11}{12} - \tfrac{1}{4}$ (k) $3\tfrac{3}{4} - \tfrac{5}{12}$ (l) $2\tfrac{1}{2} - \tfrac{1}{3}$

    (m) $3\tfrac{3}{5} - \tfrac{1}{4}$ (n) $2\tfrac{2}{3} - \tfrac{1}{5}$ (o) $3\tfrac{3}{4} - \tfrac{3}{5}$

    (p) $2\tfrac{1}{2} - 1\tfrac{2}{5}$ (q) $6\tfrac{4}{5} - 2\tfrac{2}{15}$ (r) $5\tfrac{6}{7} - 1\tfrac{1}{3}$

    (s) $4\tfrac{2}{3} - 1\tfrac{5}{12}$ (t) $2\tfrac{5}{6} - 1\tfrac{4}{9}$ (u) $3\tfrac{1}{3} - \tfrac{3}{4}$

    (v) $4\tfrac{1}{2} - \tfrac{7}{12}$ (w) $6\tfrac{1}{4} - \tfrac{7}{8}$ (x) $3\tfrac{2}{3} - 1\tfrac{4}{5}$

    (y) $2\tfrac{1}{3} - 1\tfrac{5}{6}$

1.10 Multiplying by fractions and fractions of a quantity

One quarter of the spectators at a local football match support the away team. If there are 240 supporters at the match, how many are away team supporters?

To calculate $\frac{1}{4}$ of a quantity, you divide by 4.
So, the number of away team
supporters $= \frac{1}{4}$ of $240 = 240 \div 4 = 60$

The number of home team
supporters $= \frac{3}{4}$ of $240 = (240 \div 4) \times 3 = 60 \times 3 = 180$

Example 1
(a) $\frac{1}{5}$ of $155 = 155 \div 5 = 31$
(b) $\frac{4}{5}$ of $155 = (155 \div 5) \times 4 = 31 \times 4 = 124$
(c) $\frac{1}{3}$ of $69 = 69 \div 3 = 23$
(d) $\frac{2}{3}$ of $69 = (69 \div 3) \times 2 = 46$

The word 'of' can be replaced with a multiplication sign.

Example 2
(a) $\frac{3}{4}$ of $48 = \frac{3}{4} \times 48 = (48 \div 4) \times 3 = 12 \times 3 = 36$
(b) $\frac{5}{8}$ of $64 = \frac{5}{8} \times 64 = (64 \div 8) \times 5 = 8 \times 5 = 40$

Exercise 1J
1. Calculate $\frac{1}{5}$ of:
   (a) 10   (b) 25   (c) 125   (d) 250   (e) 1 000

2. Find $\frac{1}{4}$ of:
   (a) 20   (b) 44   (c) 64   (d) 100   (e) 600

3. Calculate $\frac{1}{3}$ of:
   (a) 18   (b) 6   (c) 3   (d) 36   (e) 300

4. Multiply by $\frac{1}{2}$:
   (a) 50   (b) 18   (c) 44   (d) 72   (e) 96

5. Calculate $\frac{1}{8}$ of:
   (a) 16   (b) 8   (c) 80   (d) 800   (e) 1 600

6. Multiply by $\frac{1}{6}$:
   (a) 42   (b) 54   (c) 48   (d) 66   (e) 72

MODULE 5

7. Multiply by $\frac{1}{7}$:
   (a) 14   (b) 21   (c) 56   (d) 63   (e) 700

8. Calculate $\frac{1}{10}$ of:
   (a) 50   (b) 70   (c) 210   (d) 450   (e) 600

9. Find $\frac{3}{5}$ of:
   (a) 20   (b) 45   (c) 25   (d) 150   (e) 2 000

10. Calculate $\frac{3}{4}$ of:
   (a) 24   (b) 40   (c) 20   (d) 88   (e) 500

11. Calculate $\frac{2}{3}$ of:
   (a) 12   (b) 21   (c) 30   (d) 48   (e) 150

12. Multiply by $\frac{2}{5}$:
   (a) 60   (b) 15   (c) 45   (d) 70   (e) 100

13. Calculate $\frac{3}{8}$ of:
   (a) 8   (b) 24   (c) 640   (d) 248   (e) 360

14. Multiply by $\frac{5}{6}$:
   (a) 36   (b) 66   (c) 48   (d) 240   (e) 180

15. Multiply by $\frac{4}{7}$:
   (a) 28   (b) 35   (c) 70   (d) 84   (e) 840

16. Calculate $\frac{7}{10}$ of:
   (a) 20   (b) 40   (c) 350   (d) 500   (e) 1 000

17. Of the 120 apples in a box, $\frac{2}{5}$ are damaged when the box is dropped. How many are not damaged?

18. Police estimate that $\frac{5}{8}$ of the 24 000 spectators at a football match support the home team. How many support the away team?

19.

SUPER SALE $\frac{1}{3}$ OFF

FOR EXAMPLE
Coat £90 reduced by £30 to £60

Find the amount the following items will be reduced by and their new cost:

(a)   A dress costing £60
(b)   A pair of trousers costing £45
(c)   A top costing £30
(d)   A pair of shoes costing £36
(e)   A shirt costing £18
(f)   A jacket costing £48
(g)   A belt costing £12
(h)   A pair of socks costing £2·40

20. There are 240 marks available in an examination. Marianna scores $\frac{7}{8}$ of the marks and Barry scores $\frac{4}{5}$ of the marks. How many marks do Marianna and Barry score each?

Summary

1. A factor is a number which divides exactly into another number
For example, 6 is a factor of 18.

2. An **even number** has 2 as a factor.

3. An **odd** number does not have 2 as a factor.

4. A **prime** number has only two factors.

5. If any number divides exactly by 3, it is called a **multiple** of 3.

6. Equivalent fractions are different ways of writing the same fraction. $\frac{3}{4}$ and $\frac{6}{8}$ are equivalent fractions.

Checkout AS1

1. Find all the factors of:
(a) 20   (b) 25
(c) 42   (d) 54

2. Write down the next five even numbers after:
(a) 42   (b) 264

3. Write down the next five odd numbers after:
(a) 51   (b) 377

4. Write down all the prime numbers in this list: 6, 9, 7, 2, 15, 21, 23, 27, 31, 37, 50, 51, 53

5. Write down the first five multiples of:
(a) 4   (b) 12

6. Complete these pairs of equivalent fractions:
(a) $\frac{3}{4} = \frac{}{12}$ (b) $\frac{1}{2} = \frac{}{24}$
(c) $\frac{3}{8} = \frac{}{16}$ (d) $\frac{4}{5} = \frac{}{25}$

MODULE 5

7. Fractions can be simplified by dividing the top and bottom by the same number.

7. Simplify:
   (a) $\frac{6}{8}$ (b) $\frac{14}{35}$
   (c) $\frac{10}{16}$ (d) $\frac{15}{45}$

8. Fractions can be added and subtracted by making the denominators the same.
   $$\frac{3}{4} + \frac{2}{3} = \frac{9}{12} + \frac{8}{12} = \frac{17}{12} = 1\frac{5}{12}$$
   $$2\frac{1}{2} - 1\frac{4}{5} = 1\frac{5}{10} - \frac{8}{10} = 1 - \frac{3}{10} = \frac{7}{10}$$

8. (a) $\frac{3}{4} + \frac{3}{4}$ (b) $\frac{4}{5} + \frac{3}{5}$
   (c) $\frac{5}{11} + \frac{9}{11}$ (d) $3\frac{2}{3} + \frac{2}{3}$
   (e) $\frac{3}{4} - \frac{1}{4}$ (f) $\frac{5}{6} - \frac{1}{6}$
   (g) $\frac{7}{9} - \frac{4}{9}$ (h) $\frac{2}{3} - \frac{1}{3}$
   (i) $\frac{2}{3} + \frac{4}{5}$ (j) $\frac{3}{4} + \frac{5}{6}$
   (k) $1\frac{2}{3} + \frac{2}{9}$ (l) $4\frac{3}{5} + \frac{7}{10}$
   (m) $\frac{4}{5} - \frac{2}{3}$ (n) $\frac{7}{8} - \frac{3}{4}$
   (o) $1\frac{4}{5} - \frac{3}{10}$ (p) $3\frac{1}{3} - \frac{8}{9}$

9. To calculate $\frac{1}{4}$ of a quantity, you divide by 4.
   $\frac{1}{4}$ of $240 = 240 \div 4 = 60$

9. Calculate $\frac{1}{5}$ of:
   (a) 25   (b) 40
   (c) 250   (d) 600

10. The word 'of' can be replaced with a multiplication sign.
    $\frac{2}{5}$ of $45 = \frac{2}{5} \times 45 = (2 \times 45) \div 5 = 90 \div 5 = 18$

10. Calculate $\frac{3}{4}$ of:
    (a) 16   (b) 64
    (c) 100   (d) 300

Revision exercise AS1

1. Jack writes down the numbers

        8,   9,   13,   15,   16,   29,   35.

   State which of the numbers are
   (a) odd numbers,
   (b) multiples of 5,
   (c) powers of two,
   (d) prime numbers.   [SEG]

2. From this list of numbers

        2,   3,   6,   17,   23,   24,   28,   49,   72,   112

   Choose:
   (a) a square number,
   (b) a multiple of 9,
   (c) a factor of 56,
   (d) a prime number greater than 10.   [NEAB]

3. The cost of postage depends on the weight of the letter and whether it is sent first class or second class. The table below shows the postage rates.

Weight up to	60 g	100 g	150 g	200 g
First Class	26p	39p	52p	66p
Second Class	19p	31p	40p	50p

Find the total cost of sending the following:
two letters, each weighing 50 g, first class,
one letter weighing 140 g second class and
one letter weighing 180 g first class. [SEG]

4. Leah is starting work and expects income tax and national insurance to take $\frac{1}{4}$ of her pay.
Leah gives her parents $\frac{1}{3}$ of what she has left.
What percentage of her pay will Leah have left for herself? [SEG]

5. State which of the numbers

$$7 \quad 9 \quad 10 \quad 12 \quad 13 \quad 15 \quad 17$$

(a) are even numbers,
(b) are multiples of 3,
(c) are prime numbers,
(d) are factors of 24. [SEG]

6. State which of the numbers

$$5 \quad 7 \quad 8 \quad 15 \quad 16 \quad 20 \quad 23$$

(a) are odd numbers,
(b) are prime numbers,
(c) are multiples of 4. [SEG]

7. One day at St. George's School

$\frac{1}{4}$ of the pupils walked to school
$\frac{3}{8}$ of the pupils came by bus
the remaining 30 pupils came by car.

(a) Work out $\frac{1}{4} + \frac{3}{8}$.
Give your answer as a fraction.
(b) What fraction of the pupils came by car?
(c) How many pupils are there in the school altogether? [NEAB]

MODULE 5

8. (a) Find the prime factors of 108.
   (b) Hence write 108 as a product of prime factors.   [SEG]

9. (a) $24 = 3 \times 8$ or $24 = 8 \times 3$
      Write down two other multiplications for which the
      answer is 24.
   (b) Write down **all** the factors of 24.
   (c) Copy and fill in the missing numbers in this factor tree.

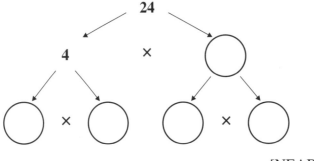

[NEAB]

10. Express 72 as a product of its prime factors.   [SEG]

11. A list of numbers is given below.

    9   12   15   19   23   29   31   34

   (a) State which of these numbers are
       (i)   even numbers,
       (ii) factors of 72.
   (b) Write down two numbers from the given list which add
       up to 50.   [SEG]

12. State which of the numbers

    2   3   14   15   16   17   18   24

   (a) are odd numbers,
   (b) are multiples of 6,
   (c) are prime numbers,   [SEG]

AS2 Shape and Space 1

Engineers use angles to construct buildings.

This unit will show you how to:
- Describe a turn using angles
- Use a protractor
- Measure angles, acute and obtuse angles
- Draw triangles
- Make scale drawings
- Work with bearings

Before you start:

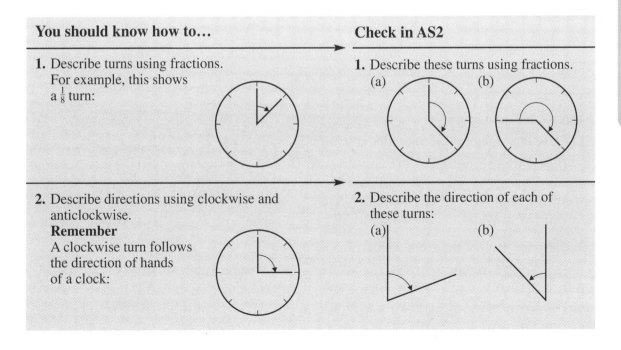

You should know how to...	Check in AS2
1. Describe turns using fractions. For example, this shows a $\frac{1}{8}$ turn:	**1.** Describe these turns using fractions. (a) (b)
2. Describe directions using clockwise and anticlockwise. **Remember** A clockwise turn follows the direction of hands of a clock:	**2.** Describe the direction of each of these turns: (a) (b)

2.1 Turning

This is a bird's eye view of a telescope mounted on a stand.

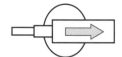

The telescope can be turned on its stand. These pictures show the telescope turned anticlockwise through $\frac{1}{4}, \frac{1}{2}, \frac{3}{4}$ and full turns.

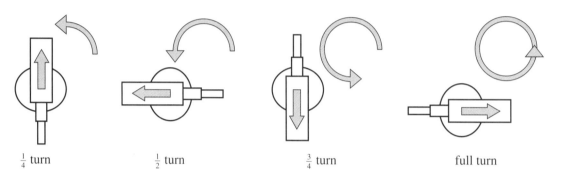

| $\frac{1}{4}$ turn | $\frac{1}{2}$ turn | $\frac{3}{4}$ turn | full turn |

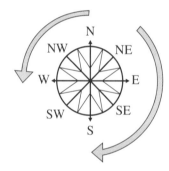

Somebody looking North turns anticlockwise to look West. This is a $\frac{1}{4}$ turn.
Somebody looking NE turns clockwise to look South. This is a $\frac{3}{8}$ turn.

Exercise 2A

1. Describe each of these anticlockwise turns:

(a) North to South	(b) NE to SW	(c) West to South	(d) East to North
(e) SE to NW	(f) North to NW	(g) South to NE	(h) East to South
(i) SW to NW	(j) West to North	(k) SW to South	(l) SW to East
(m) SW to West	(n) North to SE	(o) NW to NE	(p) West to NE

2. Describe each of these clockwise turns:

(a) North to South	(b) NE to SW	(c) West to South	(d) East to North
(e) SE to NW	(f) North to NW	(g) South to NE	(h) East to South
(i) SW to NW	(j) West to North	(k) SW to South	(l) SW to East
(m) SW to West	(n) North to SE	(o) NW to NE	(p) West to NE

2.2 Turning through an angle

The angle turned through can be measured in degrees. There are 360 degrees in a full turn. The word degree is usually replaced with a small circle, so 360 degrees is written 360°.

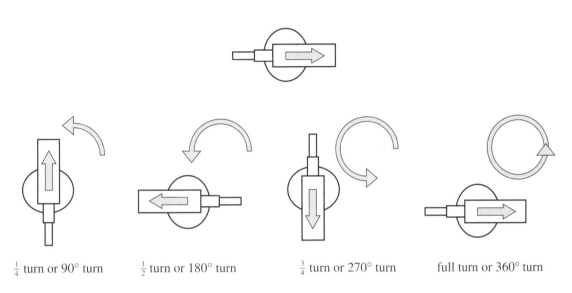

$\frac{1}{4}$ turn or 90° turn $\frac{1}{2}$ turn or 180° turn $\frac{3}{4}$ turn or 270° turn   full turn or 360° turn

Exercise 2B

1. Describe each of these anticlockwise turns in degrees:

    (a) West to South   (b) NE to NW
    (c) East to West   (d) East to South
    (e) SE to NW   (f) East to North
    (g) South to West   (h) NE to SW
    (i) West to North   (j) NW to SW
    (k) West to East   (l) NW to NE
    (m) North to NW   (n) West to SW
    (o) SE to East   (p) East to NE

2. Describe each of these clockwise turns in degrees:

    (a) West to South   (b) NE to NW
    (c) East to West   (d) East to South
    (e) SE to NW   (f) East to North
    (g) South to West   (h) NE to SW
    (i) West to North   (j) NW to SW
    (k) West to East   (l) NW to NE
    (m) North to NW   (n) West to SW
    (o) SE to East   (p) East to NE

MODULE 5

2.3 The protractor

Angles are measured with a protractor.

To look at Boat A, the telescope must be turned anticlockwise through 30°.

To look at Boat B, the telescope must be turned anticlockwise through 145°.

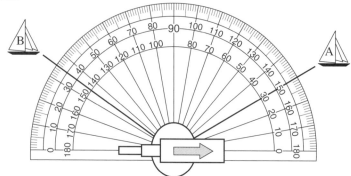

Exercise 2C

1. What anticlockwise angle must the telescope be turned through to look at each boat?

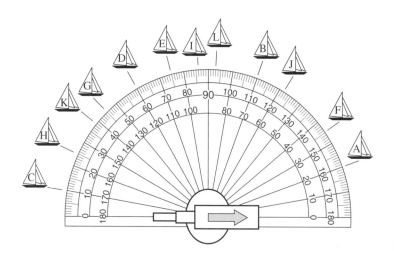

2. What clockwise angle must the telescope be turned through to look at each boat?

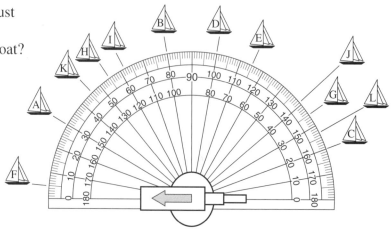

2.4 Measuring angles, acute and obtuse angles

An angle less than 90° is called an **acute** angle.
An angle greater than 90° but less than 180° is called an **obtuse** angle.

Angle *a* is an acute angle.   Angle *b* is an obtuse angle.

Note:

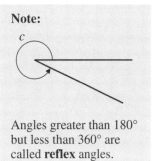

Angles greater than 180° but less than 360° are called **reflex** angles.

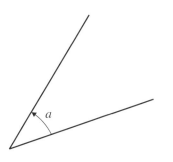

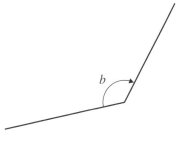

Example

Measure each angle.
Carefully place your protractor on each angle.

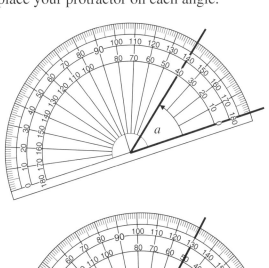

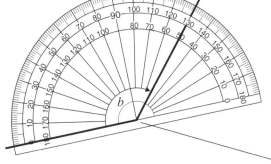

Read the size of the angle from the correct scale.
Angle *a* is acute so it is 40°.
Angle *b* is obtuse so it is 130°.

Hint:
Make sure the protractor is in place over the angle.

MODULE 5

Exercise 2D

1. Measure each angle and state whether it is an acute angle or an obtuse angle.

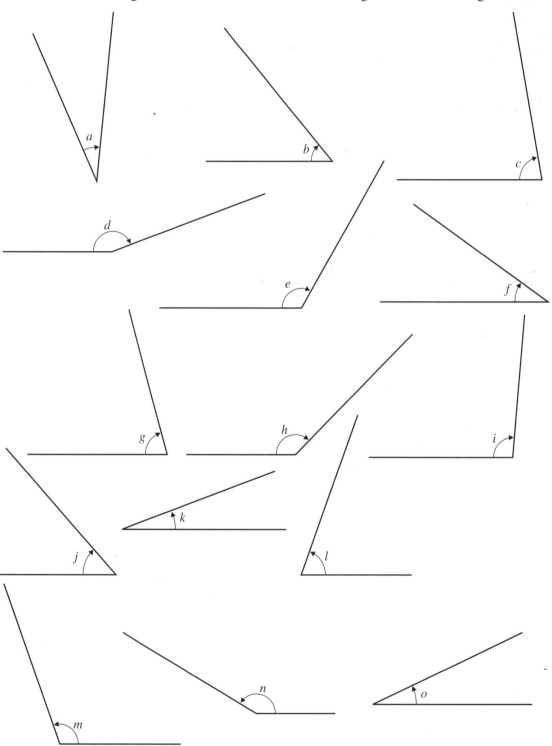

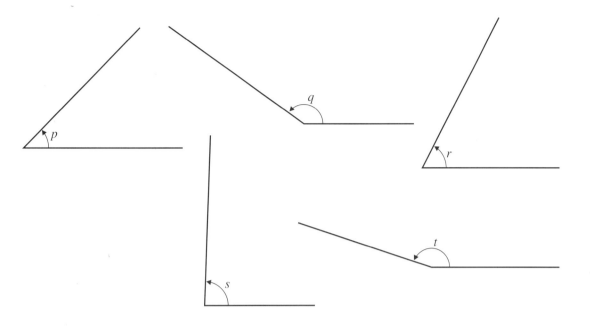

2.5 Drawing angles

To draw a clockwise angle of 50°, first draw a straight line and
mark a point for the centre of the angle.

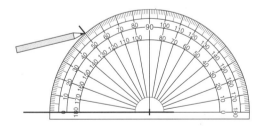

Place a protractor carefully on the line and the point and make a
mark at the 50° point on the protractor scale.

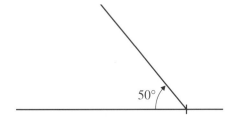

Remove the protractor. Draw and label the angle.

50°

These diagrams show the stages in drawing an anticlockwise angle of 135°.

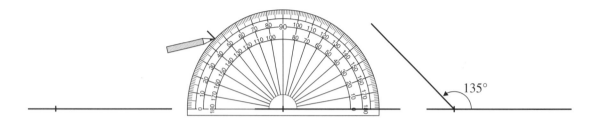

Exercise 2E

1. Draw and label each of the following clockwise angles.

(a) 20°	(b) 60°	(c) 80°.	(d) 100°
(e) 120°	(f) 140°	(g) 160°	(h) 35°
(i) 75°	(j) 95°	(k) 115°	(l) 135°
(m) 155°	(n) 175°		

2. Draw and label each of the following anticlockwise angles.

(a) 30°	(b) 50°	(c) 70°	(d) 110°
(e) 130°	(f) 150°	(g) 170°	(h) 45°
(i) 65°	(j) 85°	(k) 105°	(l) 125°
(m) 145°	(n) 165°		

2.6 Naming angles

You will see angles named in different ways.

For example, in this triangle,

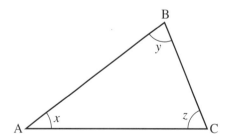

Angle x can also be called angle BAC or angle CAB.

Angle y can also be called angle ABC or angle CBA.

Angle z can also be called angle ACB or angle BCA.

Exercise 2F

In each triangle, write down two different ways to name the
angles marked *x*, *y* and *z*.

1.

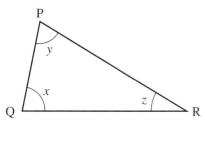

2.

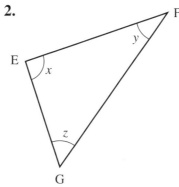

3.

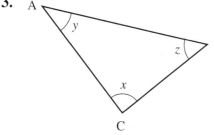

4.

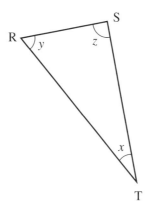

5.

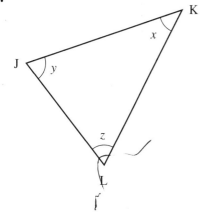

6.

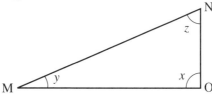

MODULE 5

2.7 Drawing triangles

To draw accurate triangles you need to use geometrical equipment: ruler, protractor and compasses. Make sure your pencil is sharp!

Example 1

Draw the triangle ABC with AB = 10 cm, angle CAB = 30° and angle CBA = 60°.

First, draw a rough sketch.

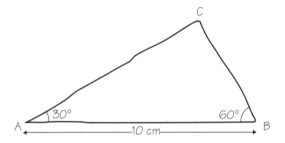

Then draw, using a ruler and protractor, an accurate triangle.

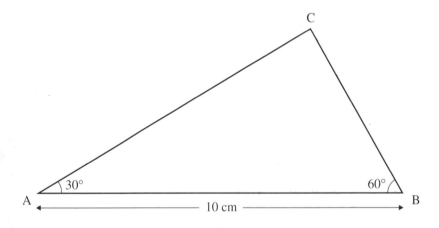

Example 2

Draw the triangle ABC with AB = 4 cm, BC = 5 cm and AC = 2 cm.

Draw the line AB, 4 cm long.

A ———————————— B

Open a pair of compasses to 5 cm. Put the point on B and draw an arc.

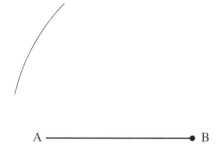

Open the compasses to 2 cm. Put the point on A and draw an arc.

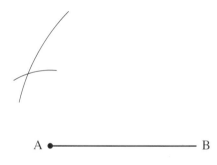

Connect A and B to the point where the arcs cross.

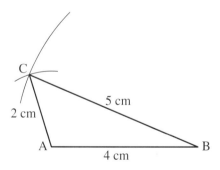

Exercise 2G

1. Draw the triangle XYZ with XY = 8 cm, angle ZXY = 40°
   and angle ZYX = 50°.

2. Draw the triangle PQR with PQ = 10 cm, angle RPQ = 60°
   and angle RQP = 60°.

3. Draw the triangle JKL with JK = 6 cm, angle LJK = 45°
   and angle LKJ = 45°.

MODULE 5

4. Draw the triangle ABC with AB = 5 cm, angle CAB = 30° and angle CBA = 70°.

5. Draw the triangle CDE with CD = 12 cm, angle ECD = 20° and angle EDC = 90°.

6. Draw the triangle MNO with MN = 10 cm, MO = 8 cm and NO = 6 cm.

7. Draw the triangle RST with RS = 8 cm, ST = 8 cm and RT = 8 cm.

8. Draw the triangle ABC with AB = 9 cm, AC = 7 cm and BC = 6 cm.

9. Draw the triangle XYZ with XY = 10 cm, XZ = 8 cm and YZ = 8 cm.

10. Draw the triangle JKL with JK = 6 cm, JL = 9 cm and KL = 3 cm.

2.8 Scale drawing

If something is too big to draw full size, you can use a **scale**.

Example

Newquay is 15 km to the east and 20 km to the north of Camborne. Use a drawing with a scale of 1 cm = 5 km to find the direct distance from Newquay to Camborne.

Using a scale of 1 cm = 5 km, the distances become 3 cm and 4 cm. The scale drawing looks like this.

> **Hint:**
> If 5 km = 1 cm
> then 15 km = 3 cm
> and 20 km = 4 cm

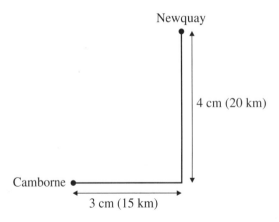

The distance between Newquay and Camborne on the scale drawing is 5 cm.
The real distance between Newquay and Camborne is 25 km.

> **Hint:**
> If 1 cm = 5 km
> then 5 cm = 25 km

Exercise 2H

1. This sketch shows three buildings in the village of Plumpton.

• Church

• Village hall   • Post office

The church is 50 m due north of the village hall.
(a) Use a scale of 1 cm = 10 m to draw the positions of the church and the village hall.
(b) The post office is 70 m due east of the village hall. Add the post office to your drawing.
(c) Use your drawing to find the direct distance between the church and the post office.

2. This sketch shows a ladder resting against a vertical wall. The ladder reaches 5 m up the wall and its base is 2 m from the wall.
(a) Use a scale of 1 cm = 1 m to make an accurate drawing of the ladder.
(b) Use your drawing to find the length of the ladder.

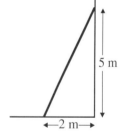

3. This sketch shows the relative position of Northampton, Peterborough and Bury St. Edmunds.

• Peterborough

• Northampton   • Bury St. Edmunds

Northampton is 110 km due west of Bury St. Edmunds.
(a) Use a scale of 1 cm = 10 km to draw the positions of Northampton and Bury St. Edmunds.
(b) Peterborough is 55 km from Northampton and 75 km from Bury St. Edmunds. Use a pair of compasses to add the position of Peterborough to your drawing.

MODULE 5

4. A tree has a shadow 20 m long when the Sun's
   rays are at an angle of 60° to the ground.

   (a) Use a scale of 1 cm = 4 m to make an accurate scale
   drawing of the tree.
   (b) Use your drawing to find the height of the tree.

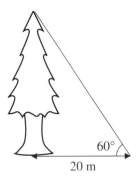

5. Thetford is 35 km to the east and 25 km to the south of
   Norwich.

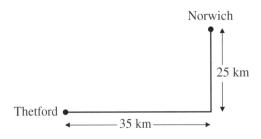

   (a) Use a scale of 1 cm = 5 km to draw the positions of
   Norwich and Thetford.
   (b) Use your drawing to find the direct distance from
   Norwich to Thetford.

6. Tiverton is 40 km to the east and 20 km to the south of
   Barnstaple.

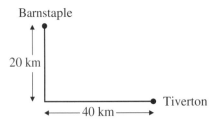

   (a) Use a scale of 1 cm = 5 km to draw the positions of
   Barnstaple and Tiverton.
   (b) Use your drawing to find the direct distance from
   Barnstaple to Tiverton.

7. Two ports, A and B are 140 km apart along a coastline.
Port A is due west of Port B. A ship C is at sea off the coastline.

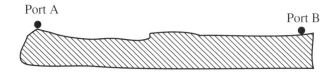

(a) Use a scale of 1 cm = 20 km to draw the positions of Port A and Port B.
(b) Ship C is 80 km from Port A and 100 km from Port B.
Use a pair of compasses to add the position of Ship C to your drawing.
(c) Estimate the shortest distance between Ship C and the coastline.

8. Colchester is 24 km due east of Braintree.

(a) Use a scale of 1 cm = 2 km to draw the positions of Colchester and Braintree.
(b) Braintree is 6 km to the east and 15 km to the north of Chelmsford.
Add the position of Chelmsford to your drawing.
(c) Use your drawing to find the direct distance between Colchester and Chelmsford.

2.9 Bearings

A **bearing** is an angle giving a direction. All bearings are measured clockwise from North.

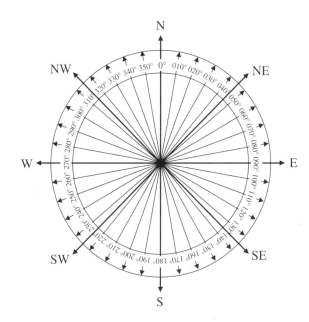

MODULE 5

Bearings are always written with three digits. These diagrams show how bearings are used to describe directions.

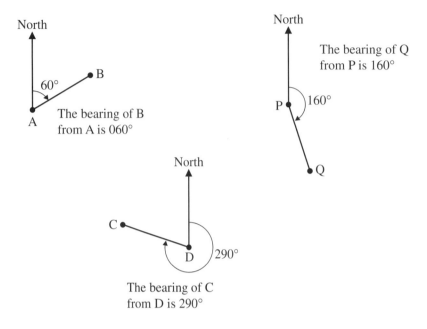

The bearing of B from A is 060°

The bearing of Q from P is 160°

The bearing of C from D is 290°

Example

Royal Tunbridge Wells is 16 km on a bearing of 158° from Sevenoaks. Use a scale of 1 cm = 4 km to draw the positions of Royal Tunbridge Wells and Sevenoaks.

These are the stages in completing the drawing.

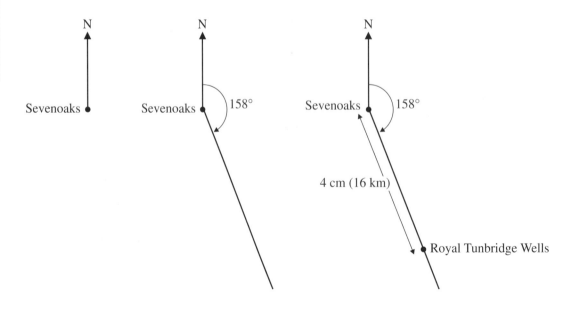

4 cm (16 km)

Exercise 2I

1. This map shows part of a coastline and a lighthouse. 1 cm on the map represents 2 km.

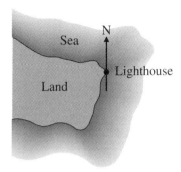

A ship is 18 km from the lighthouse on a bearing of 080°.
Copy the map and show the position of the ship.

2. Horsham is 40 km on a bearing of 052° from
Chichester. This is a rough sketch.

Use a scale of 1 cm = 5 km to draw the accurate
positions of Horsham and Chichester.

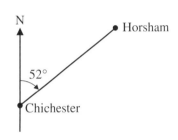

3. Skelmersdale is 18 km on a bearing of 133° from
Southport. This is a rough sketch.

Use a scale of 1 cm = 5 km to draw the accurate
positions of Skelmersdale and Southport.

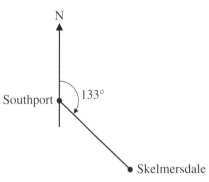

4. Camborne is 25 km on a bearing of 217° from
Newquay. This is a rough sketch.

Use a scale of 1 cm = 5 km to draw the accurate
positions of Camborne and Newquay.

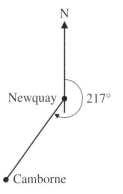

MODULE 5

5. Taunton is 33 km on a bearing of 286° from Yeovil. This is a rough sketch.

Use a scale of 1 cm = 5 km to draw the accurate positions of Taunton and Yeovil.

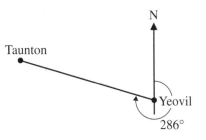

6. Melton Mowbray is 23 km on a bearing of 049° from Leicester. Nottingham is 35 km on a bearing of 355° from Leicester. This is a rough sketch.

Use a scale of 1 cm = 5 km to draw the accurate positions of Leicester, Melton Mowbray and Nottingham.

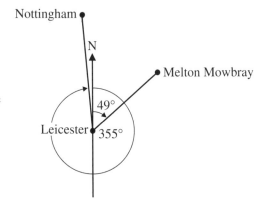

7. Milton Keynes is 35 km to the east and 35 km to the north of Oxford. This is a rough sketch.
  (a) Use a scale of 1 cm = 5 km to draw the accurate positions of Milton Keynes and Oxford.
  (b) Use your drawing to find the bearing of Milton Keynes from Oxford.

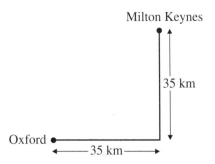

8. In the village of Rempham Vasey the village hall is 160 m north of the church.
  (a) Use a scale of 1 cm = 20 metres to draw the positions of the village hall and the church.
  (b) The local shop is on a bearing of 135° from the church. Add this bearing to your drawing.
  (c) The local shop is 240 m from the village hall. Use a pair of compasses to mark the position of the local shop on your drawing.
  (d) Use your drawing to find the bearing of the local shop from the village hall.

Summary

Checkout AS2

---

1. Turns can be described as fractions of a whole turn.

1. (a) Describe a clockwise turn from North to West.
(b) Describe an anticlockwise turn from SE to West.

---

2. An angle is a measure of turn.
Angles can be measured in degrees.

2. (a) How many degrees are there in a clockwise turn from West to NW?
(b) How many degrees are there in an anticlockwise turn from NE to SE?

---

3. **Acute** angles are less than 90°.
Obtuse angles are more than 90° but less than 180°.

3. (a) Is angle A below an acute angle or an obtuse angle?
(b) Is angle B below an acute angle or an obtuse angle?

---

4. You use a protractor to measure angles.

4. Measure each of these angles.

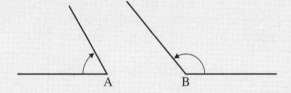

---

5. You can draw angles using a protractor.

5. (a) Draw a clockwise angle of 55°.
(b) Draw an anticlockwise angle of 120°.

---

6. You will see angles named in different ways.

6. Write down two ways to name the angles marked x, y and z.

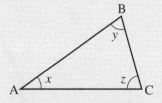

---

7. Triangles can be constructed with a ruler, protractor and pair of compasses.

7. (a) Draw the triangle EFG with EF = 8 cm, angle GEF = 45° and angle GFE = 80°.
(b) Draw the triangle ABC with AB = 7 cm, BC = 5 cm and AC = 10 cm.

MODULE 5

8. Scale drawings are used if something is too big to draw full size.

8. In the village of Jessingham the church is 160 m due north of the pub. The local shop is due east of the pub and 200 m from the church.
   (a) Use a scale of 1 cm = 20 m to draw the positions of the church, pub and local shop.
   (b) How far is the local shop from the pub?

9. A **bearing** is an angle giving a direction. All bearings are measured clockwise from North. Bearings are always written with three digits.

9. Salisbury is 30 km on a bearing of 120° from Warminster. Use a scale of 1 cm = 5 km to draw the positions of Salisbury and Warminster.

Revision exercise AS2

1. The map shows the M25 motorway.
   A helicopter is at the point marked Junction 2.
   The helicopter pilot flies directly to Junction 27.

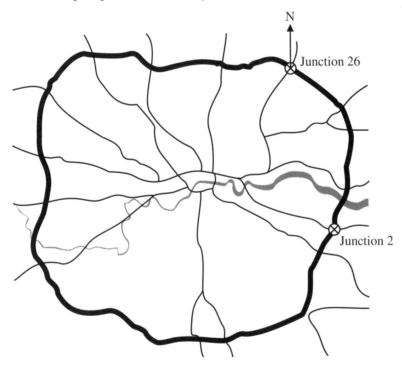

The map is drawn to a scale of 1 cm to 7 km.

(a) Use the map to find the direct flight distance, in kilometres, between Junction 2 and Junction 27.

Later the helicopter pilot flies from Junction 27 on a bearing of 205°, and lands on the motorway.

(b) Copy the motorway using tracing paper, and mark with a cross the place where the helicopter lands.   [SEG]

2. The diagram shows an accurate plan of a race.

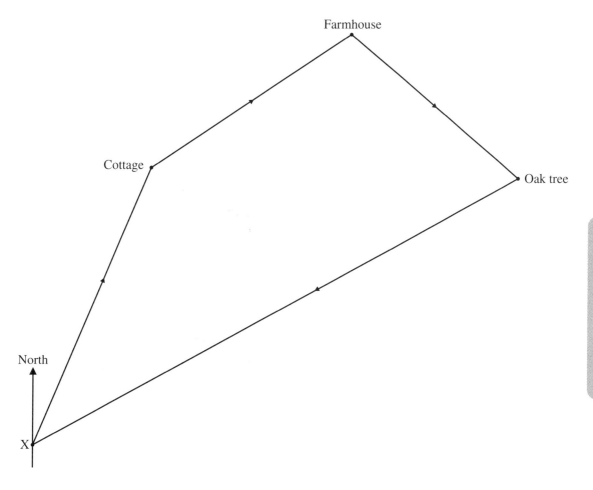

(a) The start and finish of the race is at **X**.
   (i) What is the bearing of the cottage from **X**.
   (ii) What is the bearing of **X** from the oak tree?

(b) The plan has been drawn using a scale of 1 mm to represent 10 m.
Use the map to estimate the length of the race in kilometres.
Give your answer to the nearest tenth of a kilometre.

[SEG]

3. This map shows part of Shropshire.

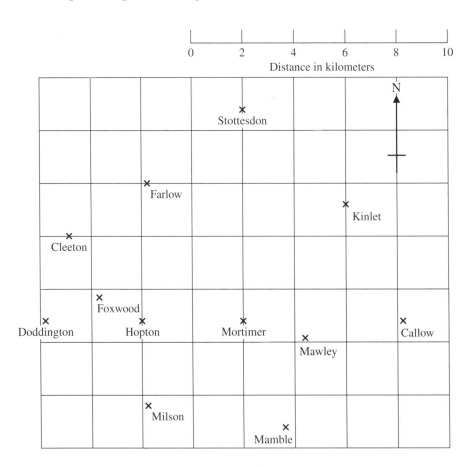

(a) Which place is about 8 kilometres West of Mortimer?

(b) What is the direction of Kinlet from Mortimer?

(c) What is the bearing of Cleeton from Mortimer?

[NEAB]

4. A scale drawing of a school playing field is shown.

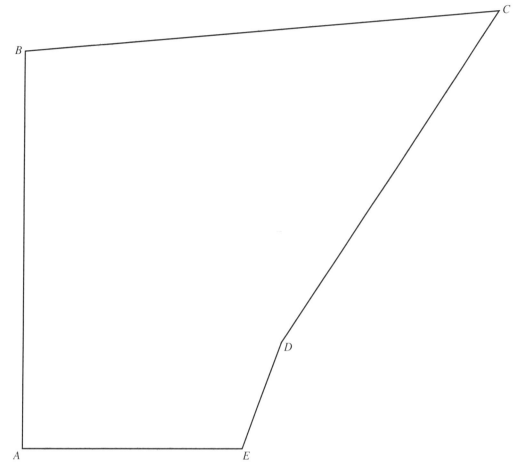

(a) (i) Measure the size of angle *AED*.

(ii) Choose the word from the list which describes angle *AED*.

Acute   Right-Angled   Obtuse   Reflex

Peter is standing at a point *X*, in the field.
Angle *EAX* = 64°.
Angle *EDX* = 135°.

(b) (i) Draw these angles on a copy of the diagram and mark, with a cross, where Peter is standing.
The scale of the drawing is 1 cm to 20 m.

(ii) How far from corner *B* is Peter?   [SEG]

MODULE 5

5. Janice is building a scale model of her house.
   She uses a scale of 1 : 50.

   The width of a window on her model is 3 centimetres.

   (a) What is the width of the window on her house?

   The height of Janice's front door is 2·1 metres.

   (b) (i) What is this height in millimetres?
       (ii) Calculate the height of the model door in
            millimetres.   [SEG]

Not to scale

6. Measure the size of angles x and y shown in the diagram.

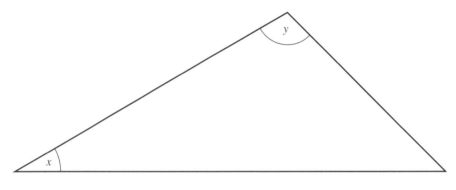

[NEAB]

7. In triangle *PQR*, *PQ* = 7·2 cm, *PR* = 4·5 cm and the angle at
   P is 75°.

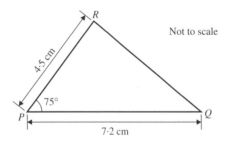

Not to scale

   (a) Make an accurate drawing of the triangle.

   (b) Measure and write down the length of *QR*.   [SEG]

AS3 ALGEBRA 1

If you make x calls per quarter it will cost you 60 + 5x pounds. If you opt for Pay As You Go you can make a saving of 20xy per cent.

That much?

This unit will show you how to:

- Use letters to represent quantities
- Use the rules of BoDMAS
- Substitute in formulae
- Collect like terms

Before you start:

You should know how to...	Check in A3
1. Add and subtract negative numbers.	**1.** Calculate:

Hint: Use a number line to help you:

$$^-7 + 6 = {}^-1$$
$$+6$$

$^-10 \ ^-9 \ ^-8 \ ^-7 \ ^-6 \ ^-5 \ ^-4 \ ^-3 \ ^-2 \ ^-1 \ 0 \ 1 \ 2 \ 3 \ 4 \ 5$

$$^-7$$
$$3 - 7 = {}^-4$$

Note: $5 - {}^-2 = 5 + 2 = 7!$

1. Calculate:
(a) $8 + 3$ (b) $^-8 + 3$
(c) $^-8 - 3$ (d) $8 - 3$
(e) $8 + {}^-3$ (f) $^-8 + {}^-3$
(g) $^-8 - {}^-3$ (h) $8 - {}^-3$

3.1 Using letters to represent quantities in addition and subtraction problems

Wilma Flint is a fence erector. When working out the number of posts and panels she needs for a fence she uses this rule:

> The number of posts is always one more than the number of panels.

If the letter f represents the number of fence panels, the number of posts needed is $f + 1$.

Example

The letter g represents the number of computer games that Henry owns. Use the letter g to write the number of games owned by:

(a) Susan, who owns 5 games more than Henry
(b) Anton, who owns 8 games less than Henry.

(a) Susan owns $g + 5$ games.
(b) Anton owns $g - 8$ games.

Exercise 3A

1. The letter m represents Jarvinder's score in a mathematics test. Use the letter m to write the scores of:
   (a) Neal, who scored 15 marks less than Jarvinder
   (b) Ashley, who scored 2 marks more than Jarvinder
   (c) Claire, who scored 6 marks less than Jarvinder
   (d) Ruth, who scored 8 marks more than Jarvinder
   (e) Gurpal, who scored 1 mark more than Jarvinder
   (f) Stacey, who scored 10 marks less than Jarvinder.

2. The letter y represents Daniel's age in years.
   Use the letter y to write the ages of:
   (a) Kelly Marie, who is 2 years older than Daniel
   (b) Kimberly, who is 4 years younger than Daniel
   (c) Christopher, who is 7 years older than Daniel
   (d) Gary, who is 1 year older than Daniel
   (e) Robert, who is 9 years younger than Daniel
   (f) Carmen, who is 2 years younger than Daniel.

3. The letter *h* represents Sally's height in centimetres.
Use the letter *h* to write the heights of:

(a) John, who is 15 cm taller than Sally
(b) Surbajit, who is 12 cm shorter than Sally
(c) Penny, who is 10 cm taller than Sally
(d) Jemma, who is 4 cm shorter than Sally
(e) Duncan, who is 1 cm taller than Sally
(f) Nathan, who is 11 cm shorter than Sally.

4. Seven friends buy a bag of cherries to share. The letter *c*
represents the number of cherries that Chris ate.
Use the letter *c* to write the number of cherries eaten by:

(a) Sarah, who ate 5 more cherries than Chris
(b) Emily, who ate 16 less cherries than Chris
(c) Melissa, who ate 3 more cherries than Chris
(d) Gavin, who ate 1 less cherry than Chris
(e) Natalie, who ate 6 more cherries than Chris
(f) Andrew, who ate 2 less cherries than Chris.

3.2 Using letters to represent quantities in multiplication and division problems

Billy Rubble is a builder. When he fits doors he knows that for
each door he will need 3 hinges. If the letter *d* represents the
number of doors he is installing in a house, he needs *d* × 3
hinges.

The multiplication sign is not used in algebra and numbers are
written before letters. So, you write:

> The number of hinges needed is 3*d*

If the letter *h* represents the number of hinges Billy has in stock,
this is enough hinges to fit *h* ÷ 3 doors.

Division in algebra is shown by putting one quantity over the
other. So, you write:

> The number of doors that can be fitted is $\dfrac{h}{3}$.

Example

There are *r* bread rolls in a Family Pack. Use the letter *r* to write
the number of bread rolls in:

(a) An Everyday Pack which has half as many rolls as a Family Pack.

(b) A Value Pack which has twice as many rolls as a Family Pack.

(a) An Everyday Pack has $\frac{r}{2}$ rolls.   (b) A Value Pack has 2*r* rolls.

Exercise 3B

1. The letter *a* represents John Brown's age in years.
   Use the letter *a* to write the ages of:
   (a) John's mother, who is twice as old as John
   (b) John's sister, whose age is John's age divided by 3
   (c) John's grandmother, who is 3 times as old as John
   (d) John's brother, whose age is John's age divided by 4
   (e) John's great-grandfather, who is 5 times as old as John
   (f) John's daughter, whose age is John's age divided by 20.

2. The letter *m* represents the number of marbles that Kevin owns.
   Use the letter *m* to write the number of marbles owned by:
   (a) Sandra, who owns 4 times as many marbles as Kevin
   (b) Gwen, who owns Kevin's number divided by 7
   (c) Nilha, who owns Kevin's number divided by 9
   (d) Sheila, who owns 3 times as many marbles as Kevin
   (e) Aaron, who owns 6 times as many marbles as Kevin
   (f) Vikram, who owns Kevin's number divided by 2.

3. Billy Rubble fits *d* doors in a new house.
   Use the letter *d* to write the number of:
   (a) Hinges needed, if he fits 4 to each door
   (b) Handles needed, if he fits 2 to each door
   (c) Screws needed, if he fits 16 to each door
   (d) Locks needed, if he fits 1 to each door
   (e) Wood framing needed, if he fits 5 metres to each door
   (f) Wood stain needed, if he uses $\frac{1}{2}$ litre on each door.

4. Betty Bun the baker has made *b* bread rolls.
   How many packets can she fill if:
   (a) There are 4 rolls in a packet
   (b) There are 6 rolls in a packet
   (c) There are 8 rolls in a packet
   (d) There are 12 rolls in a packet
   (e) There are 16 rolls in a packet
   (f) Each packet has the slogan '12 rolls plus 3 free'?

3.3 Formulae

Siloben is 3 years older than Gurpreet.

When Gurpreet is 12 years old, Siloben is 15 years old.
When Gurpreet is 14 years old, Siloben is 17 years old.
When Gurpreet is 16 years old, Siloben is 19 years old.

You can write a general rule like this:

Siloben's age = Gurpreet's age + 3

A general rule like this is called a **formula**. Formulae are usually written using letters to represent the quantities.

If you let S represent Siloben's age and G represent Gurpreet's age, the formula becomes:

$S = G + 3$

mum!

Example

A washing machine repairer calculates the cost of a repair like this:

Cost $(c) = £45 + £20 \times$ number of hours worked (h)

(a) Calculate the cost if the repair takes:
　(i) 2 hours　　(ii) $1\frac{1}{2}$ hours

(b) Write a formula using the letters in brackets.

(a) (i)　Cost $= £45 + £20 \times 2 = £45 + £40 = £85$
　　(ii)　Cost $= £45 + £20 \times 1\frac{1}{2} = £45 + £30 = £75$
(b)　$c = 45 + 20h$

Exercise 3C

1. A plumber adds a call-out fee of £25 onto the cost of any repairs. He uses this formula to calculate his total bill.

Total bill $(b) =$ cost of repairs $(r) + £25$

(a) Calculate the total bill if the cost of repairs is:
　(i) £30　　(ii) £50　　(iii) £80　　(iv) £100
(b) Write a formula using the letters in brackets.

2. Helen works in a fast food restaurant. She uses this formula to calculate her wages in pounds:

> Wages (w) = number of hours worked (n) × £4·50

(a) Calculate Helen's wage if she works:
    (i) 5 hours
    (ii) 10 hours
    (iii) 20 hours
    (iv) 15 hours
(b) Write a formula using the letters in brackets.

3. Anna Deal sells cars. She offers customers the option of credit using this formula:

> Total cost (T) = £1 000 + 24 × monthly payment (M)

(a) Calculate the cost of buying a car if the monthly payments are:
    (i) £200   (ii) £100   (iii) £300   (iv) £150
(b) Write a formula using the letters in brackets.

4. An approximate rule for changing temperatures in degrees Celsius (C) into temperatures in degrees Fahrenheit (F) is:

> Temperature in Fahrenheit (F) = 2 × temperature in Celsius (C) + 30

(a) Change each of these temperatures to Fahrenheit:
    (i) 30°C   (ii) 40°C   (iii) 50°C   (iv) 100°C
(b) Write a formula using the letters in brackets.

5. The cost, in pence, of an advertisement in a newspaper is calculated using this formula:

> Cost (C) = 25 × number of words (w) + 40

(a) Work out the cost of placing an advertisement with:
    (i) 20 words   (ii) 30 words   (iii) 16 words   (iv) 50 words
(b) Write a formula using the letters in brackets.

6. A school has a minibus which costs £20 each time it is used. A PE teacher uses this formula to calculate how much to charge her players when she uses the minibus:

> Cost per player (c) = 20 ÷ number of players travelling (p)

(a) Calculate the cost per player if the number travelling is:
    (i) 5   (ii) 10   (iii) 8   (iv) 16
(b) Write a formula using the letters in brackets.

7. This formula links foot length (*L*) measured in inches with shoe size (*S*):

    Shoe size (*S*) = 3 × length (*L*) − 25

    (a) What shoe sizes fit feet of length:
       (i)   10 inches
       (ii) 12 inches
       (iii) 11 inches
       (iv) 9 inches?
    (b) Write a formula using the letters in brackets.

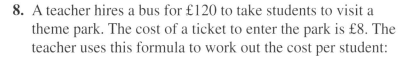

8. A teacher hires a bus for £120 to take students to visit a theme park. The cost of a ticket to enter the park is £8. The teacher uses this formula to work out the cost per student:

    Cost per student (*c*) = 120 ÷ number of students travelling (*n*) + 8

    (a) Work out the cost per student if the number of students travelling is:
       (i) 12   (ii) 24   (iii) 30   (iv) 40
    (b) Write a formula using the letters in brackets.

3.4 Substitution

An **expression** is a collection of letters and numbers.

For example: $3a + 2b$ is an expression.

If you know the values of the letter *a* and *b*, you can **substitute** them for the letters in the expression and find its value.

For example, if $a = 4$ and $b = 5$, then the value of the expression is:

$$3 \times 4 + 2 \times 5 = 12 + 10 = 22$$

Example

If $x = 5$ and $y = 7$, find the value of:

(a) $x + 9$ (b) $y - 5$ (c) $3x$ (d) $2y$ (e) $3x - 2y$

(a) $5 + 9 = 14$ (b) $7 - 5 = 2$ (c) $3 \times 5 = 15$ (d) $2 \times 7 = 14$ (e) $15 - 14 = 1$

Exercise 3D

1. If $m = 7$, find the value of:
    (a) $m + 3$ (b) $m + 4$ (c) $9 + m$ (d) $m - 3$ (e) $8 - m$
    (f) $3m$ (g) $3m + 5$ (h) $3m - 3$ (i) $2m + 1$ (j) $2m - 1$

MODULE 5

2. If $s = 6$, find the value of:

(a) $s + 6$ (b) $15 + s$ (c) $s - 4$ (d) $12 - s$ (e) $s - 6$

(f) $3s$ (g) $3s - 4$ (h) $2s + 5$ (i) $4s - 20$ (j) $18 - 2s$

3. If $y = 5$, find the value of:

(a) $y + 10$ (b) $12 + y$ (c) $8 - y$ (d) $y - 3$ (e) $5 - y$

(f) $3y$ (g) $3y + 4$ (h) $2y - 5$ (i) $2y + 5$ (j) $25 - 4y$

4. If $x = 20$, find the value of:

(a) $x + 1$ (b) $11 + x$ (c) $x - 10$ (d) $30 - x$ (e) $x + x$

(f) $2x$ (g) $x + x + x$ (h) $3x$ (i) $x + x - 3$ (j) $2x - 3$

5. If $z = 16$, find the value of:

(a) $z + 16$ (b) $z + z$ (c) $2z$ (d) $18 - z$ (e) $z - 6$

(f) $3z$ (g) $z + z + z$ (h) $z + 16 + z$ (i) $3z - 40$ (j) $50 - 3z$

6. If $a = 3$ and $b = 4$, find the value of:

(a) $7 + a$ (b) $b + 16$ (c) $3a$ (d) $2b$ (e) $3a + 2b$

(f) $a + 2b$ (g) $3a - b$ (h) $2b - a$ (i) $a + b + 7$ (j) $2a + 3b + 1$

7. If $x = 4$ and $y = 1$, find the value of:

(a) $x + y$ (b) $x + x + y$ (c) $2x + y$ (d) $2x - y$ (e) $x - 2y$

(f) $3x + 4y$ (g) $x + 5y$ (h) $2x - 5y$ (i) $2x - 2$ (j) $2y - 2$

8. If $m = 7$ and $n = 4$, find the value of:

(a) $m + n$ (b) $m + n + n$ (c) $m + 2n$ (d) $2m + m$ (e) $3m$

(f) $n + 2n + n$ (g) $4n$ (h) $3m + 2n$ (i) $2m - 3n$ (j) $m + n - 10$

9. If $q = 10$ and $r = 15$, find the value of:

(a) $3q$ (b) $2r$ (c) $3q + 2r$ (d) $3q - 2r$ (e) $2q + 3r$

(f) $2q + 45$ (g) $30 - 2r$ (h) $60 - 3r$ (i) $6q - 60$ (j) $4r - 6q$

10. If $j = 18$ and $k = 12$, find the value of:

(a) $k + k$ (b) $k + k + k$ (c) $3k$ (d) $3k - 2j$ (e) $5k - 50$

(f) $j + k$ (g) $2j + 2k$ (h) $3j + 3k$ (i) $j - k$ (j) $2j - 2k$

3.5 Substitution involving BoDMAS

The expression xy means $x \times y$

The expression $\dfrac{x}{y}$ means $x \div y$

The expression $3xy$ means $3 \times x \times y$

The expression $3(x + y)$ means calculate $x + y$ and then multiply by 3

There should never be any doubt in which order multiplications, divisions, additions or subtractions are to be done.
The word **BoDMAS** will help you remember the order is always:

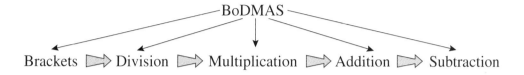

BoDMAS

Brackets ⇨ Division ⇨ Multiplication ⇨ Addition ⇨ Subtraction

Example

If $a = 4$ and $b = 2$, find the value of:

(a) ab (b) $3ab$ (c) $a + ab$ (d) $\dfrac{a}{b} - 1$ (e) $3(a + b)$

(a) $4 \times 2 = 8$
(b) $3 \times 4 \times 2 = 24$
(c) $4 + 4 \times 2 = 4 + 8 = 12$ (multiplication before addition)
(d) $4 \div 2 - 1 = 2 - 1 = 1$ (division before subtraction)
(e) $3 \times (4 + 2) = 3 \times 6 = 18$ (brackets before multiplication)

Exercise 3E

1. If $a = 3$ and $b = 4$, find the value of:

(a) ab (b) $5ab$ (c) $b + ab$ (d) $a + ab$ (e) $ab + ba$

(f) $2ab$ (g) $\dfrac{6b}{a}$ (h) $2(a + b)$ (i) $3(a + 4)$ (j) $5(b + 3)$

2. If $x = 2$ and $y = 1$, find the value of:

(a) xy (b) $3xy$ (c) $x + xy$ (d) $\dfrac{x}{y} + y$ (e) $\dfrac{12}{x} + 3y$

(f) $2x + 2y$ (g) $2(x + y)$ (h) $3(x + y)$ (i) $3x + 3y$ (j) $x(4y - 3)$

3. If $m = 4$ and $n = 5$, find the value of:

(a) mn (b) $2mn$ (c) $2nm$ (d) $\dfrac{10m}{n}$ (e) $\dfrac{8n}{m}$

(f) $3(n - m)$ (g) $3n - 3m$ (h) $5(m + n)$ (i) $5m + 5n$ (j) $n(m + n)$

4. If $p = 5$ and $q = 10$, find the value of:

(a) pq (b) qp (c) $\dfrac{30}{p}$ (d) $\dfrac{30}{q}$ (e) $\dfrac{30}{(p + q)}$

(f) $2p + 2q$ (g) $2(p + q)$ (h) $3(q - p)$ (i) $3q - 3p$ (j) $p(12 - q)$

MODULE 5

5. If $e = 3$ and $f = 7$, find the value of:

(a) ef (b) fe (c) $\dfrac{30}{e}$ (d) $\dfrac{28}{f}$ (e) $\dfrac{40}{(e+f)}$

(f) $40(e+f)$ (g) $40e + 40f$ (h) $e + ef$ (i) $e(1+f)$ (j) $f(e+1)$

6. If $x = 5$, $y = 10$ and $z = 2$, find the value of:

(a) xy (b) xz (c) zy (d) $xy + z$ (e) zxy

(f) $3(x+y)$ (g) $z(x+y)$ (h) $y(x-z)$ (i) $x(y-z)$ (j) $\dfrac{xy}{z}$

7. If $s = 3$, $t = 2$ and $u = 4$, find the value of:

(a) st (b) ut (c) us (d) $2st$ (e) $20 - 2ut$

(f) $u + st$ (g) $u(s+t)$ (h) $us + ut$ (i) $\dfrac{us}{t}$ (j) $u + \dfrac{s}{t}$

8. If $p = 3$, $q = 1$ and $r = 2$, find the value of:

(a) $2pq$ (b) pqr (c) $r(p+3)$ (d) $2pr$ (e) $q(r+2)$
(f) $qr + 3q$ (g) $3(pq + r)$ (h) $3pq + 3r$ (i) $p(q+r)$ (j) $pq + pr$

9. If $a = 3$, $b = 4$ and $c = 5$, find the value of:

(a) ab (b) $a + cb$ (c) bc (d) abc (e) $a + bc$
(f) $ab + bc$ (g) $b(a+c)$ (h) $2(ab + ac)$ (i) $2a(b+c)$ (j) $c(ab+1)$

10. If $x = 9$, $y = 3$ and $z = 2$, find the value of:

(a) $2y - 7$ (b) $2x - yz$ (c) $6y - zx$ (d) $3(x-z)$ (e) $3x - 3z$

(f) $x(y+z)$ (g) $xy + xz$ (h) $x(y-z)$ (i) $xy - xz$ (j) $\dfrac{4x}{yz}$

3.6 Substitution involving powers

The expression x^2 means $x \times x$. x^2 is read as 'x squared'.

The expression y^3 means $y \times y \times y$. y^3 is read as 'y cubed'.

The expression x^5 means $x \times x \times x \times x \times x$. x^5 is read as 'x to the power 5'.

The expression $2x^3$ means $2 \times x \times x \times x$

The expression $2xy^2$ means $2 \times x \times y \times y$

The expression $2x^2y$ means $2 \times x \times x \times y$

The expression $(x + y^2)$ means $(x + y) \times (x + y)$

The expression $\sqrt{x}$ means find a number which, when you square it, gives you x. $\sqrt{x}$ is read as 'the square root of x'.

Example

If $a = 3$ and $b = 4$, find the value of:

(a) a^2 (b) b^3 (c) a^5 (d) $2a^3$ (e) $2ab^2$ (f) $2a^2b$ (g) $(a + b)^2$
(h) $\sqrt{b}$ (i) $\sqrt{a}$

(a) $3 \times 3 = 9$ (b) $4 \times 4 \times 4 = 64$
(c) $3 \times 3 \times 3 \times 3 \times 3 = 243$ (d) $2 \times 3 \times 3 \times 3 = 54$
(e) $2 \times 3 \times 4 \times 4 = 96$ (f) $2 \times 3 \times 3 \times 4 = 72$
(g) $(3 + 4)^2 = 7^2 = 7 \times 7 = 49$ (h) $\sqrt{b} = \sqrt{4} = 2$ (because $2 \times 2 = 4$)
(i) $\sqrt{a} = \sqrt{3} = 1 \cdot 7$ (using $\sqrt{\ }$ key on a calculator)

Exercise 3F

You will need a calculator to complete this exercise.

1. If $e = 1, f = 2$ and $g = 3$, find the value of:
   (a) e^2 (b) f^2 (c) g^2 (d) e^3 (e) f^3 (f) g^3
   (g) e^4 (h) f^4 (i) g^4 (j) e^5 (k) $\sqrt{e}$

2. If $a = 5, b = 6$ and $c = 7$, find the value of:
   (a) a^2 (b) b^2 (c) c^2 (d) a^3 (e) b^3 (f) c^3
   (g) a^4 (h) b^4 (i) c^4 (j) a^5 (k) $\sqrt{a}$

3. If $x = 8, y = 9$ and $z = 10$, find the value of:
   (a) x^2 (b) y^2 (c) z^2 (d) x^3 (e) y^3 (f) z^3
   (g) x^4 (h) y^4 (i) z^4 (j) x^5 (k) $\sqrt{y}$ (l) $\sqrt{z}$

4. If $e = 5, f = 6$ and $g = 7$, find the value of:
   (a) $2e^2$ (b) $2f^2$ (c) $2g^2$ (d) ef^2 (e) e^2f (f) fg^2
   (g) f^2g (h) eg^2 (i) e^2g (j) $(e + f)^2$ (k) $\sqrt{(2e + f)}$

5. If $x = 2$ and $y = 3$, find the value of:
   (a) $2x^2$ (b) $2y^3$ (c) $3x^4$ (d) $2y^2$ (e) x^5
   (f) x^6 (g) xy (h) x^2y (i) xy^2 (j) $x^2 + y^2$

6. If $a = 1$ and $b = 2$, find the value of:
   (a) a^2 (b) b^3 (c) $a^3 + b^2$ (d) a^4 (e) a^7
   (f) ab (g) a^2b (h) ab^2 (i) $2ab^2$ (j) $(2a + b)^2$

7. If $m = 4$ and $n = 5$, find the value of:
   (a) m^2 (b) $n^2 + m^2$ (c) $n^3 + m^3$ (d) $2n^2$ (e) $2m^2$
   (f) $2n^2 + 2m^2$ (g) $2(n^2 + m^2)$ (h) $n^2 - m^2$ (i) $(n - m)(m + n)$ (j) $3m^2$

8. If $a = 3, s = 4$ and $u = 6$, find the value of:
   (a) as (b) u^2 (c) $2as$ (d) $u^2 - 2as$ (e) u^3
   (f) $(a + s)^2$ (g) $u^2 + us$ (h) $u(u + s)$ (i) $s(u - a)$ (j) $su - sa$

MODULE 5

9. If $x = 3$, $y = 4$ and $z = 8$, find the value of:

   (a) $x + 2$ (b) $12 - 2y$ (c) $5z - 11$ (d) $3(2x + y)$ (e) xy .

   (f) $x(y + z)$ (g) z^3 (h) zy^2 (i) z^2y (j) $(x + y)^3$

10. If $a = 10$, $b = 5$ and $c = 1$, find the value of:

   (a) $a + b$ (b) $a - b$ (c) $5b - 7$ (d) abc (e) $2ab + c$

   (f) $\dfrac{ac}{b}$ (g) a^3b (h) ab^3 (i) $a^3 + b^3$ (j) $(a + b)^2$

3.7 Substitution with negative numbers

A negative number multiplied by a positive number gives a
negative answer.

Examples

(a) $4 \times {}^-3 = {}^-12$ (b) ${}^-5 \times 5 = {}^-25$

(c) If $p = {}^-2$, $q = 4$ and $r = {}^-3$, then:

   $p + q = {}^-2 + 4 = 2$

   $q - p = 4 - {}^-2 = 4 + 2 = 6$

   $3r = 3 \times {}^-3 = {}^-9$

   $p - q = {}^-2 - 4 = {}^-6$

   $4p = 4 \times {}^-2 = {}^-8$

   $4p + 3r = 4 \times {}^-2 + 3 \times {}^-3 = {}^-8 + {}^-9 = {}^-17$

   $3r - 2q = 3 \times {}^-3 - 2 \times 4 = {}^-9 - 8 = {}^-17$

   $4r - 5p = 4 \times {}^-3 - 5 \times {}^-2 = {}^-12 - {}^-10 = {}^-12 + 10 = {}^-2$

Exercise 3G

1. If $m = {}^-7$, find the value of:

   (a) $m + 3$ (b) $m + 4$ (c) $9 + m$ (d) $m - 3$ (e) $8 - m$

   (f) $3m$ (g) $3m + 5$ (h) $3m - 3$ (i) $2m + 1$ (j) $2m - 1$

2. If $s = {}^-6$, find the value of:

   (a) $s + 6$ (b) $15 + s$ (c) $s - 4$ (d) $12 - s$ (e) $s - 6$

   (f) $3s$ (g) $3s - 4$ (h) $2s + 5$ (i) $4s - 20$ (j) $18 - 2s$

3. If $y = {}^-5$, find the value of:

   (a) $y + 10$ (b) $12 + y$ (c) $8 - y$ (d) $y - 3$ (e) $5 - y$

   (f) $3y$ (g) $3y + 4$ (h) $2y - 5$ (i) $2y + 5$ (j) $25 - 4y$

4. If $x = {}^-20$, find the value of:

   (a) $x + 1$ (b) $11 + x$ (c) $x - 10$ (d) $30 - x$ (e) $x + x$

   (f) $2x$ (g) $x + x + x$ (h) $3x$ (i) $x + x - 3$ (j) $2x - 3$

5. If $z = {}^-16$, find the value of:

(a) $z + 16$ (b) $z + z$ (c) $2z$ (d) $18 - z$ (e) $z - 6$

(f) $3z$ (g) $z + z + z$ (h) $z + 16 + z$ (i) $3z - 40$ (j) $50 - 3z$

6. If $a = 2$ and $b = {}^-4$, find the value of:

(a) $7 + a$ (b) $b + 16$ (c) $3a$ (d) $2b$ (e) $3a + 2b$

(f) $a + 2b$ (g) $3a - b$ (h) $2b - a$ (i) $a + b + 7$ (j) $2a + 3b + 1$

7. If $x = {}^-4$ and $y = 4$, find the value of:

(a) $x + y$ (b) $x + x + y$ (c) $2x + y$ (d) $2x - y$ (e) $x - 2y$

(f) $3x + 4y$ (g) $x + 5y$ (h) $2x - 5y$ (i) $2x - 2$ (j) $2y - 2$

8. If $m = 5$ and $n = {}^-4$, find the value of:

(a) $m + n$ (b) $m + n + n$ (c) $m + 2n$ (d) $2m + m$ (e) $3m$

(f) $n + 2n + n$ (g) $4n$ (h) $3m + 2n$ (i) $2m - 3n$ (j) $m + n - 10$

9. If $q = {}^-10$ and $r = 5$, find the value of:

(a) $3q$ (b) $2r$ (c) $3q + 2r$ (d) $3q - 2r$ (e) $2q + 3r$

(f) $2q + 45$ (g) $30 - 2r$ (h) $60 - 3r$ (i) $6q - 60$ (j) $4r - 6q$

10. If $j = {}^-18$ and $k = {}^-12$, find the value of:

(a) $k + k$ (b) $k + k + k$ (c) $3k$ (d) $3k - 2j$ (e) $5k - 50$

(f) $j + k$ (g) $2j + 2k$ (h) $3j + 3k$ (i) $j - k$ (j) $2j - 2k$

3.8 Substitution in formulae

A formula is a rule to calculate a value.

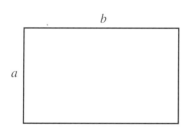

For example, the formula $P = 2a + 2b$ can be used to calculate the perimeter (P) of a rectangle if you know the side lengths a and b.

Example 1

$S = 180n - 360$. Find the value of S when $n = 10$

so $n = 10$

so $S = 180 \times 10 - 360 = 1\,800 - 360 = 1\,440$

MODULE 5

Example 2

The cost C pence, of a newspaper advertisement of n words is given by the formula

$$C = 30n + 40$$

Find the cost of an advertisement of 20 words.

$$n = 20$$

so $\quad C = 30 \times 20 + 40 = 600 + 40 = 640$ pence $= £6{\cdot}40$

Example 3

When a stone is dropped over a cliff, the distance d metres it has fallen after t seconds is given by the formula

$$d = 5t^2$$

How far will a stone fall in 3 seconds?

$$t = 3$$

so $\quad d = 5 \times 3 \times 3 = 45$ metres.

Exercise 3H

1. Use the formula $p = f + 1$ to calculate the value of p when:

    (a) $f = 3$ (b) $f = 5$ (c) $f = 8$

    (d) $f = 25$ (e) $f = 50$ (f) $f = 31$

2. Use the formula $C = 3d$ to calculate the value of C when:

    (a) $d = 4$ (b) $d = 3$ (c) $d = 2$

    (d) $d = 1$ (e) $d = 1{\cdot}5$ (f) $d = 2{\cdot}1$

3. Use the formula $P = 2a + 2b$ to calculate the perimeter of a rectangle when:

    (a) $a = 3$ cm, $b = 5$ cm   (b) $a = 6$ cm, $b = 7$ cm

    (c) $a = 2$ m, $b = 1$ m   (d) $a = 8$ mm, $b = 10$ mm

    (e) $a = 3{\cdot}5$ cm, $b = 4$ cm   (f) $a = 2{\cdot}5$ m, $b = 3{\cdot}5$ m

4. Use the formula $V = RI$ to calculate the value of V when:

    (a) $R = 100$, $I = 2$ (b) $R = 50$, $I = 3$

    (c) $R = 240$, $I = 1$ (d) $R = 100$, $I = 2{\cdot}5$

    (e) $R = 40$, $I = 6$ (f) $R = 50$, $I = 3{\cdot}5$

5. Use the formula $T = 4f - 5g$ to calculate the value of T when:

    (a) $f = 6$, $g = 4$ (b) $f = 10$, $g = 6$

    (c) $f = 2{\cdot}5$, $g = 1$ (d) $f = 5$, $g = 4$

    (e) $f = 4{\cdot}5$, $g = 1{\cdot}5$ (f) $f = 2$, $g = 2$

6. Use the formula $v = u + at$ to calculate the value of v when:

   (a) $u = 0, a = 2, t = 3$ (b) $u = 1, a = 3, t = 5$

   (c) $u = 6, a = 4, t = 1$ (d) $u = 0, a = 5, t = 4$

   (e) $u = 4, a = 4, t = 4$ (f) $u = 3, a = 0, t = 5$

7. Use the formula $s = 2t + 32$ to calculate the value of s when:

   (a) $t = 1$ (b) $t = 2$ (c) $t = 3$

   (d) $t = 0$ (e) $t = {}^-1$ (f) $t = {}^-2$

8. Use the formula $d = \dfrac{C}{3}$ to calculate the value of d when:

   (a) $C = 9$ (b) $C = 12$ (c) $C = 21$

   (d) $C = 30$ (e) $C = 72$ (f) $C = 4 \cdot 5$

9. Use the formula $A = 3r^2$ to calculate the value of A when:

   (a) $r = 2$ (b) $r = 3$ (c) $r = 1$

   (d) $r = 4$ (e) $r = 5$ (f) $r = 1 \cdot 5$

10. Use the formula $A = \dfrac{(a + b)h}{2}$ to calculate the value of A when:

   (a) $a = 2, b = 3, h = 4$ (b) $a = 1, b = 1, h = 2$

   (c) $a = 8, b = 5, h = 3$ (d) $a = 1 \cdot 5, b = 2 \cdot 5, h = 4$

   (e) $a = 2, b = 2 \cdot 5, h = 2$ (f) $a = 3, b = 2, h = 7$

3.9 Collecting like terms

Remember: an **expression** is a collection of letters and numbers. For example:

$$3ab + 2b + 7 \text{ is an } \textbf{expression}.$$

These are the **terms** of the expression.

Terms with the same letter part are called **like terms**.

        $3a$ and $2a$ are like terms

        $7y$, $2y$ and y are like terms.

An expression can be **simplified** by **collecting like terms**.

Example

(a) $3a + 2a = 5a$ (b) $7y + 2y + y = 10y$ (c) $5x - 4x = x$

Hint:

x is $1x$ – you don't need to write the 1!

Exercise 3I

Simplify each expression by collecting like terms.

1. $5a + 6a$	**2.** $7y + 3y$	**3.** $2w + w$	**4.** $x + 5x$	**5.** $8m + 5m$
6. $2q + 2q$	**7.** $v + v$	**8.** $4r + 7r$	**9.** $3b + 17b$	**10.** $5g + 5g$
11. $8w - 3w$	**12.** $4x - x$	**13.** $5t - 4t$	**14.** $9e - 6e$	**15.** $7u - u$
16. $6u - 5u$	**17.** $5y - 2y$	**18.** $8i - 2i$	**19.** $9r - 8r$	**20.** $2x - x$

21. $3x + 5x + 6x$ **22.** $6y + 5y + y$ **23.** $5t + t + 3t$

24. $8a + 5a + 6a$ **25.** $7b + b + b$ **26.** $x + x + x + x$

27. $2w + w + 5w$ **28.** $d + 2d + 3d$ **29.** $7e + 3e + e$

30. $5r + 6r + 7r$ **31.** $4x + 7x - 3x$ **32.** $5a + a - 3a$

33. $2q + 3q - q$ **34.** $b + 3b - 2b$ **35.** $x + 5x - 5x$

36. $3x - 6x + 4x$ **37.** $x - 4x + 6x$ **38.** $4z - 7z + 4z$

39. $3e - 8e + 7e$ **40.** $5a - 7a + 9a$ **41.** $9x - 5x - x$

42. $7y - 2y - 3y$ **43.** $8m - m - 3m$ **44.** $9u - 4u - 2u$

45. $6y - 2y - 3y$ **46.** $8z - z - z$ **47.** $9b - 5b - 3b$

48. $11d - 5d - 3d$ **49.** $6h - h - 2h$ **50.** $10a - 5a - a$

3.10 Simplifying with different types of term

Example

Simplify:

(a) $3a + 2b + a + 3b$

(b) $5x + 3y - x + y$

(c) $5r + 8 - 2r + 2$

(d) $4x - 5y - 2x + 4y$

> **Remember:**
> The sign in front of the number goes with the number.

(a)
$$3a + 2b + a + 3b$$
$$= 3a + a + 2b + 3b$$
$$= 4a + 5b$$

(b)
$$5x + 3y - x + y$$
$$= 5x - x + 3y + y$$
$$= 4x + 4y$$

(c)
$$5r + 8 - 2r + 2$$
$$= 5r - 2r + 8 + 2$$
$$= 3r + 10$$

(d)
$$4x - 5y - 2x + 4y$$
$$= 4x - 2x - 5y + 4y$$
$$= 2x - y$$

Exercise 3J

Simplify each expression by collecting like terms.

1. $4x + y + 3x + 2y$ **2.** $5t + 3s + 4t + 3s$ **3.** $4m + 2n + 5m + n$

4. $3a + b + a + 3b$ **5.** $4y + 5y + 2z + z$ **6.** $5r + 6r + 3s + 2s$

7. $7y + 2 + 3y + 2$ 8. $6u + 3v + v + u$ 9. $8 + n + 3 + 5n$
10. $3e + 2e + 5f + f$ 11. $5x + 2y - x + y$ 12. $6a + 5b - 5a + 3b$
13. $x + 3y + x - 2y$ 14. $2 + 3f + 2f - 1$ 15. $3m + 2n - 2m + n$
16. $5x - 3x + y + y$ 17. $7 - 2 + 3v + v$ 18. $2p + 3q + p - q$
19. $5r + 2s - 3r + s$ 20. $6a + 3b + b - 5a$ 21. $4x + 5y - x - y$
22. $4a + 7 - 3a - 6$ 23. $8e - 7e + 4f - 2f$ 24. $5s + 6 - 4s - 5$
25. $6x + 4y - 3x - 2y$ 26. $4r - 2s - r + 4s$
27. $6x - 5y - x + 6y$ 28. $8u - 8 - 4u + 10$
29. $5a + 3b - 2a - 2b$ 30. $6y + 4z - 5y - 3z$
31. $3a + 2b + a - 4b$ 32. $5x + 7y + 2x - 9y$
33. $6e + 5f + e - 8f$ 34. $7u + 5t + 8u - 10t$
35. $6y + 3z + 2y - 4z$ 36. $6a + 2b - 4a - 5b$
37. $4m - 2n - 2m + n$ 38. $4a + 7 - 2a - 8$
39. $6y - 9 + y - 11$ 40. $7x - 3y - 4x - 2y$

3.11 More simplification

The perimeter of a rectangle is the total distance round the outside.

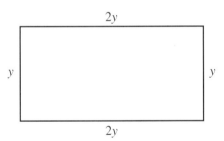

The perimeter of this rectangle is $2y + y + 2y + y = 6y$

Exercise 3K

Find an expression for the perimeter of each shape.

1.
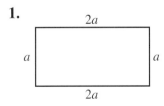

2.
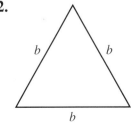

3.
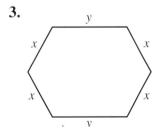

4.
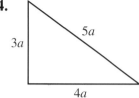

5.
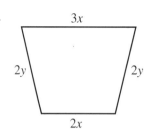

6.
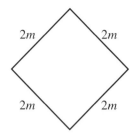

7.
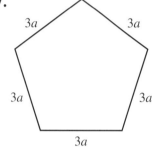

8.
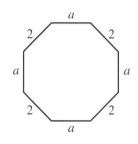

9.
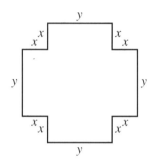

10.
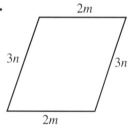

11.
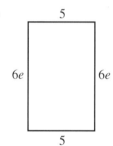

12.
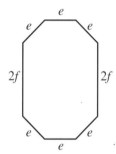

Summary

1. Letters can be used to represent quantities.

Checkout AS3

1. The letter *s* represents the number of 'pic-n-mix' sweets that Priya has chosen. Use the letter *s* to write the number of sweets chosen by:
   (a) Kimberly, who has chosen 3 more sweets than Priya.
   (b) Wendy, who has chosen 3 less sweets than Priya.
   (c) Billy, who has chosen 3 times as many sweets as Priya.
   (d) Tariq, who has chosen half as many sweets as Priya.

MODULE 5

2. Formulae can be used to solve problems.

2. A mechanic uses this formula to calculate the cost in pounds of repair:
Total cost (C) =cost of parts (P)
    + hours worked (H) × 20
(a) Calculate the cost of repairs if:
(i) Parts cost £50 and 3 hours are worked
(ii) Parts cost £85 and 5 hours are worked.
(b) Write the formula using the letters in brackets.

---

3. You can substitute numbers for letters to find the value of an expression.

3. If $x = 2$, $y = 3$ and $z = 4$, find the value of:
(a) $x + 1$ (b) $z - 2$ (c) $4y$
(d) $18 - x$ (e) $y + 2z$ (f) $4x - 2y$
(g) xy (h) $5yz$ (i) $x + yz$

(j) $4(x + y)$ (k) $\dfrac{3z}{(x + z)}$ (l) $xy + 3xz$

(m) x^2 (n) z^3 (o) xy^2

---

4. A negative number × a positive number = a negative number.

4. If $a = 2$ and $b = {}^-3$, find the value of:
(a) $a + b$ (b) $a - b$ (c) $3a$
(d) $4b$ (e) $5a + 2b$ (f) $3a - 5b$
(g) $14 + 3b$ (h) $3a - 10$ (i) $a + b + 1$
(j) $3a + 2b + 6$ (k) $3(a + b)$ (l) $ab + b$

---

5. You can substitute in formulae.

5. (a) Use the formula $p = 3t + 7$ to find the value of p when:
(i) $t = 5$ (ii) $t = 1$ (iii) $t = {}^-1$
(b) Use the formula $y = mx + c$ to find the value of y when:
(i) $m = 3$, $x = 2$ and $c = 1$
(ii) $m = 2$, $x = {}^-2$ and $c = 5$

---

6. You can simplify an expression by collecting like terms.

6. (a) Simplify each expression by collecting like terms:
(i) $5t + 7t$ (ii) $7y + 4y + y$
(iii) $9a - 3a$ (iv) $3a + 2b + 3a + 5b$
(v) $6x + 7y - 4x + y$ (vi) $3d + 2e + 2d - e$
(vii) $6x + 3y + x - 4y$ (viii) $7a - 3b - 2a + b$
(ix) $9p - 3q - 2p - 3q$ (x) $7u + 3v - 8v - 4u$
(b) Write an expression for the perimeter of this shape.

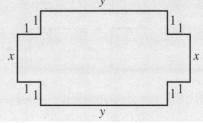

Revision exercise AS3

1. (a) Simplify
   (i) $4a + 5a$,
   (ii) $4a - 2b + 2a + 3b$,
   (iii) $3 \times b \times b$.   [SEG]

2. (a) Lucy has 12 sweets.
       Jason has four less than Lucy.
       How many sweets does Jason have?

   (b) Mary has p sweets.
       Write down the number of sweets each person has:
       (i)   Carol has five more than Mary
       (ii) Abdul has twice as many as Mary
       (iii) Tina has three fewer than Abdul.   [NEAB]

3. (a) Simplify the algebraic expression

   $$6x + 7 - 2x + 4.$$

   (b) Using the formula

   $$a = 5b - \frac{c}{4},$$

   find the value of a when $b = 12$ and $c = 24$.   [SEG]

4. Judy has some books in her bag.
   The number of books in her bag is x.
   Judy puts 3 more books in her bag.

   (a) Write an expression to show the total number of books
       in Judy's bag.

   The number of books in David's bag is y.
   He takes out $\frac{1}{4}$ of the books from his bag.

   (b) Write an expression to show the total number of
       books that are **not** taken out of David's bag.   [SEG]

5. Here is a rule for working out a sequence of numbers

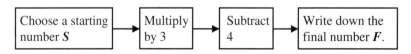

| Choose a starting number S | → | Multiply by 3 | → | Subtract 4 | → | Write down the final number F. |

Write down an **equation** connecting the final number,
F and the starting number S.   [NEAB]

6. The formula
$$F = \frac{9}{5}C + 32$$
is used to change temperatures in degrees Centigrade (C) to temperatures in degrees Fahrenheit (F).
A thermometer reads a temperature of 15 °C.
What is the equivalent temperature in degrees Fahrenheit?
[NEAB]

7. The cost of hiring a coach is £40 plus £2 for every mile travelled.
For example, a journey of 25 miles would cost
$$£40 + 25 \times £2 = £90$$

(a) How much will it cost for a journey of 72 miles?

(b) Write down an expression for the cost in £ of a journey of M miles.

(c) A journey costs £124.
   (i) Use your answer to part (b) to form an equation using this information.
   (ii) How many miles did the coach travel on this journey? [NEAB]

8. A formula to estimate the number of rolls of wallpaper, R, for a room is

$$R = \frac{ph}{5}$$ where p is the perimeter of the room in metres and h is the height of the room in metres.

The perimeter of Carol's bedroom is 15·5 m and it is 2·25 m high.
How many rolls of wallpaper will she have to buy? [NEAB]

9. Cars can be hired from Andy's Car Hire.

(a) (i) How much does it cost to hire a car for 5 days?
   (ii) Mrs Mansi paid £222 altogether to hire a car.
      For how many days did she hire the car?

> **Andy's Car Hire**
>
> **£23 per day**
> **plus a fixed charge of £15**

Cars can also be hired from Belinda's Car Hire.

(b) Using T for the total cost in £, and d for the number of days hired, write a formula for T in terms of d.

(c) Mr Li wants to hire a car for 6 days.
Which is cheaper, Andy's or Belinda's, and by how much? [SEG]

> **Belinda's Car Hire**
>
> **£25 per day**
> **no fixed charge**

MODULE 5

AS4 SHAPE AND SPACE 2

This unit will show you how to:

- Describe two- and three-dimensional shapes
- Draw nets of 3-D shapes
- Use isometric drawings to draw 3-D shapes
- Draw plans and elevations of 3-D shapes

Before you start:

You should know how to...	Check in AS4
1. Use compasses, a ruler and a protractor to construct triangles. Look back to page 234 to remind yourself how to do this.	**1.** Make an accurate drawing of each triangle: (a) 70° 40° 12 cm (b) 6 cm 9 cm 10 cm

4.1 Two- and three-dimensional shapes

When a two-dimensional shape is extended into three dimensions it makes a 3-D shape.

For example, a square can become a cube or a cuboid.

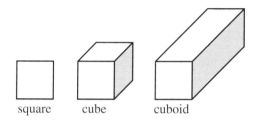

square   cube   cuboid

These are some of the words used to describe 3-D shapes.

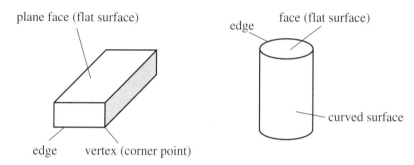

plane face (flat surface)   edge   face (flat surface)

curved surface

edge   vertex (corner point)

Exercise 4A

Copy and complete this table which continues on page 272.

Name	3-D shape	Plane faces	Curved surfaces	Vertices	Edges
Cube		6	0	8	12
Cuboid					
Cylinder					
Triangular prism					

MODULE 5

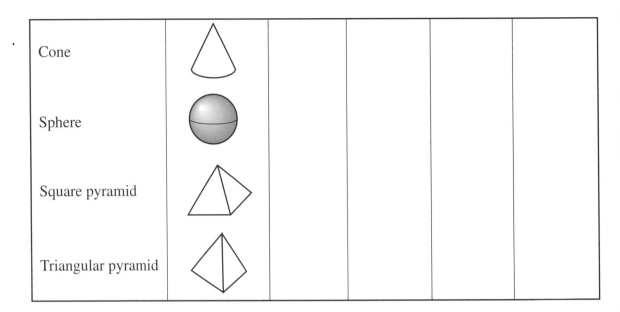

Cone					
Sphere					
Square pyramid					
Triangular pyramid					

4.2 Nets

A **net** is a flat shape which can be folded into a 3-D shape.

This net can be folded to make a cube.

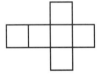

Exercise 4B

1. Copy these shapes on squared paper. Cut them out and fold them. Which shapes are nets for a cube?

(a) 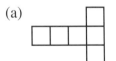   (b) 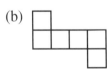   (c)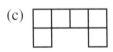

(d) 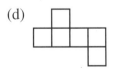   (e)   (f)

(g) 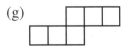   (h)   (i)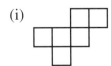

MODULE 5

2. This is a sketch of a net for a cuboid which is 2 cm by 4 cm by 3 cm.

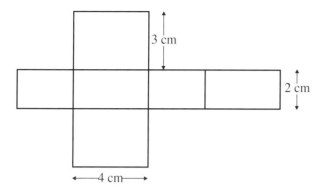

(a) Draw the net accurately, cut it out and fold it.

(b) Draw a net for a cuboid which is 1 cm by 5 cm by 6 cm, cut it out and fold it.

3. This is a sketch of a net for a triangular prism.

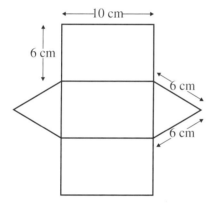

(a) Draw the three rectangles accurately on squared paper.

(b) Use a pair of compasses to add the two triangles.

(c) Cut out the net and fold it.

4. This is a sketch of a net for a triangular-based pyramid, made from four equilateral triangles.

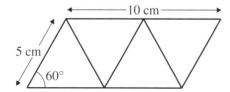

Hint:

An **equilateral** triangle has 3 equal angles. All three angles are 60°.

(a) Draw the net accurately, cut it out and fold it.

(b) Sketch a different net which would make the same pyramid.

5. This is a sketch of a net of a 3-D shape.

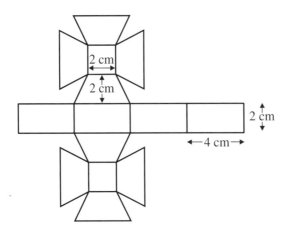

(a) Describe the 3-D shape you think the net will make.
(b) Draw the net accurately on squared paper, adding glue flaps where you think they are needed.
(c) Cut out the net and glue it together.
(d) How many plane faces does the 3-D shape have?
(e) How many edges does the 3-D shape have?
(f) How many vertices does the 3-D shape have?

4.3 Isometric drawings

You can use isometric paper to draw 3-D shapes.

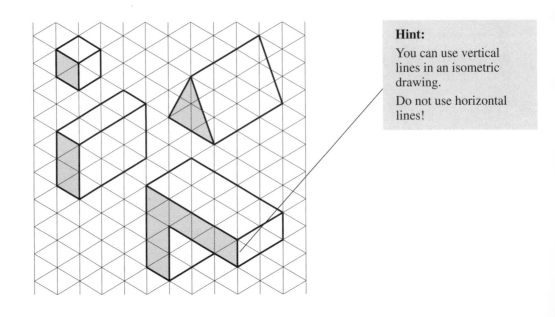

Hint:

You can use vertical lines in an isometric drawing.

Do not use horizontal lines!

Exercise 4C

1. These are isometric drawings of the
   3-D letters, T, R, I and P.

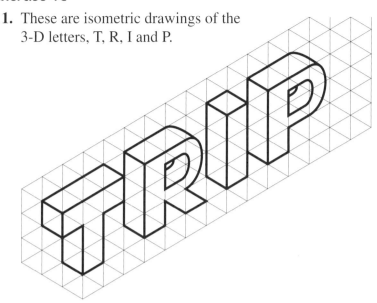

   (a) Copy the drawings.
   (b) Make an isometric drawing of a 3-D letter H.
   (c) Make an isometric drawing of a 3-D letter K.
   (d) Make an isometric drawing of a complete name.

2. These isometric drawings show the same 3-D shape in four different positions.

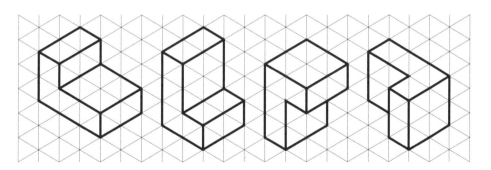

   Copy this 3-D shape and draw it in three different positions.

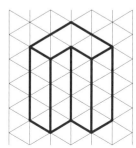

4.4 Plans and elevations

Plans and elevations can also be used to draw 3-D shapes.

This is a 3-D cross with a plan and two elevations.

The **plan** is the view from directly above the 3-D shape.

The side elevation is drawn directly beside the front elevation so that edges and vertices line up.

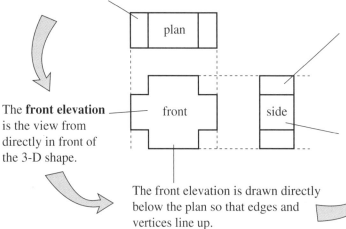

The **front elevation** is the view from directly in front of the 3-D shape.

The **side elevation** is the view from one side of the 3-D shape.

The front elevation is drawn directly below the plan so that edges and vertices line up.

Exercise 4D

Draw a plan, front elevation and side elevation for each 3-D shape.
Line your drawings up carefully.

1.

2.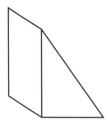

3.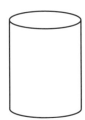

4.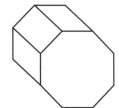

5.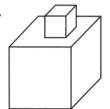

6.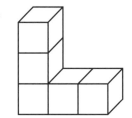

7. 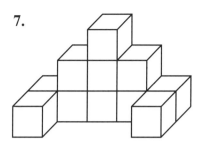   **8.** 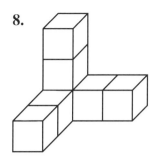   **9.**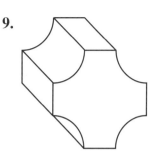

Summary

1. These are some of the words used to describe 3-D shapes.

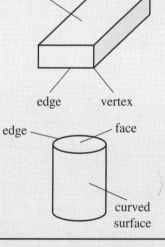

2. A **net** is a 2-D shape which can be folded to make a 3-D shape.

3. You can use isometric paper to draw 3-D shapes.

Checkout AS4

1. List the number of curved surfaces, plane faces, edges and vertices for each 3-D shape.
   (a) a cuboid   (b) a cylinder

2. (a) Draw a net for a cube.
   (b) Draw a net for a cuboid which is 3 cm by 4 cm by 5 cm.

3. Use isometric paper to draw the 3-D letters, L, W and A.

4. The **plan** is the view from directly above the 3-D shape.

The **front elevation** is the view from directly in front of the 3-D shape.

The **side elevation** is the view from one side of the 3-D shape.

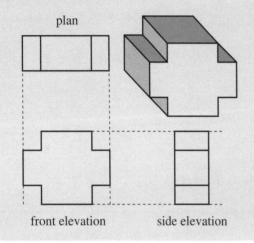

plan

front elevation   side elevation

4. Draw a plan, front view and side elevation for this 3-D shape. Line your drawing up carefully.

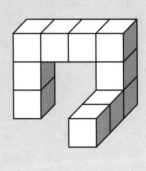

Revision exercise AS4

1. The diagram shows a box.

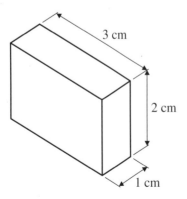

3 cm

2 cm

1 cm

Draw a full sized net for this box.   [SEG]

2. (a) Sketch a cube.

  (b) Which **two** of these shapes are nets for a cube?

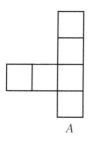

A

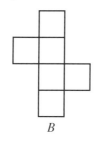

B

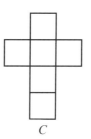

C

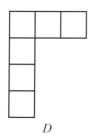

D

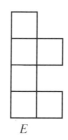

E

[NEAB]

3. The diagram shows a net of a cuboid.

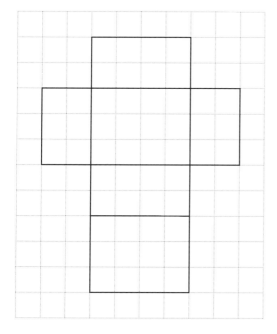

On isometric paper show what the cuboid looks like when the net is folded.   [SEG]

MODULE 5

4. The diagram shows a solid.

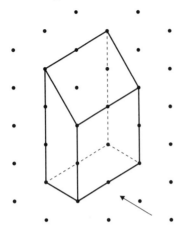

On squared paper draw the elevation of this solid, from the direction shown by the arrow.   [AQA]

5. The diagram shows an open box.

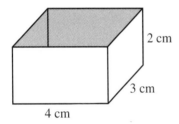

2 cm

3 cm

4 cm

(a) Draw an accurate net of the open box on squared paper.   [NEAB]

AS5 SHAPE AND SPACE 3

Geometric shapes are used in design and architecture.

This unit will show you how to:

- Use angle facts to work out missing angles
- Find angles in triangles
- Describe and recognise types of triangle and quadrilateral
- Find the angle sum of a polygon

Before you start:

You should know how to...	Check in AS5
1. Describe turns in degrees. For example From NE to S clockwise is $3 \times 45° = 135°$	**1.** Describe these turns in degrees: (a) W to E clockwise (b) S to W clockwise (c) E to NW clockwise (d) N to NW anticlockwise (e) E to SW anticlockwise (f) SE to N anticlockwise

5.1 Lines and angles

Remember:

There are 90° in a
quarter turn.

90°

There are 180° in a
half turn.

180°

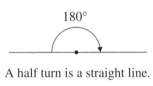

A half turn is a straight line.

There are 360° in a
full turn.

360°

Look back to page 227 if you need more help.

Examples

Find the angles *a*, *b* and *c* in these diagrams.

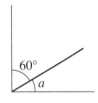
60°
a

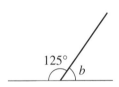
125°
b

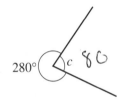
280° *c* 80

$a = 90° - 60° = 30°$ $b = 180° - 125° = 55°$ $c = 360° - 280° = 80°$

Exercise 5A

Find each angle marked with a letter in these diagrams.

1.

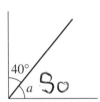
40°
a 50

2.

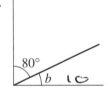
80°
b 10

3.

c 45 50
45°

4.

965
d
25° 5=30

5.

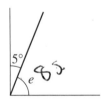
5°
e 85

6.

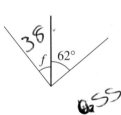
38
f 62°
55

7.

34°
56 *g*

8.

h 57°
33

9.

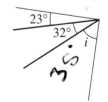
23°
32° *i*
35

MODULE 5

10.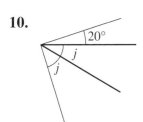

11.

12.

13.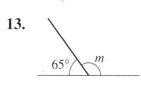

14.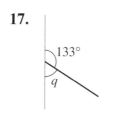

15.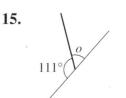

16.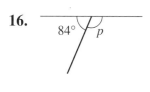

17.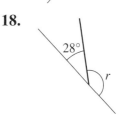

18.

19.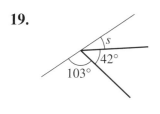

20.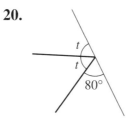

21.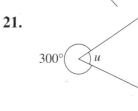

22.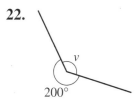

23.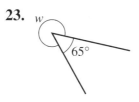

24.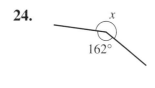

25..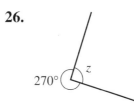

26.

27.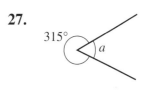

28.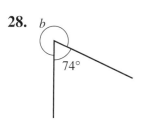

29.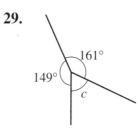

30.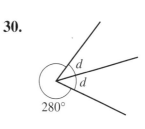

MODULE 5

5.2 Opposite angles

Two pairs of opposite angles are created when straight lines cross.
Opposite angles are always equal.

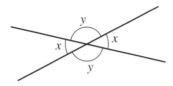

Example

Find the angles e, f and g.

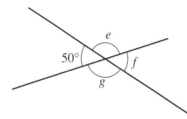

angle $f = 50°$ (because angle f and $50°$ are opposite angles)
angle $e = 130°$ (because angle e and $50°$ make a straight line)
angle $g = 130°$ (because angle g and angle e are opposite angles)

Exercise 5B

Find each angle marked with a letter in these diagrams.

1.

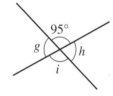

2.

3.

4.

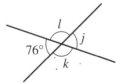

5.

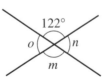

6.

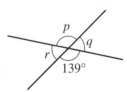

7.

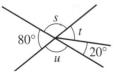

8.

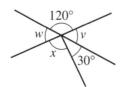

9.

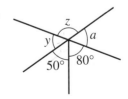

5.3 Parallel lines and angles

When a line crosses a pair of parallel lines, two sets of identical opposite angles are formed.

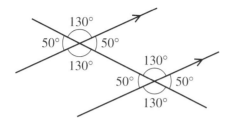

Example

Find the angles e, f, g, h, i, j and k.

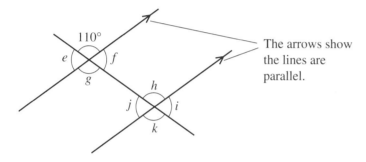

The arrows show the lines are parallel.

angle $g = 110°$ (because angle g and $110°$ are opposite angles)
angle $e = 70°$ (because angle e and $110°$ make a straight line)
angle $f = 70°$ (because angle e and angle f are opposite angles)
angle $j = 70°$ (because the two pairs of opposite angles are identical)
angle $i = 70°$ (because the two pairs of opposite angles are identical)
angle $h = 110°$ (because the two pairs of opposite angles are identical)
angle $k = 110°$ (because the two pairs of opposite angles are identical)

Exercise 5C

Find each angle marked with a letter in these diagrams.

1.
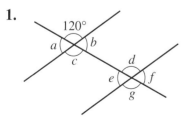

2.
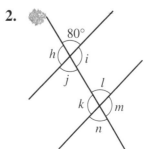

MODULE 5

3.

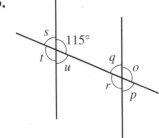

4.

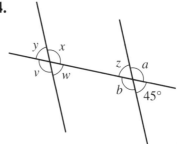

5.

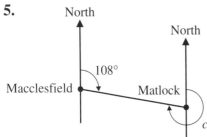

6.

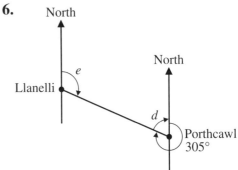

7.

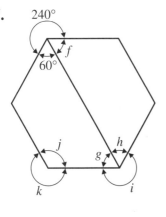

8.

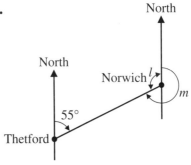

5.4 Angles in triangles

The three angles in any triangle add up to 180°.

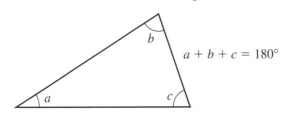

$$a + b + c = 180°$$

If you know two angles, you can find the third angle.

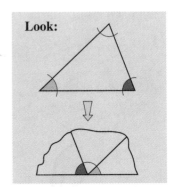

Look:

Example

Find angle *a*.

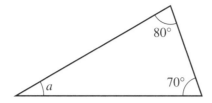

angle $a = 180° - (80° + 70°) = 180° - 150° = 30°$

Exercise 5D

Find each angle marked with a letter in these diagrams.

1.

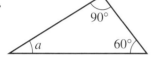

2.

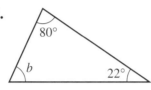

3.

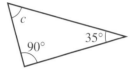

4.

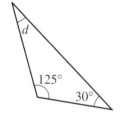

5.

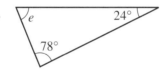

6.

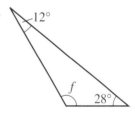

7.

8.

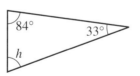

9.

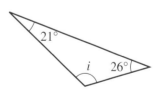

10.

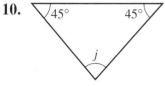

11.

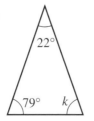

12.

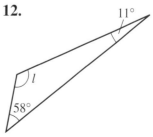

MODULE 5

Exterior angle of a triangle

These angles are **interior** angles because they are inside the triangle.

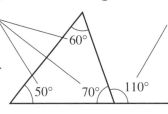

This is an **exterior** angle because it is outside the triangle.

Example

Find the missing angles in these triangles:

(a)

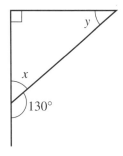

(b)

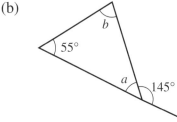

(a) First find x
$130° + x = 180°$
so $x = 50°$
Interior angles add to $180°$
so $50° + 90° + y = 180°$
$y = 40°$

(b) First find a
$145° + a = 180°$
$a = 35°$
Interior angles add to $180°$
so $35° + 55° + b = 180°$
$b = 90°$

Notice that

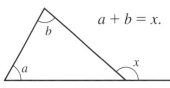

$a + b = x.$

This activity will help you prove it.

Activity – copy and complete

For this triangle:

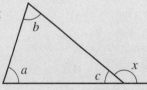

Theorem: $a + b = x$.

Proof:

Angles on a straight line add to $180°$
$x + c = \underline{}°$
so $x = \underline{}° - c$

Notice these two have the same right hand side. That means that:
$x = \underline{} + \underline{}$

Angles in a triangle add to $180°$
so $a + b + c = \underline{}°$
so $a + b = \underline{}° - c$

MODULE 5

5.5 Types of triangle

An **isosceles** triangle has two equal sides and two equal angles.

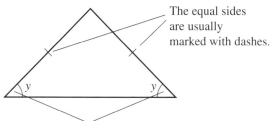

The equal sides are usually marked with dashes.

The equal angles are formed between the equal sides and the third side.

An **equilateral** triangle has three equal sides and three equal angles of 60°.

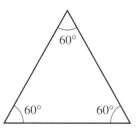

Example

Find each angle marked with a letter in these diagrams.

(a)

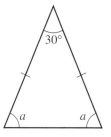

(b)

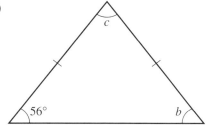

The triangle is isosceles.
$a + a = 180° - 30° = 150°$
$a = 150° ÷ 2 = 75°$

The triangle is isosceles.
$b = 56°$ (because it is the other equal angle)
$c = 180° - (56° + 56°) = 68°$

Exercise 5E

Find each angle marked with a letter in these diagrams.

1.

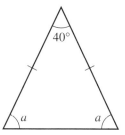

2.

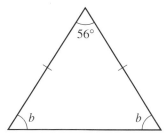

MODULE 5

3.

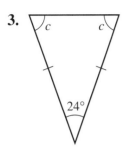

4.

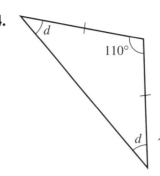

5.

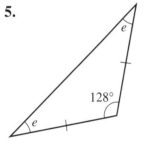

6.

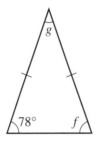

7.

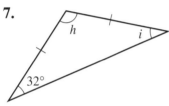

8.

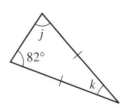

9.

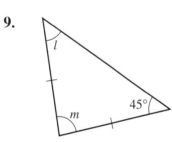

10.

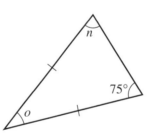

5.6 Quadrilaterals

A quadrilateral is a shape with four straight sides.
These shapes are all quadrilaterals.

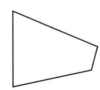

Some quadrilaterals have special names. These are given in the
next exercise.

Exercise 5F

Use centimetre squared paper for this exercise.

1. A quadrilateral with one pair of parallel sides is called a **trapezium**.

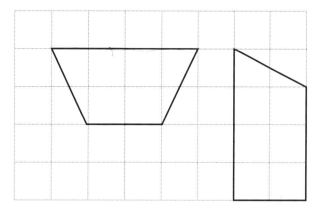

Draw four different trapeziums.

2. A quadrilateral with two pairs of parallel sides is called a **parallelogram**.

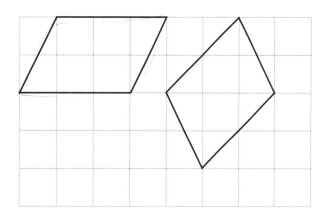

Draw four different parallelograms.

3. A quadrilateral with four equal sides is called a **rhombus**.

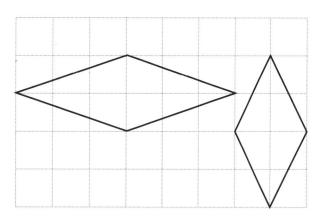

Draw four different rhombuses.

MODULE 5

4. A quadrilateral with internal angles of 90° is called **rectangle**.

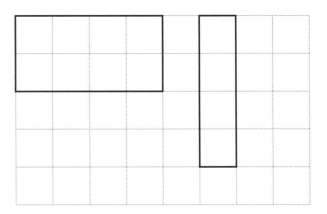

Draw four different rectangles.

5. A quadrilateral with four equal sides **and** internal angles of 90° is called a **square**.

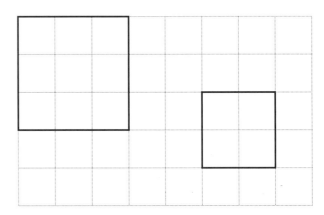

Draw four different squares.

6. Draw a robot made up only from quadrilaterals. Use each type of quadrilateral at least once. Label one of each type of quadrilateral. Here is an example:

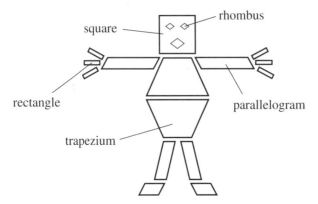

5.7 Polygons

A **polygon** is a shape with straight sides.

A triangle is a polygon with three sides.

A quadrilateral is a polygon with four sides.

This is a polygon with six sides, called a **hexagon**.

A **regular** polygon has all its sides and angles equal. This is a regular polygon with five sides, called a **pentagon**.

The angles inside a polygon are called interior angles. It also has exterior angles.

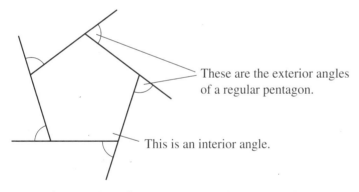

These are the exterior angles of a regular pentagon.

This is an interior angle.

The **exterior** angles of any polygon add up to 360°.
Each exterior angle of a regular pentagon is 360° ÷ 5 = 72°.
Each interior angle of the pentagon makes an angle of 180° with an exterior angle.
Each interior angle of a regular pentagon = 180° − 72° = 108°.

Example

Find the angles p and q in this regular hexagon.

The exterior angles add up to 360°.
$p = 360 \div 6 = 60°$
Each interior angle makes an angle of 180° with an exterior angle.
$q = 180° − 60° = 120°$

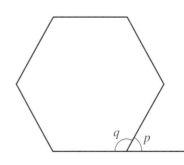

Exercise 5G

1. A polygon with eight sides is called an **octagon**.
    Find the angles p and q in this regular octagon.

    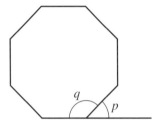

2. A polygon with nine sides is called a **nonagon**.
    Find the angles m and n in this regular nonagon.

    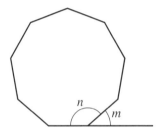

3. A polygon with ten sides is called a **decagon**.
    Find the angles c and d in this regular decagon.

    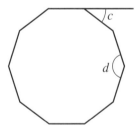

4. A polygon with twelve sides is called a **dodecagon**.
    Find the angles a and b in this regular dodecagon.

    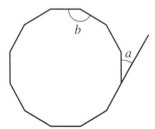

5.8 Angle sum of a polygon

The interior angles of any triangle add up to 180°.
There is a similar fixed sum for the interior angles of any other type of polygon.
You can find the sum by dividing the polygon into triangles.

Example
Find the sum of the interior angles in a pentagon.

First, divide the pentagon into triangles.

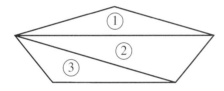

The interior angles in each triangle add up to 180°.
The interior angles in a pentagon add up to 3 × 180° = 540°.

Exercise 5H

1. Find the angle x in this pentagon.

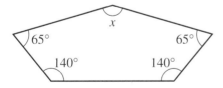

2. (a) Find the sum of the interior angles in a quadrilateral.
   (b) Find the angle a in this diagram.

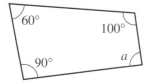

MODULE 5

3. (a) Find the sum of the interior angles in a hexagon.
   (b) Find the angle z in this diagram.

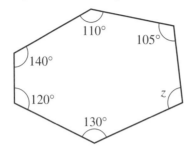

4. (a) Find the sum of the interior angles in an octagon.
   (b) Find the angle y in this diagram.

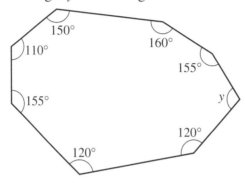

Summary and Checkout AS5

- A right angle is 90°. A straight line is 180°. A circle is 360°. Missing angles can be found in right angles, straight lines and circles.

  1. Find the angles marked with letters.

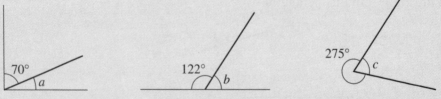

- Two pairs of opposite angles are created when straight lines cross. Pairs of opposite angles are always equal.

  2. Find the angles e, f and g.

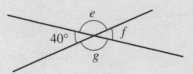

- When a pair of parallel lines is crossed by a third line, two sets of identical opposite angles are formed.

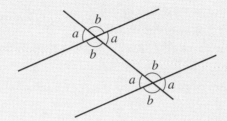

3. Find the angles marked with letters.

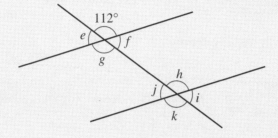

- The three angles in any triangle add up to 180°. If two angles are known, the third angle can be calculated.

4. Find angle *a*.

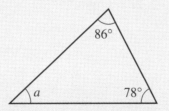

- An **isosceles** triangle has two equal sides and two equal angles. The equal angles are formed between the equal sides and the third side. The equal sides are usually marked with dashes. An **equilateral** triangle has three equal sides and three equal angles of 60°.

5. Find each angle marked with a letter in these diagrams.

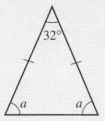

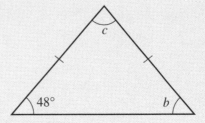

MODULE 5

- A quadrilateral is a shape with four straight sides.

  Some quadrilaterals have special names.

  A quadrilateral with one pair of parallel sides is called a **trapezium**.

  A quadrilateral with two pairs of parallel sides is called a **parallelogram**.

  A quadrilateral with four equal sides is called a **rhombus**.

  A quadrilateral with internal angles of 90° is called a **rectangle**.

  A quadrilateral with four equal sides **and** internal angles of 90° is called a **square**.

6. Lucy is making a decorative surround for a mirror using small mosaic tiles in the shape of quadrilaterals. Draw a possible design. Try to use each type of quadrilateral at least once. Label one of each type of quadrilateral.

- A **polygon** is a shape with straight sides.
  A **triangle** has three sides.
  A **quadrilateral** has four sides.
  A **pentagon** has five sides.
  A **hexagon** has six sides.
  A **heptagon** has seven sides.
  An **octagon** has eight sides.
  A **nonagon** has nine sides.
  A **decagon** has ten sides.
  A **dodecagon** has twelve sides.

  The exterior angles of any polygon add up to 360°.

7. Find the angles p and q in this regular hexagon.

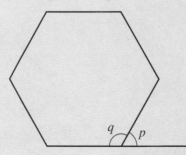

• There is a fixed sum for the interior angles of any polygon.
  You can calculate the sum by dividing the polygon into triangles.

8. (a) Find the sum of the interior angles in a hexagon.
   (b) Find the angle *z* in this diagram.

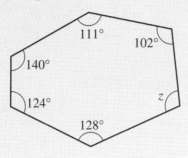

Revision exercise AS5

1. A sketch of a six-sided shape is shown below.

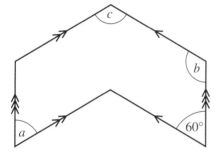

Not drawn to scale

It has three pairs of parallel lines.
An angle of 60° is shown.
Work out the sizes of the angles marked *a*, *b* and *c*.

[NEAB]

2.

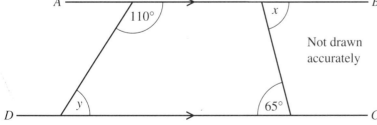

Not drawn
accurately

AB is parallel to *DC*.
(a) Work out the size of angle *x*.
    Give a reason for your answer.
(b) Work out the size of angle *y*.
    Give a reason for your answer.   [NEAB]

3. (a) The diagram shows a rectangle *ABCD*.
M is the mid point of *DC*.
Angle *AMB* = 80°.
AM = *MB*.

Work out the sizes of angles *x* and *y*.

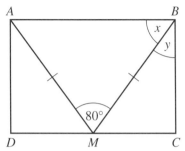

Not to scale

(b) The diagram shows a quadrilateral *PQRS*.
PQ = *QR* and *PS* = *SR*.

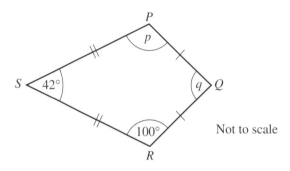

Not to scale

(i) Which of the following correctly describes the
quadrilateral *PQRS*?

Diamond Kite Rhombus Parallelogram Trapezium

(ii) Angle *PSR* = 42° and angle *QRS* = 100°.
Work out the sizes of angles *p* and *q*. [SEG]

4. This is a shape with five sides.
It is made from 5 triangles *A*, *B*, *C*, *D* and *E*.

(a) What is the mathematical name for a
shape with five sides?

(b) Triangles *A*, *B* and *C* are all equilateral
triangles.
What is special about the angles in
equilateral triangles?

(c) Triangles *D* and *E* are congruent.
What does the word congruent mean?

(d) One of the angles in triangle *D* is 30°.
Write down the sizes of the other 2 angles. [NEAB]

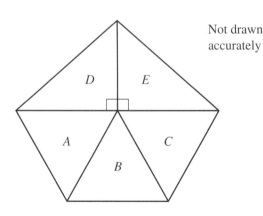

Not drawn
accurately

5. Here are three identical sectors cut out of card.
The angle of each sector is marked *a*.

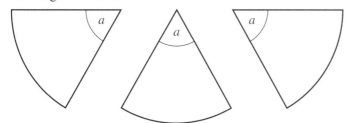

(a) What is the mathematical name for shapes that are identical?

(b) These three sectors fit together to form half a circle.

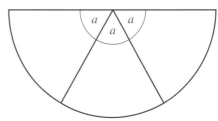

    (i)   Write down the value in degrees of $a + a + a$.

    (ii) Simplify $a + a + a$.

    (iii) Calculate the size of angle *a*.   [NEAB]

6. (a) In the diagram *AB* is parallel to *CD*.

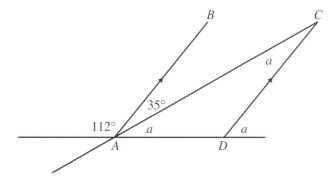

In each case give the size of the angle
(i)   Angle *a*
(ii) Angle *b*
(iii) Angle *c*

(b) The diagram shows a kite.
Give the value of the angle *d*.

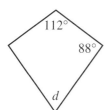

[NEAB]

MODULE 5

AS6 ALGEBRA 2

Equations in algebra are all about balancing.

This unit will show you how to:

- Multiply and divide negative numbers
- Multiply terms of an expression
- Expand brackets and factorise expressions
- Solve equations

Before you start:

You should know how to...	Check in AS6
1. Add and subtract negative numbers. **Remember** $5 + {}^-2 = 5 - 2 = 3$ $5 - {}^-2 = 5 + 2 = 7$ So $+-$ or $-+$ means $-$ and $++$ or $--$ means $+$ **Hint** Use a number line to help you.	**1.** Work out: (a) $7 + 4$ (b) $7 + {}^-4$ (c) ${}^-7 + 4$ (d) ${}^-7 + {}^-4$ (e) $7 - 4$ (f) ${}^-7 - 4$ (g) $7 - {}^-4$ (h) ${}^-7 - {}^-4$
2. Substitute numbers into algebraic expressions. For example If $x = 3$, $y = 4$ and $z = 2$, $xz + \dfrac{y}{z} = 3 \times 2 + \dfrac{4}{2}$ $= 3 \times 2 + 2$ $= 6 + 2 = 8$ **Remember** $\dfrac{y}{z}$ means $y \div z$ and xz means $x \times z$	**2.** If $x = 4$, y $= 5$ and $z = -2$, find the value of: (a) $x + y$ (b) $3x$ (c) $5y$ (d) $7z$ (e) $7x + 3y$ (f) xy (g) x^2 (h) $\dfrac{x}{z}$

6.1 Multiplying negative numbers

A multiplication with one negative and one positive number gives a negative answer.

Example

(a) $4 \times {}^-3 = {}^-12$ (b) ${}^-5 \times 5 = {}^-25$

A multiplication with two negative numbers gives a positive answer.

Example

(a) ${}^-4 \times {}^-3 = 12$ (b) ${}^-5 \times {}^-5 = 25$

Exercise 6A

1. $4 \times {}^-2$	2. $5 \times {}^-3$	3. $2 \times {}^-3$	4. ${}^-3 \times 2$	5. $4 \times {}^-4$
6. $6 \times {}^-3$	7. $8 \times {}^-2$	8. $9 \times {}^-3$	9. $5 \times {}^-4$	10. $6 \times {}^-1$
11. ${}^-3 \times 8$	12. ${}^-2 \times 6$	13. ${}^-7 \times 4$	14. ${}^-8 \times 5$	15. ${}^-9 \times 1$
16. ${}^-7 \times 3$	17. ${}^-8 \times 4$	18. ${}^-7 \times 5$	19. ${}^-9 \times 2$	20. ${}^-10 \times 3$
21. ${}^-3 \times {}^-3$	22. ${}^-3 \times {}^-1$	23. ${}^-1 \times {}^-7$	24. ${}^-8 \times {}^-6$	25. ${}^-9 \times {}^-5$
26. ${}^-9 \times {}^-7$	27. ${}^-4 \times {}^-9$	28. ${}^-5 \times {}^-6$	29. ${}^-5 \times {}^-1$	30. ${}^-7 \times {}^-2$
31. ${}^-9 \times {}^-6$	32. ${}^-6 \times {}^-7$	33. ${}^-8 \times 8$	34. $9 \times {}^-9$	35. ${}^-9 \times 8$
36. ${}^-1 \times {}^-8$	37. $4 \times {}^-6$	38. ${}^-6 \times 6$	39. $2 \times {}^-2$	40. ${}^-7 \times {}^-7$

6.2 Dividing negative numbers

A division with one negative and one positive number gives a negative answer.

Example

(a) ${}^-12 \div 3 = {}^-4$ (b) $24 \div {}^-6 = {}^-4$

A division with two negative numbers gives a positive answer.

Example

(a) ${}^-12 \div {}^-3 = 4$ (b) ${}^-24 \div {}^-6 = 4$

Exercise 6B

1. $^-16 \div 4$	**2.** $^-12 \div 6$	**3.** $^-32 \div 8$	**4.** $^-42 \div 6$	**5.** $^-15 \div 3$
6. $^-56 \div 8$	**7.** $^-24 \div 6$	**8.** $^-9 \div 3$	**9.** $^-27 \div 9$	**10.** $^-45 \div 5$
11. $24 \div {}^-3$	**12.** $63 \div {}^-9$	**13.** $35 \div {}^-7$	**14.** $4 \div {}^-2$	**15.** $81 \div {}^-9$
16. $21 \div {}^-7$	**17.** $20 \div {}^-5$	**18.** $18 \div {}^-2$	**19.** $18 \div {}^-9$	**20.** $14 \div {}^-7$
21. $^-14 \div {}^-7$	**22.** $^-30 \div {}^-6$	**23.** $^-40 \div {}^-8$	**24.** $^-48 \div {}^-6$	**25.** $^-49 \div {}^-7$
26. $^-6 \div {}^-3$	**27.** $^-10 \div {}^-5$	**28.** $^-18 \div {}^-6$	**29.** $^-8 \div {}^-4$	**30.** $^-4 \div {}^-1$
31. $^-5 \div 1$	**32.** $5 \div {}^-1$	**33.** $^-5 \div {}^-1$	**34.** $16 \div {}^-8$	**35.** $^-16 \div 8$
36. $^-16 \div {}^-8$	**37.** $^-36 \div 9$	**38.** $28 \div {}^-7$	**39.** $^-54 \div {}^-9$	**40.** $^-64 \div {}^-8$

6.3 Multiplying letter terms by number terms

To multiply a letter term by a number term, write out in full
what the multiplication means and then simplify.

Example 1

$3 \times 2a = 3 \times 2 \times a = 6 \times a = 6a$

Remember, a multiplication with one negative and one positive
number gives a negative answer.

Example 2

(a) $4 \times {}^-3b = 4 \times {}^-3 \times b = {}^-12 \times b = {}^-12b$

(b) $^-5 \times 6z = {}^-5 \times 6 \times z = {}^-30 \times z = {}^-30z$

Remember, a multiplication with two negative numbers gives a
positive answer.

Example 3

$^-4 \times {}^-3x = {}^-4 \times {}^-3 \times x = 12 \times x = 12x$

Exercise 6C

1. $4 \times 2x$	**2.** $6y \times 3$	**3.** $7 \times 2p$	**4.** $5 \times 5a$	**5.** $6z \times 6$
6. $8u \times 3$	**7.** $5 \times 4m$	**8** $3b \times 7$	**9.** $7q \times 3$	**10.** $6 \times 6w$
11. $4 \times {}^-3e$	**12.** $5 \times {}^-6t$	**13.** $3 \times {}^-2x$	**14.** $3 \times {}^-y$	**15.** $4 \times {}^-u$
16. $5 \times {}^-x$	**17.** $1 \times {}^-a$	**18.** $9 \times {}^-2d$	**19.** $10 \times {}^-4r$	**20.** $6 \times {}^-6y$
21. $^-3 \times 2x$	**22.** $^-4 \times 5c$	**23.** $^-7p \times 6$	**24.** $^-3 \times x$	**25.** $^-4 \times y$
26. $^-z \times 2$	**27.** $^-3 \times 5t$	**28.** $^-1 \times t$	**29.** $^-1 \times x$	**30.** $^-4z \times 4$
31. $^-2 \times {}^-2x$	**32.** $^-3 \times {}^-5m$	**33.** $^-2 \times {}^-6p$	**34.** $^-4x \times {}^-2$	**35.** $^-2y \times {}^-5$
36. $^-1 \times {}^-2t$	**37.** $^-1 \times {}^-t$	**38.** $^-e \times {}^-3$	**39.** $^-e \times {}^-1$	**40.** $^-4 \times {}^-4x$

6.4 Multiplying letter terms by letter terms

To multiply a letter term by a letter term, write out in full what
the multiplication means and then simplify.

Examples

(a) $3x \times 4y = 3 \times x \times 4 \times y = 3 \times 4 \times x \times y = 12 \times x \times y = 12xy$

(b) $8m \times m = 8 \times m \times m = 8 \times m^2 = 8m^2$

(c) $^-3e \times 2f = ^-3 \times e \times 2 \times f = ^-3 \times 2 \times e \times f = ^-6 \times e \times f = ^-6ef$

(d) $^-6x \times ^-x = ^-6 \times x \times ^-1 \times x = ^-6 \times ^-1 \times x \times x = 6 \times x \times x = 6x^2$

Exercise 6D

1. $2a \times 2b$	**2.** $5s \times 3t$	**3.** $4a \times b$	**4.** $7u \times 7v$	**5.** $2c \times 8d$
6. $a \times 6b$	**7.** $7y \times x$	**8.** $5r \times 6s$	**9.** $6x \times 4y$	**10.** $7p \times 5q$
11. $6z \times z$	**12.** $7u \times u$	**13.** $x \times 5x$	**14.** $3a \times 2a$	**15.** $2x \times 2x$
16. $3y \times 3y$	**17.** $4r \times 2r$	**18.** $6e \times 2e$	**19.** $5t \times 5t$	**20.** $3w \times 7w$
21. $^-3a \times 2b$	**22.** $5m \times ^-2n$	**23.** $3a \times ^-b$	**24.** $^-x \times 2y$	**25.** $y \times ^-2x$
26. $^-3z \times 2z$	**27.** $^-3a \times 2a$	**28.** $^-4r \times r$	**29.** $x \times ^-3x$	**30.** $4b \times ^-3b$
31. $^-3e \times ^-2f$	**32.** $^-2x \times ^-4y$	**33.** $^-e \times ^-f$	**34.** $^-r \times ^-s$	**35.** $^-4m \times ^-3n$
36. $^-x \times ^-2x$	**37.** $^-3y \times ^-2y$	**38.** $^-3a \times ^-4a$	**39.** $^-x \times ^-x$	**40.** $^-y \times ^-y \times ^-y$

6.5 Expanding brackets with a number term outside

To **expand** a bracket means to multiply each term in the bracket
by the term outside the bracket.

Examples

(a) $3(a + 5) = 3 \times a + 3 \times 5 = 3a + 15$

(b) $5(2x - 3) = 5 \times 2x - 5 \times 3 = 10x - 15$

(c) $6(2w - 3x) = 6 \times 2w - 6 \times 3x = 12w - 18x$

Exercise 6E

Expand each bracket.

1. $3(x + 2)$	**2.** $5(y + 1)$	**3.** $8(w + 3)$	**4.** $7(3 + e)$	**5.** $6(a + 4)$
6. $4(x - 1)$	**7.** $5(t - 3)$	**8.** $9(e - 5)$	**9.** $3(4 - w)$	**10.** $5(x - 4)$
11. $3(2a + 4)$	**12.** $4(5b + 3)$	**13.** $6(5e + 3)$	**14.** $2(3x + 2)$	**15.** $5(6t + 4)$
16. $7(3r - 4)$	**17.** $8(2x - 3)$	**18.** $2(4 - 3m)$	**19.** $5(1 - w)$	**20.** $6(4 - 2w)$
21. $5(2a + 3b)$	**22.** $6(a + 4b)$	**23.** $7(2x + 2y)$	**24.** $6(3e + 4f)$	**25.** $4(6t + 5u)$
26. $3(4x - 5y)$	**27.** $5(2a - 3b)$	**28.** $5(3b - 2a)$	**29.** $6(2w - 4x)$	**30.** $5(5m - 5n)$

MODULE 5

6.6 Expanding and simplifying

Examples

(a) $2(s + 1) + 3(2s + 5) = 2s + 2 + 6s + 15 = 8s + 17$

(b) $2(3 + y) + 4(2y - 1) = 6 + 2y + 8y - 4 = 10y + 2$

Exercise 6F

Expand each bracket and simplify.

1. $3(x + 2) + 4(x + 3)$
2. $4(y + 3) + 5(y + 1)$
3. $5(2a + 3) + 4(a + 3)$
4. $2(2z + 1) + 5(3 + 4z)$
5. $6(4q + 3) + 3(2q + 2)$
6. $3(x + 3) + 2(2x + 5)$
7. $4(2w + 1) + 3(2w + 1)$
8. $2(2w + 4) + 3(4 + 3w)$
9. $5(2w + 3) + 4(w - 2)$
10. $6(x + 3) + 3(x - 6)$
11. $5(x + 3) + 2(x - 5)$
12. $4(a + 3) + 2(a - 5)$
13. $5(2w + 1) + 4(2w - 2)$
14. $4(3e + 2) + 3(e - 3)$
15. $2(2x - 1) + 3(x + 1)$
16. $2(2x - 1) + 3(x - 1)$
17. $4(2y - 3) + (3y + 5)$
18. $3(2x - 4) + 2(x + 1)$
19. $5(2w - 2) + 3(w - 2)$
20. $4(2z - 3) + 5(3z - 2)$

6.7 Expanding brackets with a letter term outside

Examples

(a) $m(8 + 3n) = m \times 8 + m \times 3n = 8m + 3mn$

(b) $a(a - 5) = a \times a - a \times 5 = a^2 - 5a$

(c) $2x(3x + 2y) = 2x \times 3x + 2x \times 2y = 6x^2 + 4xy$

Exercise 6G

Expand each bracket.

1. $b(3 + 5a)$
2. $a(5 - 3b)$
3. $y(2 - 5x)$
4. $x(x + 2)$
5. $y(y + 7)$
6. $z(2z + 1)$
7. $m(2m - 1)$
8. $d(3 + 2d)$
9. $a(5a - 3)$
10. $2b(b - 1)$
11. $b(2b - 2)$
12. $3s(s - 1)$
13. $5r(2r + 3)$
14. $a(1 + b)$
15. $x(2 - y)$
16. $a(a + b)$
17. $d(d + 2e)$
18. $m(3 - 2n)$
19. $2a(3a + 4b)$
20. $2x(4y + 6x)$
21. $3u(2v + 3u)$
22. $4r(4r + 2s)$
23. $r(16r - 8s)$
24. $2x(5x - 3y)$
25. $4p(3q - 2p)$

6.8 Expanding brackets with negative terms

Take extra care when there is a negative term outside a bracket.

Examples

(a) $^-2(2x + 7) = {^-2} \times 2x + {^-2} \times 7 = {^-4x} - 14$

(b) $^-4(2a - 7) = {^-4} \times 2a - {^-4} \times 7 = {^-8a} - {^-28} = {^-8a} + 28 = 28 - 8a$

(c) $^-(3a + 2b) = {^-1} \times (3a + 2b) = {^-1} \times 3a + {^-1} \times 2b = {^-3a} - 2b$

(d) $^-m(2m - 3n) = {^-m} \times 2m - {^-m} \times 3n = {^-2m^2} - {^-3mn} = {^-2m^2} + 3mn = 3mn - 2m^2$

Exercise 6H

Expand each bracket.

1. $^-2(a + 3)$	2. $^-4(x + 1)$	3. $^-2(2b + 3)$	4. $^-2(3 + 2z)$
5. $^-5(4 + 6t)$	6. $^-9(2w + 1)$	7. $^-2(5 + 5r)$	8. $^-6(2b + 2)$
9. $^-3(x + 5)$	10. $^-7(1 + x)$	11. $^-2(x - 1)$	12. $^-2(1 - x)$
13. $^-4(s - 1)$	14. $^-4(1 - s)$	15. $^-3(2w - 1)$	16. $^-4(1 - 2w)$
17. $^-5(3x - 5)$	18. $^-5(5 - 3x)$	19. $^-4(2p - 3)$	20. $^-4(3 - 2p)$
21. $^-(x + 2)$	22. $^-(y + 3)$	23. $^-(a + b)$	24. $^-(2a + 3b)$
25. $^-(2x + y)$	26. $^-(x - 1)$	27. $^-(y - 2x)$	28. $^-(2a - 3b)$
29. $^-(3x - 2y)$	30. $^-(3p - 5q)$	31. $^-a(a + b)$	32. $^-x(2x + y)$
33. $^-d(3 + 2d)$	34. $^-v(4v + 2)$	35. $^-s(2s + t)$	36. $^-t(t - s)$
37. $^-2w(2w - 3)$	38. $^-4x(2x - 2y)$	39. $^-2a(3a - 3b)$	40. $^-5m(2n - 4m)$

6.9 Factorisation by extracting a number term outside a bracket

Look at the expression $4x + 6$.

The terms $4x$ and 6 have 2 as a common factor. This means you can write the expression using a bracket:

$$4x + 6 = 2(2x + 3)$$

This is called **factorising** the expression. You can test each answer by expanding the bracket again.

Examples

(a) $6y + 12 = 6(y + 2)$ Test: $6(y + 2) = 6y + 12$

(b) $10a - 15 = 5(2a - 3)$ Test: $5(2a - 3) = 10a - 15$

MODULE 5

Exercise 6I

Factorise each expression.

1. $3x + 9$	**2.** $5x + 15$	**3.** $6a + 18$	**4.** $4m + 12$	**5.** $7b + 14$
6. $4r - 16$	**7.** $5t - 20$	**8.** $9w - 18$	**9.** $3w - 15$	**10.** $4y - 24$
11. $3w + 21$	**12.** $6m - 36$	**13.** $7y + 21$	**14.** $11a - 22$	**15.** $12w + 24$
16. $6e + 9$	**17.** $8u + 12$	**18.** $15a + 20$	**19.** $12b + 18$	**20.** $12w + 15$
21. $12y - 16$	**22.** $20v - 25$	**23.** $18c - 24$	**24.** $6t - 15$	**25.** $14m - 21$
26. $15x + 18$	**27.** $16t - 24$	**28.** $30r + 35$	**29.** $30p - 12$	**30.** $28z + 21$

6.10 Factorisation by extracting a letter term outside a bracket

Examples

(a) $x + 2xy = x(1 + 2y)$ Test: $x(1 + 2y) = x + 2xy$

(b) $9x + 6xy = x(9 + 6y) = 3x(3 + 2y)$ Test: $3x(3 + 2y) = 9x + 6xy$

(c) $a^2 + ab = a(a + b)$ Test: $a(a + b) = a^2 + ab$

Exercise 6J

Factorise each expression.

1. $a + ab$	**2.** $2x + xy$	**3.** $3p + 5pq$	**4.** $3t + 2st$	**5.** $5a + 7ab$
6. $6xy + x$	**7.** $4st + 3t$	**8.** $5e - 4ef$	**9.** $7u - 5uv$	**10.** $3ab - 5b$
11. $6ab + 9a$	**12.** $8u + 12uv$	**13.** $15e + 20ef$	**14.** $9x + 12xy$	**15.** $12r + 16rs$
16. $20xy - 25y$	**17.** $18ab - 12b$	**18.** $4yz - 6y$	**19.** $15e - 12ef$	**20.** $20pq - 30q$
21. $x^2 + xy$	**22.** $x^3 + xy$	**23.** $2ab + a^2$	**24.** $5st + t^2$	**25.** $5st + 10t^2$
26. $x^2 + 2xy$	**27.** $2x^2 + 2xy$	**28.** $2x^2 + 4xy$	**29.** $7a^3 + 14ab$	**30.** $2ab + 3a^2b$

6.11 Solving equations by subtracting

An **equation** is a statement about the value of a letter.
For example this equation:

$$x + 5 = 20$$

means that if you add 5 to the value of the letter x you will get the answer 20.

You **solve** an equation by working out the value of the letter.

To help solve an equation, you can **subtract any number from both sides of the equation**.

Example 1

Solve the equation:	$x + 5 = 20$
Subtract 5 from both sides:	$x + 5 - 5 = 20 - 5$
This gives the solution:	$x = 15$

Example 2

Solve the equation:	$a + 30 = 20$
Subtract 30 from both sides:	$a + 30 - 30 = 20 - 30$
This gives the solution:	$a = {}^-10$

Exercise 6K

Solve the equations.

1. $x + 7 = 11$	**2.** $y + 9 = 12$	**3.** $a + 7 = 14$
4. $s + 8 = 9$	**5.** $x + 7 = 8$	**6.** $y + 4 = 4$
7. $c + 15 = 23$	**8.** $z + 11 = 23$	**9.** $f + 5 = 50$
10. $m + 6 = 14$	**11.** $x + 3 = 2$	**12.** $y + 7 = 3$
13. $a + 5 = 0$	**14.** $e + 9 = 3$	**15.** $t + 8 = 3$
16. $x + 7 = 1$	**17.** $d + 2 = {}^-2$	**18.** $z + 3 = {}^-4$
19. $y + 4 = 0$	**20.** $d + 7 = {}^-1$	

6.12 Solving equations by adding

To help solve an equation, you can **add any number to both sides of the equation**.

Example 1

Solve the equation:	$x - 5 = 20$
Add 5 to both sides:	$x - 5 + 5 = 20 + 5$
This gives the solution:	$x = 25$

Example 2

Solve the equation:	$a - 30 = {}^-20$
Add 30 to both sides:	$a - 30 + 30 = {}^-20 + 30$
This gives the solution:	$a = 10$

Exercise 6L

Solve the equations.

1. $x - 5 = 15$	**2.** $e - 7 = 10$	**3.** $a - 8 = 3$
4. $z - 5 = 0$	**5.** $t - 9 = 1$	**6.** $u - 5 = 5$
7. $d - 5 = 3$	**8.** $r - 20 = 1$	**9.** $x - 7 = 0$
10. $d - 6 = 16$	**11.** $d - 5 = {}^-1$	**12.** $x - 6 = {}^-2$
13. $t - 5 = {}^-3$	**14.** $y - 7 = {}^-7$	**15.** $u - 9 = {}^-3$
16. $x - 2 = {}^-2$	**17.** $b - 4 = {}^-10$	**18.** $z - 3 = {}^-4$
19. $p - 1 = {}^-6$	**20.** $g - 3 = {}^-6$	

6.13 Solving equations by dividing

To help solve an equation, you can **divide both sides of the equation by any number.**

Remember, a division with one negative and one positive number gives a negative answer.

Example 1

(a) $^-12 \div 3 = {}^-4$ (b) $24 \div {}^-6 = {}^-4$

Remember, a division with two negative numbers gives a positive answer.

Example 2

(a) $^-12 \div {}^-3 = 4$ (b) $^-24 \div {}^-6 = 4$

Example 3

Solve the equation: $3x = 15$

Divide both sides by 3: $\dfrac{3x}{3} = \dfrac{15}{3}$

This gives the solution: $x = 5$

Example 4

Solve the equation: $^-2x = 14$

Divide both sides by $^-2$: $\dfrac{^-2x}{^-2} = \dfrac{14}{^-2}$

This gives the solution: $x = {}^-7$

Example 5

Solve the equation: $\qquad\qquad {}^-x = {}^-8$

Divide both sides by $^-1$: $\qquad \dfrac{{}^-x}{{}^-1} = \dfrac{{}^-8}{{}^-1}$

This gives the solution: $\qquad x = 8$

Exercise 6M

Solve the equations.

1. $4x = 16$	**2.** $5r = 25$	**3.** $2w = 18$	**4.** $6y = 36$	**5.** $5m = 30$
6. $2a = 16$	**7.** $7u = 21$	**8.** $8y = 24$	**9.** $5t = 40$	**10.** $4c = 12$
11. $^-4y = 20$	**12.** $^-9x = 27$	**13.** $^-6t = 30$	**14.** $^-2x = 18$	**15.** $^-7u = 28$
16. $6y = {}^-18$	**17.** $4r = {}^-32$	**18.** $3y = {}^-15$	**19.** $2z = {}^-20$	**20.** $6t = {}^-6$
21. $^-4x = {}^-8$	**22.** $^-3x = {}^-27$	**23.** $^-5f = {}^-40$	**24.** $^-8v = {}^-16$	**25.** $^-9x = {}^-36$
26. $^-x = {}^-7$	**27.** $^-a = {}^-21$	**28.** $^-s = 7$	**29.** $^-3r = 30$	**30.** $^-2m = {}^-40$

6.14 Solving equations by multiplying

To help solve an equation, you can **multiply both sides of the equation by any number.**

Remember, a multiplication with one negative and one positive number gives a negative answer.

Example 1

(a) $^-4 \times 3 = {}^-12$ (b) $6 \times {}^-4 = {}^-24$

Remember, a multiplication with two negative numbers gives a positive answer.

Example 2

(a) $^-4 \times {}^-3 = 12$ (b) $^-6 \times {}^-4 = 24$

Example 3

Solve the equation: $\qquad\qquad \dfrac{x}{3} = 4$

Multiply both sides by 3: $\qquad \dfrac{x}{3} \times 3 = 4 \times 3$

This gives the solution: $\qquad\qquad x = 12$

MODULE 5

Example 4

Solve the equation: $\dfrac{x}{-2} = 5$

Multiply both sides by $^-2$: $\dfrac{x}{-2} \times ^-2 = 5 \times ^-2$

This gives the solution: $x = ^-10$

Example 5

Solve the equation: $\dfrac{w}{-3} = ^-5$

Multiply both sides by $^-3$: $\dfrac{w}{-3} \times ^-3 = ^-5 \times ^-3$

This gives the solution: $w = 15$

Exercise 6N

Solve the equations.

1. $\dfrac{x}{4} = 4$　　2. $\dfrac{c}{5} = 3$　　3. $\dfrac{a}{6} = 2$　　4. $\dfrac{t}{7} = 1$

5. $\dfrac{y}{3} = 3$　　6. $\dfrac{m}{7} = 5$　　7. $\dfrac{x}{6} = 8$　　8. $\dfrac{z}{2} = 5$

9. $\dfrac{t}{4} = 6$　　10. $\dfrac{h}{9} = 5$　　11. $\dfrac{j}{5} = ^-4$　　12. $\dfrac{y}{3} = ^-5$

13. $\dfrac{z}{6} = ^-7$　　14. $\dfrac{d}{3} = ^-1$　　15. $\dfrac{r}{2} = ^-9$　　16. $\dfrac{d}{8} = ^-1$

17. $\dfrac{y}{-5} = 6$　　18. $\dfrac{u}{-2} = 15$　　19. $\dfrac{x}{-3} = 10$　　20. $\dfrac{t}{-1} = 12$

21. $\dfrac{x}{-2} = ^-9$　　22. $\dfrac{z}{-3} = ^-8$　　23. $\dfrac{r}{-5} = ^-9$　　24. $\dfrac{m}{-9} = ^-5$

25. $\dfrac{s}{-2} = ^-10$　　26. $\dfrac{e}{8} = 7$　　27. $\dfrac{e}{-8} = 7$　　28. $\dfrac{e}{8} = ^-7$

29. $\dfrac{e}{-8} = ^-7$　　30. $\dfrac{a}{6} = ^-8$

6.15 Equations which require several operations to solve them

Example 1

Solve the equation: $\qquad 2x + 7 = 29$

Subtract 7 from both sides: $\qquad 2x + 7 - 7 = 29 - 7$

This gives: $\qquad 2x = 22$

Divide both sides by 2: $\qquad \dfrac{2x}{2} = \dfrac{22}{2}$

This gives the solution: $\qquad x = 11$

Example 2

Solve the equation: $\qquad 30 - 5x = 5$

Subtract 30 from both sides: $\quad 30 - 5x - 30 = 5 - 30$

This gives: $\qquad {}^{-}5x = {}^{-}25$

Divide both sides by $^{-}5$: $\qquad \dfrac{{}^{-}5x}{{}^{-}5} = \dfrac{{}^{-}25}{{}^{-}5}$

This gives the solution: $\qquad x = 5$

Example 3

Solve the equation: $\qquad \dfrac{x}{5} - 7 = 1$

Add 7 to both sides: $\qquad \dfrac{x}{5} - 7 + 7 = 1 + 7$

This gives: $\qquad \dfrac{x}{5} = 8$

Multiply both sides by 5: $\qquad \dfrac{x}{5} \times 5 = 8 \times 5$

This gives the solution: $\qquad x = 40$

Exercise 6O

Solve the equations.

1. $2x + 3 = 15$ 2. $3x + 1 = 13$ 3. $5a + 7 = 42$
4. $3e + 2 = 8$ 5. $4m + 5 = 9$ 6. $7s + 4 = 18$
7. $3p + 5 = 23$ 8. $3x + 3 = 12$ 9. $5s + 2 = 42$

MODULE 5

10. $6y + 7 = 13$ **11.** $8y - 1 = 31$ **12.** $2x - 4 = 2$

13. $3a - 8 = 4$ **14.** $5z - 3 = 27$ **15.** $8x - 6 = 10$

16. $2x - 7 = 13$ **17.** $5p - 3 = 27$ **18.** $3m - 12 = 3$

19. $3t - 6 = {}^{-}3$ **20.** $4x - 10 = {}^{-}2$ **21.** $17 - 2x = 1$

22. $12 - 4x = 4$ **23.** $20 - 3a = 2$ **24.** $18 - 5x = 8$

25. $15 - 9z = 6$ **26.** $7 - 2q = 9$ **27.** $11 - 3y = 17$

28. $15 - 3z = 6$ **29.** $24 - 2m = 0$ **30.** $6 - 4y = 18$

31. $\dfrac{a}{4} + 1 = 3$ **32.** $\dfrac{z}{3} - 2 = 1$ **33.** $\dfrac{p}{4} + 5 = 10$

34. $\dfrac{q}{6} - 1 = 1$ **35.** $\dfrac{x}{5} + 7 = 8$ **36.** $\dfrac{y}{3} - 2 = 3$

37. $\dfrac{a}{4} + 3 = 2$ **38.** $\dfrac{x}{7} + 4 = 2$ **39.** $\dfrac{2x}{3} + 4 = 10$

40. $\dfrac{5x}{4} - 7 = 8$

6.16 Equations with brackets

Example

Solve the equation: $\qquad\qquad 3(2x + 5) = 21$

Expand the bracket: $\qquad\qquad 6x + 15 = 21$

Subtract 15 from both sides: $\quad 6x + 15 - 15 = 21 - 15$

This gives: $\qquad\qquad\qquad 6x = 6$

Divide both sides by 6: $\qquad \dfrac{6x}{6} = \dfrac{6}{6}$

This gives the solution: $\qquad\qquad x = 1$

Exercise 6P

Solve the equations.

1. $2(x + 1) = 12$ **2.** $2(a + 3) = 14$ **3.** $5(z + 4) = 25$

4. $6(3 + m) = 30$ **5.** $7(2 + p) = 14$ **6.** $3(z - 2) = 18$

7. $5(t - 3) = 20$ **8.** $2(x - 5) = 0$ **9.** $4(t + 1) = 16$

10. $7(q - 2) = 14$ **11.** $5(2x - 1) = 35$ **12.** $4(2a + 2) = 32$

13. $5(3z + 4) = 35$ **14.** $6(2 + 3s) = 48$ **15.** $3(3 + 2x) = 33$

16. $4(2x - 1) = 44$ **17.** $2(3x - 7) = 4$ **18.** $4(5a - 9) = 24$

19. $2(4y - 5) = {}^-2$ **20.** $3(5z - 8) = 6$ **21.** $4(3 - x) = 4$

22. $5(6 - x) = 10$ **23.** $7(8 - y) = 14$ **24.** $4(9 - y) = 20$

25. $2(8 - y) = 12$ **26.** $2(8 - y) = 20$ **27.** $3(4 - 2x) = 6$

28. $4(15 - 3a) = 12$ **29.** $3(8 - 2y) = 30$ **30.** $4(2 - 3y) = 44$

6.17 Equations with letter terms on both sides

Sometimes there are letter terms on both sides of an equation.
The first step is to get all the letter terms on one side.

Example 1

Solve the equation:	$11a - 5 = a + 25$
Subtract a from both sides:	$11a - 5 - a = a + 25 - a$
This gives:	$10a - 5 = 25$
Adding 5 to both sides gives:	$10a = 30$
Dividing both sides by 10 gives:	$a = 3$

Example 2

Solve the equation:	$3p + 2 = 18 - 5p$
Add $5p$ to both sides:	$3p + 2 + 5p = 18 - 5p + 5p$
This gives:	$8p + 2 = 18$
Subtracting 2 from both sides gives:	$8p = 16$
Dividing both sides by 8 gives:	$p = 2$

Exercise 6Q

Solve the equations.

1. $7p - 11 = 2p + 4$ **2.** $5a + 3 = a + 11$

3. $12w - 7 = 10w - 1$ **4.** $5t = 8 - 3t$

5. $2w - 7 = 8 - 3w$ **6.** $12x + 4 = 32 - 2x$

7. $x - 13 = 8 - 3x$ **8.** $c + 7 = 70 - 8c$

9. $3a - 5 = 2a + 8$ **10.** $8 - 2w = 38 - 7w$

11. $4 - s = 15 - 2s$ **12.** $3e = 8 - 5e$

13. $x = 28 - 6x$ **14.** $3x + 28 = 4 - 9x$

MODULE 5

15. $5b - 18 = 4 - 2b$ 16. $x + 7 = 2x + 8$

17. $x + 8 = 2x + 7$ 18. $2z - 5 = 3z + 9$

19. $4q - 5 = 5q - 9$ 20. $7t - 18 = 10t - 3$

21. $8 - 3b = 5b - 7$ 22. $2 - x = 4x + 12$

23. $13 - 5m = 2m - 1$ 24. $18 - 7q = 3q + 19$

25. $14 - 2k = k - 1$ 26. $3(x + 5) = 4x + 3$

27. $5(2s - 1) = 8s + 1$ 28. $3(2w - 1) = 5(w + 1)$

29. $7(3y - 5) = 2(5y - 1)$ 30. $5(6y - 4) = 2(3y + 4)$

6.18 Changing the subject of formulae

In the formula $P = 2(l + w)$ the subject is P.

You can change the subject of any formula, but you must use the rules of algebra.

Example 1

Make w the subject of the formula $\longrightarrow$ $P = 2(l + w)$

- **Step 1** Deal with any fractions or brackets. $P = 2l + 2w$

- **Step 2** Get the term with the new subject on its own on one side of the formula. $P - 2l = 2w$

- **Step 3** Divide both sides by 2 to get the subject. $\dfrac{P - 2l}{2} = w$

w is now the subject of the formula.

Example 2

Make g the subject of the formula $\longrightarrow$ $t = 2\pi\sqrt{\dfrac{l}{g}}$

- **Step 1** Deal with the $\sqrt{\ }$ by squaring both sides. $t^2 = \dfrac{4\pi^2 l}{g}$

- **Step 2** Deal with the fraction by $\times$ both sides by g. $gt^2 = 4\pi^2 l$

- **Step 3** Divide both sides by t^2 to get the subject. $g = \dfrac{4\pi^2 l}{t^2}$

g is now the subject of the formula.

(The subject of the formula can be written on the LHS or the RHS.)

Exercise 6R

1. Make y the subject of each of these formulas.

    (a) $3x = y - 5$ (b) $3y = 3x - 2$ (c) $2 = 3x + y$

    (d) $2x - 3y = 5$ (e) $2x = 3 + 2y$ (f) $2a = b(2y + 1)$

2. A formula used to calculate velocity is:

$$v = u + ft$$

> Give all answers correct
> to 2 dp.

  (a) Make t the subject of the formula.
  (b) Find a value for t when: $v = 34.5$, $u = 6.75$ and $f = 2.62$
  (c) Calculate a value for u when: $v = 175.4$, $f = 28.6$ and $t = 4.5$

3. Velocity can be calculated with this formula:

$$v^2 = u^2 + 2fs$$

  (a) Make s the subject of the formula.
  (b) Calculate a value for s when: $v = 11.6$, $u = 0.8$ and $f = 4.65$
  (c) Make v the subject of the formula.
  (d) Calculate a value for v when: $u = 0.88$, $f = 16.5$ and $s = 100.8$
  (e) Make u the subject of the formula.
  (f) Calculate a value for u when: $v = 15.65$, $f = 3.4$ and $s = 7.3$

Summary

1. A multiplication or division with one negative number gives a negative answer. A multiplication or division with two negative numbers gives a positive answer.

2. You can multiply letter terms by number terms.

3. You can multiply letter terms by letter terms.

4. You can expand brackets.

Checkout AS6

1. Calculate.
 (a) 5×4 (b) $^-5 \times 3$ (c) $4 \times ^-2$
 (d) $^-3 \times ^-8$ (e) $9 \times ^-2$ (f) $^-4 \times 4$
 (g) $^-6 \times ^-6$ (h) 7×2 (i) $18 \div ^-2$
 (j) $12 \div 3$ (k) $^-15 \div 5$ (l) $^-21 \div ^-7$
 (m) $^-30 \div 10$ (n) $^-25 \div ^-5$ (o) $8 \times ^-2$
 (p) $32 \div 4$

2. Calculate.
 (a) $3 \times 4d$ (b) $5x \times 6$ (c) $2 \times 9w$
 (d) $4 \times 5y$ (e) $^-2 \times 3e$ (f) $6y \times ^-1$
 (g) $^-4r \times 5$ (h) $^-3 \times ^-2x$

3. Calculate.
 (a) $2x \times 3y$ (b) $4r \times 5s$ (c) $2w \times 3y$
 (d) $a \times 5b$ (e) $^-2e \times 3f$ (f) $3x \times ^-2y$
 (g) $^-5t \times ^-3s$ (h) $4r \times r$ (i) $3x \times 2x$
 (j) $^-2y \times y$ (k) $^-5t \times ^-3t$ (l) $x \times ^-7x$

4. Expand these brackets.
 (a) $4(x+2)$ (b) $3(x-1)$ (c) $6(2x+3)$
 (d) $2(5t-1)$ (e) $6(3-5j)$ (f) $5(2a+3c)$
 (g) $6(2x+y)$ (h) $3(3u-2v)$ (i) $x(x+1)$
 (j) $d(d+e)$ (k) $z(2z+5)$ (l) $x(x+y)$
 (m) $s(2s+3t)$ (n) $p(2q-3p)$ (o) $3c(c+2d)$
 (p) $4y(2x-3y)$

MODULE 5

5. You can expand brackets with a negative term outside.

5. Expand these brackets.

   (a) $^-2(x + 1)$ (b) $^-3(z + 4)$ (c) $^-4(2x + 3)$
   (d) $^-7(x + 2)$ (e) $^-3(x - 1)$ (f) $^-2(2x - 4)$
   (g) $^-5(4 - x)$ (h) $^-6(2 - 5x)$ (i) $^-(y + 4)$
   (j) $^-(2x - 6)$ (k) $^-(a + b)$ (l) $^-(a - b)$
   (m) $^-x(x + 3)$ (n) $^-y(y - 2)$ (o) $^-2s(1 - s)$
   (p) $^-4t(2p - 3t)$

6. You can factorise by extracting a number term outside a bracket.

6. Factorise.

   (a) $3x + 9$ (b) $5t + 15$ (c) $4m - 20$
   (d) $7t - 14$ (e) $15x + 40$ (f) $9r + 24$
   (g) $12x - 15$ (h) $20p - 30$

7. You can factorise by extracting a letter term outside a bracket.

7. Factorise.

   (a) $x + xy$ (b) $cd + 2d$ (c) $3ab - 2b$
   (d) $4f - 2ef$ (e) $2x^2 + x$ (f) $3x^2 + 2x$
   (g) $2ab - a^2$ (h) $5x - 10xy$

8. You can solve equations by subtracting.

8. Solve.

   (a) $x + 5 = 30$ (b) $r + 7 = 7$ (c) $y + 13 = {}^-13$

9. You can solve equations by adding.

9. Solve.

   (a) $c - 7 = 3$ (b) $u - 5 = 2$ (c) $m - 5 = {}^-1$

10. You can solve equations by dividing.

10. Solve.

   (a) $3m = 30$ (b) $8t = 16$ (c) $5x = {}^-40$

11. You can solve equations by multiplying.

11. Solve.

   (a) $\dfrac{x}{3} = 4$ (b) $\dfrac{n}{5} = 2$ (c) $\dfrac{v}{4} = {}^-5$

12. You can solve equations which require several operations.

12. Solve.

   (a) $2x + 5 = 11$ (b) $3e - 8 = 22$ (c) $7 - 2e = 1$
   (d) $\dfrac{x}{5} + 1 = 4$ (e) $\dfrac{m}{3} - 1 = 9$ (f) $\dfrac{2c}{3} + 3 = 7$

13. You can solve equations with brackets.

13. Solve.

   (a) $3(x + 1) = 18$ (b) $5(2x - 3) = 25$
   (c) $3(10 - 2y) = 6$ (d) $4(2 - 2e) = 16$

14. You can solve equations with letter terms on both sides.

14. Solve.

   (a) $2x + 1 = x + 4$ (b) $3y + 2 = y + 8$
   (c) $5t - 4 = 2t + 8$ (d) $5(x + 1) = 6x + 1$

MODULE 5

Revision exercise AS6

1. Solve the following equations:
(a) $4x + 6 = 11$
(b) $2(5 + 2x) = 16$ [NEAB]

2. Solve these equations:
(a) $x - 2 = 5$
(b) $5x = 10$ [SEG]

3. Solve the equations:
(a) $2x + 10 = 29$
(b) $5x - 4 = 8 - x$ [NEAB]

4. Solve the equations:
(a) $5x - 3 = 7$
(b) $5x + 5 = 7 + x$ [NEAB]

5. Solve the equations:
(a) $5x - 2 = 13$
(b) $3(2x - 1) = 9$ [SEG]

6. Solve the equation $7 - 2x = 9$ [SEG]

7. Solve these equations:
(i) $4m = 35$
(ii) $3n - 5 = 76$
(iii) $3(p + 4) = 20 + 2p$ [SEG]

8. Solve the equations:
(a) $2x + 10 = 19$
(b) $5x + 2 = 14 - x$ [NEAB]

9. Adrian has three regular polygons, A, B and C.

A has x sides.
B has $(2x - 1)$ sides.
C has $(2x + 2)$ sides.

(a) Write an expression in terms of x, for the total number of sides of these three polygons.
Write your answer in its simplest form.
The three polygons have a total of 16 sides.

(b) (i) Form an equation and hence find the value of x.
(ii) Use your value of x to find the number of sides of polygon B. [SEG]

MODULE 5

10. The angles of a triangle are $4x + 3$, $4x - 8$ and $5x + 3$ degrees.

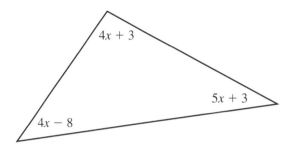

(a) Write down and simplify an equation, in terms of x, for the sum of the angles.

(b) Find the value of the largest angle in the triangle.   [NEAB]

11. Solve the equations:
   (a) $2x + 3 = 11$,
   (b) $3y + 7 = 1 - y$.   [SEG]

AS7 ALGEBRA 3

Algebra can be used to describe patterns found in nature.

The number of seeds in a sunflower 'spiral' is always a term in the Fibonnaci sequence:

1, 1, 2, 3, 5, 8, ...

The next term in the sequence is the sum of the previous two terms:

5 + 8 = 13 is the next term.

This unit will show you how to:

- Describe and continue a sequence of numbers
- Find a formula for the nth term of a sequence
- Draw a graph of a linear equation
- Recognise graphs of equations which produce curves
- Use distance and time graphs

Before you start:

<table>
<tr><td>You should know how to...</td><td>Check in AS7</td></tr>
<tr>
<td>

1. Use a formula.
   For example, for the formula
   $$y = mx + c, \text{ if } m = 2, x = 3 \text{ and } c = -4$$
   then $y = 2 \times 3 + -4$
   $= 6 - 4$
   $= 2$

</td>
<td>

1. If $x = 4$, $y = 2$ and $z = {}^{-}3$ find the value of t if:
   (a) $t = x + y$ (b) $t = 2y$
   (c) $t = 5x + 1$ (d) $t = 3x - 2y$
   (e) $t = y^2$ (f) $t = xy + z$

</td>
</tr>
<tr>
<td>

2. Solve equations.
   For example if
   $$3n + 1 = 4$$
   Take 1 from both sides.
   $$3n = 4 - 1$$
   so $3n = 3$
   Divide both sides by 3
   and $n = 3 \div 3$
   so $n = 1$

</td>
<td>

2. Solve:
   (a) $3x = 12$ (b) $4 + y = 7$
   (c) $\frac{y}{5} = 4$ (d) $t - 7 = 1$
   (e) $2t + 1 = 11$ (f) $4r - 3 = 25$
   (g) $x + 3 = 2x$ (h) $3n + 1 = n + 3$

</td>
</tr>
</table>

7.1 Producing a sequence of numbers

If you start with the number 1 and keep adding 2, you get
the numbers:

$$1, 3, 5, 7, 9, 11, 13, 15, 17, 19, 21 \ldots$$

A set of numbers like this is called a **sequence**. Each number is
called a **term** of the sequence. The way each new number is
found is called the **rule** for the sequence.

Example

The first number in a sequence is 2, the rule for forming new
numbers is to multiply by 2. Write down the first 5 terms of the
sequence.

The first 5 terms are: 2, 4, 8, 16, 32

Exercise 7A

Write down the first 5 terms of each sequence.

1. The first number is 2, the rule is to add 3.
2. The first number is 1, the rule is to multiply by 3.
3. The first number is 5, the rule is to add 4.
4. The first number is 2, the rule is to add 4.
5. The first number is 100, the rule is to subtract 3.
6. The first number is 6, the rule is to add 5.
7. The first number is 1, the rule is to multiply by 4.
8. The first number is 2, the rule is to add 5.
9. The first number is 3, the rule is to add 6.
10. The first number is 1, the rule is to add 7.
11. The first number is 100, the rule is to subtract 10.
12. The first two numbers are 1 and 1, the rule is to add the two previous terms.

7.2 Finding the next terms in a sequence

You may be asked to write down the next terms in a sequence.
Look carefully at the terms you are given to discover the rule.
Use the rule to produce the number of new terms required.

Examples

Find the next two terms in each sequence.

(a) 2, 9, 16, 23, 30 …

   The rule is to add 7. The next two terms are 37 and 44.

(b) 3, 6, 12, 24, 48 …

The rule is to multiply by 2. The next two terms are 96 and 192.

(c) 100, 95, 90, 85, 80 …

The rule is to subtract 5. The next two terms are 75 and 70.

Exercise 7B

Write down the next two terms in each sequence.

1. 7, 12, 17, 22, 27 … **2.** 110, 100, 90, 80, 70 …
3. 1, 5, 25, 125, 625 … **4.** 5, 9, 13, 17, 21 …
5. 3, 4, 7, 11, 18 … **6.** 9, 11, 13, 15, 17 …
7. 1 024, 512, 256, 128, 64 … **8.** 1, 2, 4, 7, 11 …
9. 1, 3, 9, 27, 81 … **10.** 8, 11, 14, 17, 20 …
11. 60, 56, 52, 48, 44 … **12.** 3, 18, 33, 48, 63 …
13. 1 000, 100, 10, 1, 0.1 … **14.** 7, 19, 31, 43, 55 …
15. 13, 19, 25, 31, 37 … **16.** 1, 2, 3, 5, 8 …
17. 1, 3, 6, 10, 15 … **18.** 1, 12, 23, 34, 45 …
19. 0.002, 0.02, 0.2, 2, 20 … **20.** 8, 4, 2, 1, 0.5 …

7.3 Using a formula for the *n*th term of a sequence

The sequence 1, 2, 3, 4, 5, 6, 7 … is called the sequence of natural numbers. The natural numbers can be used to number the terms of any other sequence. For example, the terms of the sequence 1, 4, 7, 10, 13 … can be numbered like this:

1st	2nd	3rd	4th	5th
1	4	7	10	13

The sequence 1, 4, 7, 10, 13 … can be formed from the natural numbers by multiplying each natural number by 3 and then subtracting 2.

$$\begin{aligned}
\text{1st term} &= 3 \times 1 - 2 = 1 \\
\text{2nd term} &= 3 \times 2 - 2 = 4 \\
\text{3rd term} &= 3 \times 3 - 2 = 7 \\
\text{4th term} &= 3 \times 4 - 2 = 10 \\
\text{5th term} &= 3 \times 5 - 2 = 13
\end{aligned}$$

A formula for the sequence can be written like this:

$$\begin{aligned}
n\text{th term} &= 3 \times n - 2 \\
&= 3n - 2
\end{aligned}$$

MODULE 5

Example

Write down the first 5 terms of a sequence if the formula for the nth term is:

nth term $= 2n + 3$

1st term $= 2 \times 1 + 3 = 5$
2nd term $= 2 \times 2 + 3 = 7$
3rd term $= 2 \times 3 + 3 = 9$
4th term $= 2 \times 4 + 3 = 11$
5th term $= 2 \times 5 + 3 = 13$

Exercise 7C

Write down the first five terms of the sequences produced by these formulae.

1. nth term $= 2n$
2. nth term $= 3n$
3. nth term $= 4n$
4. nth term $= 5n$
5. nth term $= 6n$
6. nth term $= 7n$
7. nth term $= 8n$
8. nth term $= 9n$
9. nth term $= 10n$
10. nth term $= n + 1$
11. nth term $= n + 3$
12. nth term $= n + 4$
13. nth term $= 2n + 1$
14. nth term $= 3n + 1$
15. nth term $= 4n + 1$
16. nth term $= 2n - 1$
17. nth term $= 3n - 1$
18. nth term $= 4n - 1$
19. nth term $= 5n + 2$
20. nth term $= 3n + 4$
21. nth term $= 4n - 3$
22. nth term $= 2n + 5$
23. nth term $= 5n - 4$
24. nth term $= 6n - 3$
25. nth term $= 2n + 7$
26. nth term $= 3n - 3$
27. nth term $= 4n + 5$
28. nth term $= 5n + 4$
29. nth term $= 3n + 8$
30. nth term $= 10n - 7$

7.4 Using differences

In the sequence 5, 8, 11, 14, 17 … there is a constant difference between each pair of terms. To find a formula for the nth term of a sequence, first find the constant difference between each pair of terms. In this case, the constant difference is 3.

1st		2nd		3rd		4th		5th
5	+3	8	+3	11	+3	14	+3	17

The constant difference of 3 means this sequence is based on the sequence with the formula: nth term $= 3n$.

Write this sequence in above the given sequence.

n	1st	2nd	3rd	4th	5th
$3n$	3	6	9	12	15
	5	8	11	14	17

Look carefully at the two sequences. You will see that the second sequence is formed from the first by adding 2. The formula for the nth term of the sequence is: nth term $= 3n + 2$.

Example 1

Find a formula for the nth term of the sequence: 4, 6, 8, 10, 12 …

The constant difference is 2. The sequence is based on the sequence with the formula nth term $= 2n$

n	1st	2nd	3rd	4th	5th
$2n$	2	4	6	8	10
	4	6	8	10	12

The formula is: nth term $= 2n + 2$

Example 2

Find a formula for the nth term of the sequence: 2, 7, 12, 17, 22 … and the 50th term of the sequence

The constant difference is 5. The sequence is based on the sequence with the formula: nth term $= 5n$

n	1st	2nd	3rd	4th	5th
$5n$	5	10	15	20	25
	2	7	12	17	22

The formula is: nth term $= 5n - 3$.
The 50th term $= 5 \times 50 - 3 = 247$

Exercise 7D

Find a formula for the nth term and the 50th term of each sequence.

1. 5, 7, 9, 11, 13 …
2. 6, 9, 12, 15, 18 …
3. 7, 11, 15, 19, 23 …
4. 3, 8, 13, 18, 23 …
5. 8, 14, 20, 26, 32 …
6. ⁻1, 1, 3, 5, 7 …
7. 1, 4, 7, 10, 13 …
8. 2, 6, 10, 14, 18 …
9. 4, 9, 14, 19, 24 …
10. 4, 11, 18, 25, 32 …
11. 7, 9, 11, 13, 15 …
12. 9, 12, 15, 18, 21 …
13. 11, 15, 19, 23, 27 …
14. 8, 13, 18, 23, 28 …
15. 14, 24, 34, 44, 54 …
16. 0, 2, 4, 6, 8 …
17. 5, 8, 11, 14, 17 …
18. 8, 12, 16, 20, 24 …
19. 13, 18, 23, 28, 33 …
20. 9, 19, 29, 39, 49 …

MODULE 5

7.5 Sequences based on patterns

Look at this sequence of patterns based on a hexagon with a side length of 1 unit.

1 2 3 4

The perimeters of the hexagons form the sequence 6, 10, 14, 18 ...

This sequence has a constant difference of 4.

n	1st	2nd	3rd	4th
$4n$	4	8	12	16
	6	10	14	18

The formula for the perimeter of the nth pattern is: nth perimeter $= 4n + 2$

Example

Matchsticks are placed to form this sequence of patterns.

Pattern 1   Pattern 2   Pattern 3

(a) Find a formula for the number of matchsticks needed to form the nth pattern.
(b) How many matchsticks are in the 100th pattern?
(c) Which pattern uses 51 matches?

(a) The sequence of matchsticks is:

n	1st	2nd	3rd
	3	5	7

The constant difference is 2.

n	1st	2nd	3rd
$2n$	2	4	6
	3	5	7

The formula is: number of matchsticks needed to make the nth pattern $= 2n + 1$

(b) The number of matchsticks in the 100th pattern $= 2 \times 100 + 1 = 201$

(c) We have to find n when $\qquad\qquad 2n + 1 = 51$
Subtracting 1 from both sides gives $\qquad 2n = 50$
Dividing both sides by 2 gives $\qquad\qquad n = 25$
Pattern number 25 uses 51 matches.

Exercise 7E

1. Wilma Flint builds ranch fences using 1 metre lengths of wood. She builds fences of different length like this:

Length 1 metre   Length 2 metres   Length 3 metres

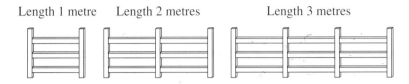

(a) How many metres of wood are used to build a fence of length 1 metre?

(b) Copy and complete this table.

Fences length in metres	1	2	3	4
Metres of wood needed		9	13	

(c) Find a formula for the number of metres of wood needed to build a fence of length n metres.

(d) How many metres of wood are needed to build a fence of length 25 metres?

(e) What length of fence can be built with 41 metres of wood?

2. A restaurant has tables which can seat 4 people. The tables are put together like this to make seating for larger parties of guests.

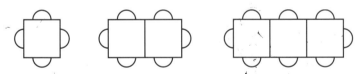

(a) Copy and complete this table.

Number of tables	1	2	3	4
Number of seats	4	6		

(b) Find a formula for the number of seats provided if n tables are put together.

(c) How many seats are provided if 20 tables are put together?

(d) How many tables are needed to provide 32 seats?

3. This sequence of patterns is made from octagons with a side length of 1 centimetre.

Pattern 1   Pattern 2   Pattern 3

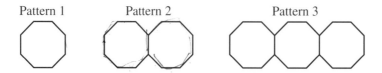

(a) What is the perimeter of pattern 2?
(b) Copy and complete this table.

Pattern number	1	2	3	4
Perimeter	8 cm		20 cm	

(c) Find a formula for the perimeter of the nth pattern.
(d) Find the perimeter of the 60th pattern.
(e) Which pattern has a perimeter of 62 centimetres?

4. Matchsticks are placed to form this sequence of patterns.

Pattern 1   Pattern 2   Pattern 3

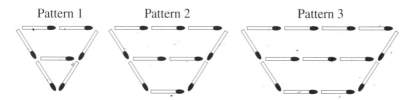

(a) Find a formula for the number of matchsticks needed to form the nth pattern.
(b) Find the number of matchsticks in the 100th pattern.
(c) Which pattern requires 40 matchsticks?

5. A supermarket displays cans of beans by building them into pyramids like this:

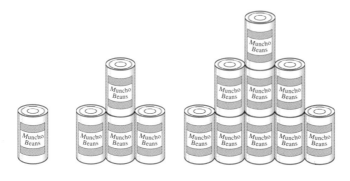

(a) Copy and complete this table.

Height of pyramid	1 can	2 cans	3 cans	4 cans
Number of cans in the bottom row	1		5	

(b) Find a formula for the number of cans in the bottom row of a pyramid n cans high.

(c) How many cans will be in the bottom row of a pyramid 25 cans high?

(d) How high is the pyramid with 29 cans in its bottom row?

7.6 Coordinates

Coordinates fix the position of a point on a square grid like this:

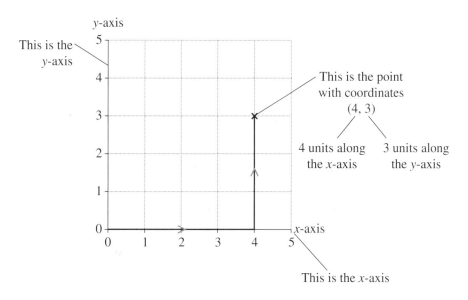

Coordinates are written in a bracket: (x, y)

(across   up)

Look at the grid below.

      A is the point with coordinates (1,4)

      B is the point with coordinates (4,1)

      C is the point with coordinates (1,0)

      D is the point with coordinates (3,3)

      E is the point with coordinates (0,2)

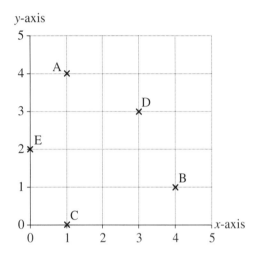

Exercise 7F

1. Write down the coordinates of the points A to J on this grid.

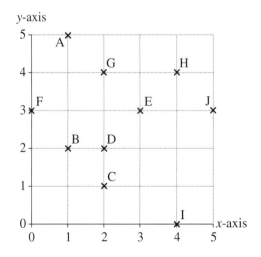

2. The outline of a jet has been drawn on this grid.
Write down the coordinates of the corner points A to M.

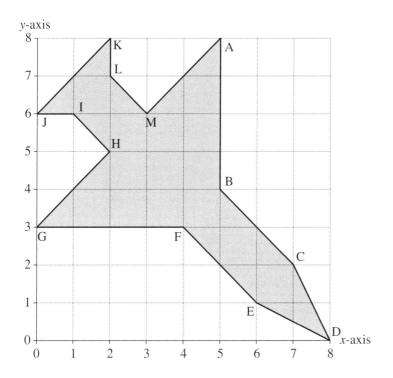

3. Draw a grid with an *x*-axis and a *y*-axis from 0 to 8. Add
each of the following points, joining them, in order, with
straight lines. Join the last point to the first point.
(2,4), (4,2), (6,2), (8,4), (8,8), (6,6), (4,6), (2,8)

4. Draw a grid with an *x*-axis and a *y*-axis from 0 to 8. Add
each of the following points, joining them, in order, with
straight lines. Join the last point to the first point.
(0,5), (0,2), (1,2), (1,0), (3,0), (3,2), (4,2), (4,0), (6,0),
(6,2), (8,2), (8,3), (6,3), (6,6), (8,6), (8,7), (5,7), (5,5),
(2,5), (2,7), (1,7), (1,5)

5. For each part of this question, draw a grid with an *x*-axis
and a *y*-axis from 0 to 10. Add each of the following sets of
points, joining them, in order, with straight lines. Join the
last point to the first point. Shade in the shapes and inside
each shape write its correct name selected from this list (use
each name once only).

You can copy this grid:

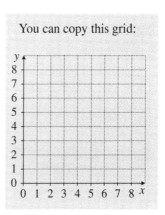

MODULE 5

Isosceles triangle, Rectangle, Pentagon, Quadrilateral, Rhombus, Trapezium, Square, Hexagon, Right-angled triangle, Parallelogram, Kite.

Hint:
Look back at Unit AS5 to find out what these words mean.

(a) (0,8), (0,10), (3,9)
(b) (0,7), (1,8), (2,8), (1,6)
(c) (5,8), (5,9), (6,10), (7,9), (7,8)
(d) (0,1), (1,2), (3,2), (2,1)
(e) (4,3), (4,4), (5,4), (5,3)
(f) (2,3), (1,5), (2,6), (3,5)
(g) (2,0), (4,1), (5,1), (7,0)
(h) (8,10), (10,10), (10,7)
(i) (5,2), (7,3), (9,2), (7,1)
(j) (4,6), (4,7), (7,7), (7,6)
(k) (6,4), (6,5), (8,6), (10,5), (10,4), (8,3)

6. The treasure map below has a key which starts like this:

Place	Location
Caves	(9,5)
Dead Person's Point	$(8\frac{1}{2}, 7\frac{1}{2})$

Copy and complete the key.

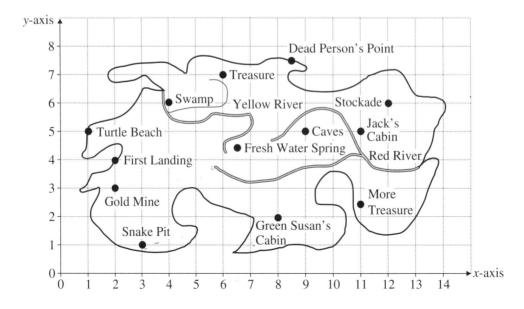

7.7 Coordinates in four quadrants

Coordinates can be extended to fix the position of a point on a square grid like this:

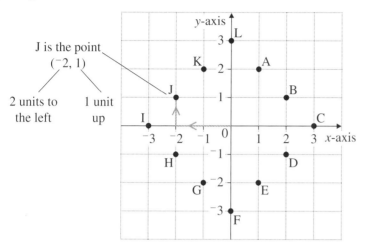

Look at the grid.

A is the point with coordinates (1,2)
C is the point with coordinates (3,0)
E is the point with coordinates (1,⁻2)
G is the point with coordinates (⁻1,⁻2)
I is the point with coordinates (⁻3,0)
K is the point with coordinates (⁻1,2)

B is the point with coordinates (2,1)
D is the point with coordinates (2,⁻1)
F is the point with coordinates (0, ⁻3)
H is the point with coordinates (⁻2,⁻1)
J is the point with coordinates (⁻2,1)
L is the point with coordinates (0,3)

Exercise 7G

1. Write down the coordinates of the points A to L on this grid.

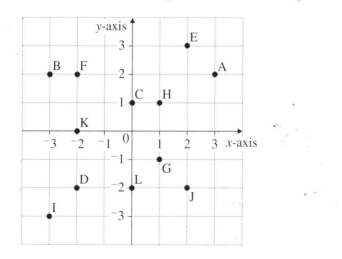

2. The outline of a cat has been drawn on this grid. Write down the coordinates of the corner points A to O.

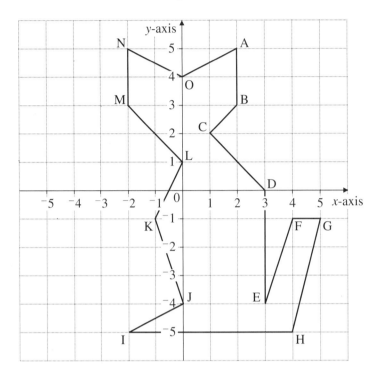

3. For each part of this question, draw a grid with an *x*-axis and a *y*-axis from ⁻4 to 4. Add each of the following sets of points, joining them, in order, with straight lines. Join the last point to the first point.

(a) (3,0), (0,3), (⁻3,0), (0,⁻3)

(b) (4,0), (3,4), (⁻4,0), (⁻3,⁻4)

(c) (⁻3,⁻3), (⁻1,⁻2), (0,4), (1,⁻2), (3,⁻3)

(d) (⁻2,4), (2,4), (3,⁻1), (2,⁻4), (⁻2,⁻4), (⁻3,⁻1)

(e) (4,⁻1), (1,⁻1), (1,0), (4,0), (0,3), (⁻4,0), (⁻1,0), (⁻1,⁻1), (⁻4,⁻1), (⁻4,⁻3), (4,⁻3)

(f) (2,0), (2½,0), (1½,1), (2,1), (1,2), (1½,2), (½,3), (1,3), (0,4), (⁻1,3), (⁻½,3), (⁻1½,2), (½,⁻3), (⁻1,2), (⁻2,1), (⁻1½,1), (⁻2½,0), (⁻2,0), (⁻3,⁻1), (⁻½,⁻1), (-½,-2), (-1,-2), (⁻½,⁻3), (1,⁻2), (½,⁻2), (½,⁻1), (3,⁻1)

You can copy this grid:

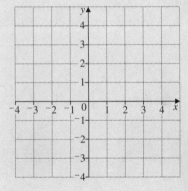

4. The points ($^-$2,1) and (4,1) are two of the corner points of a square.

    (a) Plot these points on a grid.

    (b) What are the other possible corner points for the square?

    (c) Show all the possibilities on your grid.

5. The points ($^-$2,3) and ($^-$2,$^-$1) are the vertices of the base of an isosceles triangle.

    (a) Plot these points on a grid.

    (b) List some possibilities for the third corner point of the isosceles triangle.

    (c) Show these points on your grid.

    (d) What do all these possible points have in common?

6. The points ($^-$2,$^-$1) and (4,$^-$1) are the vertices of the base of an isosceles triangle.

    (a) Plot these points on a grid.

    (b) List some possibilities for the third corner point of the isosceles triangle.

    (c) Show these points on your grid.

    (d) What do all these possible points have in common?

7.8 Drawing a graph of a linear equation

The equation $y = x + 1$ links the values of x and y.

If you choose a sequence of values for x, the equation will produce a sequence of values for y. You can show the results in a table.

x	$^-$2	$^-$1	0	1	2
$y = x + 1$	$^-$1	0	1	2	3

The table gives   ($^-$2,$^-$1)   ($^-$1,0)   (0,1)   (1,2)   (2,3)
coordinates to plot:

Plot the points and join them together.

The completed diagram is
the graph of $y = x + 1$

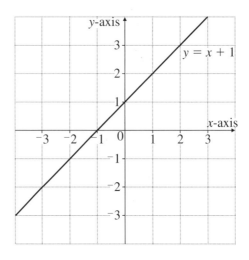

Example

Using x values from $^-2$ to 2, draw the graph of $y = 2x - 1$.

First complete a table of values for x and y.

x	$^-2$	$^-1$	0	1	2
$y = 2x - 1$	$^-5$	$^-3$	$^-1$	1	3

$(^-2, ^-5)$ $(^-1, ^-3)$ $(0, ^-1)$ $(1, 1)$ $(2, 3)$

Then, draw a grid and plot the points.

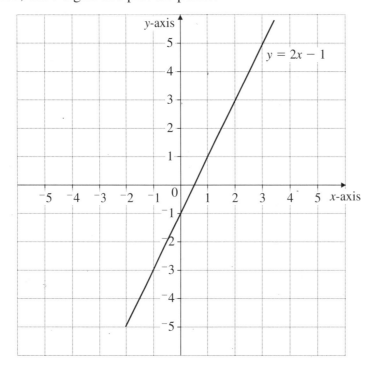

Exercise 7H

1. Draw a grid with x values from $^-3$ to 3 and y values from $^-6$ to 6.

2. Copy and complete these tables of values. As you complete each table, add the graph of the equation to the grid you drew for Question **1**.

(a)

x	$^-2$	$^-1$	0	1	2
$y = x + 2$	0				4

(b)

x	$^-2$	$^-1$	0	1	2
$y = x + 3$	1			4·	

(c)

x	$^-2$	$^-1$	0	1	2
$y = x + 4$	2		4.		

(d)

x	$^-2$	$^-1$	0	1	2
$y = x - 1$	$^-3$		$^-1$		

(e)

x	$^-2$	$^-1$	0	1	2
$y = x - 2$		$^-3$		$^-1$	

(f)

x	$^-2$	$^-1$	0	1	2
$y = x - 3$	$^-5$		$^-3$		

3. Copy and complete these tables of values. As you complete each table, add the graph of the equation to your grid.

(a)

x	$^-2$	$^-1$	0	1	2
$y = x$	$^-2$				2

(b)

x	$^-2$	$^-1$	0	1	2
$y = 2x$	$^-4$			2	

(c)

x	$^-2$	$^-1$	0	1	2
$y = 3x$	$^-6$		0		

(d)

x	⁻2	⁻1	0	1	2
y = ⁻2x	4		0		⁻4

(e)

x	⁻2	⁻1	0	1	2
y = ⁻3x	6			⁻3	⁻6

(f)

x	⁻2	⁻1	0	1	2
y = ⁻x	2		0	⁻1	

4. Draw a grid with x values from ⁻3 to 3 and y values from ⁻1 to 12.

Copy and complete these tables of values. As you complete each table, add the graph of the equation to your grid.

(a)

x	⁻2	⁻1	0	1	2
y = 3 − x	5				1

(b)

x	⁻2	⁻1	0	1	2
y = 2 − x	4			1	

(c)

x	⁻2	⁻1	0	1	2
y = 1 − x	3		1		

(d)

x	⁻2	⁻1	0	1	2
y = 4 − x	6	5	4		

(e)

x	⁻2	⁻1	0	1	2
y = 8 − 2x	12		8		4

5. Draw a grid with x values from ⁻4 to 4 and y values from ⁻2 to 2.

6. Copy and complete these tables of values. As you complete each table, add the graph of the equation to the grid you drew for Question **5**.

(a)

x		$^-2$	$^-1$	0	1	2
$y = \dfrac{x}{2}$		$^-1$		0	$\frac{1}{2}$	

(b)

x		$^-3$	$^-1$	0	1	3
$y = \dfrac{x}{3}$		$^-1$	$-\frac{1}{3}$	0		

(c)

x		$^-4$	$^-1$	0	1	4
$y = \dfrac{x}{4}$		$^-1$		0		

(d)

x		$^-2$	$^-1$	0	1	2
$y = \dfrac{^-x}{2}$		1		0		$^-1$

(e)

x		$^-3$	$^-1$	0	1	3
$y = \dfrac{^-x}{3}$		1				

(f)

x		$^-4$	$^-1$	0	1	4
$y = \dfrac{^-x}{4}$		1		0	$-\frac{1}{4}$	

7. Copy and complete these tables of values and draw the graph of the equation on a suitable grid.

(a)

x		$^-2$	$^-1$	0	1	2
$y = 2x + 1$		$^-3$				5

(b)

x	$^-2$	$^-1$	0	1	2
$y = 3x - 1$	$^-7$			2	

(c)

x	$^-2$	$^-1$	0	1	2
$y = 2x - 3$	$^-7$		$^-3$		

(d)

x	$^-2$	$^-1$	0	1	2
$y = \dfrac{x}{2} + 3$	2		3	$3\frac{1}{2}$	

(e)

x	$^-2$	$^-1$	0	1	2
$y = 3 - 2x$	7			1	$^-1$

(f)

x	$^-2$	$^-1$	0	1	2
$y = 3x - 4$	$^-10$		$^-4$	$^-1$	

7.9 Graphs of equations which produce curves

Some equations will produce curves when plotted on a graph.

For example, this table shows a sequence of y values given by the equation $y = x^2$.

x	$^-3$	$^-2$	$^-1$	0	1	2	3
$y = x^2$	9	4	1	0	1	4	9

$(^-3,9)$ $(^-2,4)$ $(^-1,1)$ $(0,0)$ $(1,1)$ $(2,4)$ $(3,9)$

When these values are plotted on a grid, it is quite clear that they cannot be connected with a straight line. The points are connected with a smooth curve to draw the graph of $y = x^2$.

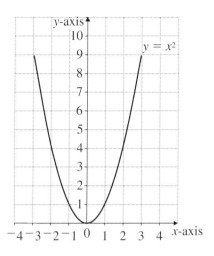

Example

Using x values from 1 to 8, draw the graph of $y = \dfrac{8}{x}$.

This is the table of values.

x	1	2	3	4	5	6	7	8
$y = \dfrac{8}{x}$	8	4	2·7	2	1·6	1·3	1·1	1

(1,8)   (2,4)   (3,2·7)   (4,2)   (5,1·6)   (6,1·3)   (7,1·1)   (8,1)

This is the graph.

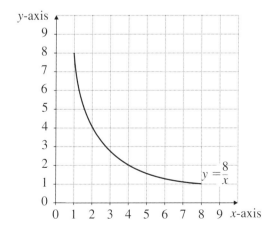

MODULE 5

Exercise 71

1. Draw a graph with x values from $^-4$ to 4 and y values from $^-4$ to 16.

2, Copy and complete these tables of values. As you complete each table, add the graph of the equation to the grid you drew for Question **1**.

(a)

x	$^-3$	$^-2$	$^-1$	0	1	2	3
$y = x^2 + 2$	11			2			11

(b)

x	$^-3$	$^-2$	$^-1$	0	1	2	3
$y = x^2 + 4$	13				5		

(c)

x	$^-3$	$^-2$	$^-1$	0	1	2	3
$y = x^2 + 6$		10				10	

(d)

x	$^-3$	$^-2$	$^-1$	0	1	2	3
$y = x^2 - 2$	7		$^-1$	$^-2$			

(e)

x	$^-3$	$^-2$	$^-1$	0	1	2	3
$y = x^2 - 4$	5	0		$^-4$	$^-3$		

3. Draw a grid with x and y values from 0 to 12.

Copy and complete these tables of values. As you complete each table, add the graph of the equation to your grid.

(a)

x	1	2	3	4	5	6	7	8	9	10	11	12
$y = \dfrac{12}{x}$	12				2·4		1·7	1·5	1·3		1·1	1

(b)

x	1	2	3	4
$y = \dfrac{4}{x}$			1·3	

(c)

x	1	2	3	4	5	6
$y = \dfrac{6}{x}$				1·5	1·2	

4. (a) Copy and complete this table of values.

x	$^-3$	$^-2$	$^-1$	0	1	2	3
x^2	9	4		0	1		
$2x$	$^-6$	$^-4$			2		6
$y = x^2 + 2x$	3		$^-1$	0		8	

(b) Draw the graph of $y = x^2 + 2x$ with values of x from $^-3$ to 3.

5. (a) Copy and complete this table of values.

x	$^-3$	$^-2$	$^-1$	0	1	2	3
x^2	9	4		0	1		
x	$^-3$	$^-2$			1		3
$y = x^2 - x$	12		2	0	0	2	

(b) Draw the graph of $y = x^2 - x$ with values of x from $^-3$ to 3.

6. (a) Copy and complete this table of values.

x	$^-3$	$^-2$	$^-1$	0	1	2	3
8	8	8	8	8	8	8	8
x^2	9	4		0	1		
$y = 8 - x^2$	$^-1$	4	7		7		$^-1$

(b) Draw the graph of $y = 8 - x^2$ with values of x from $^-3$ to 3.

7. (a) Copy and complete this table of values.

x		$^-3$	$^-2$	$^-1$	0	1	2
x^2		9	4		0	1	
$3x$		$^-9$	$^-6$	$^-3$		3	
5		5	5	5		5	
$y = x^2 + 3x + 5$		5	3		5		15

(b) Draw the graph of $y = x^2 + 3x + 5$ with values of x from $^-3$ to 2.

7.10 Using graphs to illustrate relationships

Graphs are often used to illustrate real-life relationships.
This graph shows the relationship between the distance that a car
travels and the petrol it uses.

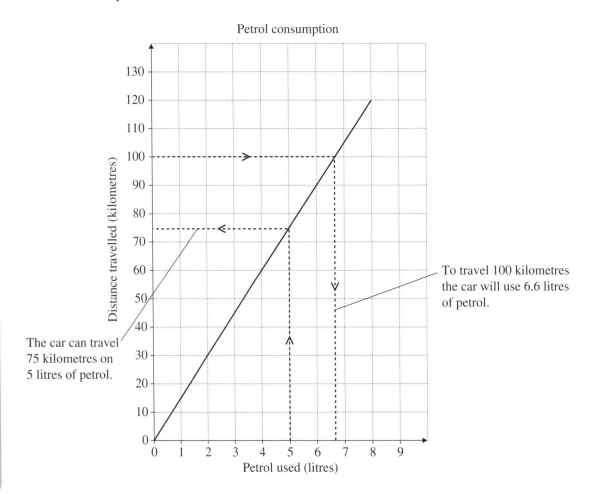

The car can travel
75 kilometres on
5 litres of petrol.

To travel 100 kilometres
the car will use 6.6 litres
of petrol.

The arrows added to the graph show how you can use it to estimate.

Exercise 7J

1. On a particular day, this table gave the conversion rate from
English pounds into French francs.

English pounds	0	2	4	6	8	10
French francs	0	20	40	60	80	100

(a) Draw a graph to show the relationship between English pounds and French francs. Using 1 centimetre squares, start your axes like this.

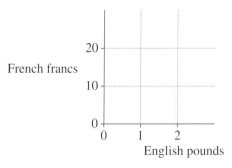

(b) Use your graph to convert these amounts into French francs.
   (i) £2·50   (ii) £7·50   (iii) £9·50
(c) Use your graph to convert these amounts into English pounds.
   (i) 5 francs   (ii) 35 francs   (iii) 55 francs

2. This table shows the correct dose of a medicine that a doctor should prescribe for a small child aged up to 1 year.

Age (months)	3	6	9	12
Dose (millilitres)	1·5	3	4·5	6

(a) Draw a graph to show the relationship between a child's age and the correct dose of the medicine. Using 1 centimetre squares, start your axes like this:

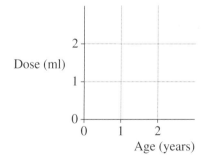

(b) Use your graph to estimate the correct dose for a child of age:
   (i) 1 month   (ii) 8 months   (iii) 11 months
(c) Use your graph to estimate the age of a child who is given a dose of:
   (i) 2 ml   (ii) 10 ml   (iii) 5 ml

3. This table shows the relationship between weight and cost for the 'pick-and-mix' sweets sold in a cinema.

Weight (grams)	0	250	500
Cost (pence)	0	200	400

(a) Draw a graph to show the relationship between weight and cost for the sweets. Using 1 centimetre squares, start your axes like this:

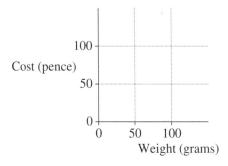

(b) Use your graph to estimate the cost of sweets which weigh:
(i) 100 grams   (ii) 300 grams   (iii) 450 grams
(c) Use your graph to estimate the weight of sweets which cost:
(i) £0·40   (ii) £2·80   (iii) £3·20

4. Melissa wants to hire a disco for her birthday. She has seen this advertisement for the 'Five High Disco'.

FIVE HIGH DISCO

£20 plus 50p
per person

(a) Copy and complete this table for the charges made by the 'Five High Disco'.

Number of people	10	30	50	70	90
Cost of disco (£)	25	35			

(b) Draw a graph to show the relationship between the number of people and the cost. Using 1 centimetre squares, start your axes like this:

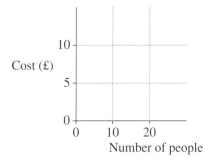

(c) Use your graph to estimate the cost of the disco if the number of people attending is:
(i) 20   (ii) 35   (iii) 65

(d) Use your graph to estimate the number of people attending if the cost is:
(i) £60   (ii) £40   (iii) £50

5. The relationship between the height of a birthday candle and the time for which it has been burning is described by this formula:

'The candle loses 1 cm in height for every minute it burns.'

(a) Draw a graph to show the change in height of a 5 centimetre birthday candle as it burns for 5 minutes. Using 1 centimetre squares, start your axes like this:

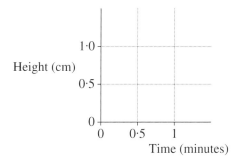

(b) Make up two questions that you could use your graph to answer. Write down your questions and their answers.

MODULE 5

7.11 Distance and time graphs

A journey of 5 kilometres from home to school takes 20 minutes. The journey starts with a 500 metre walk to the bus stop. This takes 5 minutes. There is then a 5 minute wait for a bus. The bus takes 10 minutes to complete the journey to school.

You can use this graph to show the journey.

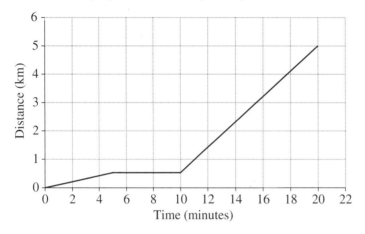

Exercise 7K

1. A family travel from their home in England to the car ferry at Dover and cross to Calais in France. They then travel to a camp site in northern France to spend the night. Their journey is shown on this graph.

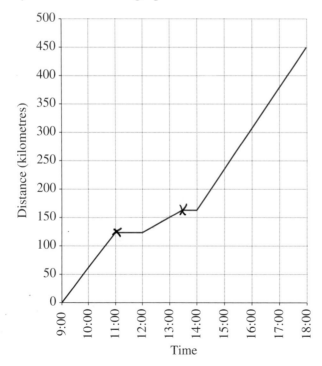

(a) At what time did they leave home?
(b) Where were they at 11:30?
(c) How long did they wait for the ferry to leave?
(d) How far from home were they at 16:00?
(e) How far was it from:
    (i)   their home to Dover
    (ii) Dover to Calais
    (iii) Calais to their camp site?
(f) At what time did their boat arrive in Calais?
(g) How long did it take the family to get to Dover?
(h) What was the average speed in kilometres per hour
    from their home to Dover?

2. Mrs Smith travelled from home by bus to the town centre to
shop. On the way home she used two buses because she
wished to visit a friend who lives along the bus route. This
graph shows her journey.

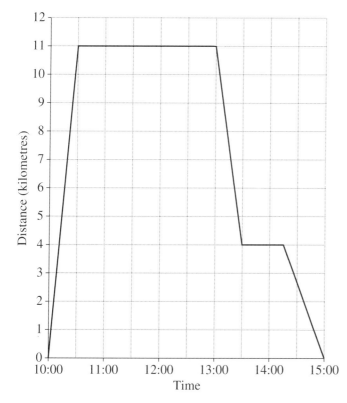

(a) How far is Mrs Smith's home from the town centre?
(b) How long did Mrs Smith's bus ride to the town centre take?
(c) What was the average speed of Mrs Smith's bus
    journey to the town centre in kilometres per hour?

    (d) How long did Mrs Smith stay in the town centre?
    (e) How long did Mrs Smith's bus ride to her friend's
        house take?
    (f) How far is the friend's house from the town centre?
    (g) What was the average speed of Mrs Smith's bus
        journey to her friend's house in kilometres per hour?
    (h) How long did Mrs Smith stay at her friend's house?
    (i) How long did the journey home from Mrs Smith's
        friend's house take?
    (j) What was the average speed of Mrs Smith's bus
        journey from her friend's house to her home in
        kilometres per hour?

3.   A slow train leaves Peterborough for London. Twenty
       minutes later a fast train leaves London for Peterborough.
       The journeys of both trains are shown on this graph.

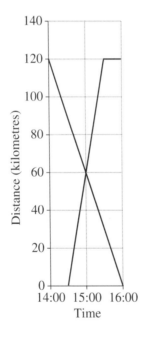

    (a) At what time did the slow train leave Peterborough?
    (b) At what time did the fast train leave London?
    (c) At what time did the slow train arrive in London?
    (d) At what time did the fast train arrive in Peterborough?
    (e) How far is it from London to Peterborough?
    (f) How far from Peterborough were the two trains when
        they passed each other?
    (g) At what time did the two trains pass each other?

MODULE 5

(h) What was the average speed in kilometres per hour of the slow train?

(i) What was the average speed in kilometres per hour of the fast train?

(j) How many minutes after the fast train arrived in Peterborough did the slow train arrive in London?

4. Two boys take part in a 10 kilometre cycle race. One cycles at a steady speed, the other cycles in spurts and then stops to rest. The steady cyclist is called Alim, the other cyclist is called Farath. This graph shows the race.

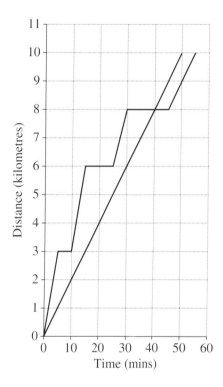

(a) How long does Farath rest for when he stops for the second time?

(b) How far has Farath cycled when he stops for the second time?

(c) How far is Farath ahead of Alim after 5 minutes?

(d) What is the greatest distance that Farath is ahead of Alim during the race?

(e) At what distance from the start does Alim overtake Farath?

(f) For what time during the race is Alim in the lead?

(g) By what distance does Alim beat Farath?

(h) How much slower than Farath is Alim to reach the 6 kilometre point in the race?

(i) At what speed, in kilometres per hour, did Farath cycle after his third rest?

(j) At what average speed in kilometres per hour would Farath have needed to cycle after his last rest to tie the race?

Summary

1. A **sequence** is a set of numbers produced using a fixed rule.

Checkout AS7

1. What are the next two numbers in each sequence?
  (a) 3, 6, 9, 12 ...
  (b) 18, 16, 14, 12 ...
  (c) 2, 4, 8, 16 ...
  (d) 400, 200, 100, 50 ...

2. A formula for the *n*th term can be used to produce a sequence.

2. Write down the first 5 terms of the sequence produced by the formula:
(a) *n*th term = 5*n* (b) *n*th term = *n* + 5
(c) *n*th term = *n* − 1 (d) *n*th term = 3*n* + 5

3. To find a formula for the *n*th term of a sequence, find the common difference between the terms. The formula will be based on the sequence produced by multiplying by this number.

3. Find a formula for the *n*th term of each sequence.
(a) 4, 9, 14, 19, 24 ... (b) 11, 14, 17, 20, 23 ...
(c) 9, 11, 13, 15, 17 ... (d) 7, 11, 15, 19, 23 ...

4. You can fix positions and plot points using coordinates.

4. The points (1,1) and (1,⁻1), are the corner points of a square.
(a) Plot these points on a grid.
(b) What are the other possible corner points for the square?
(c) Show all the possibilities on your grid.

5. You can draw the graph of an equation from a table of values.

5. Using *x* values from ⁻2 to 2, draw the graphs of:
(a) $y = x + 5$ (b) $y = x - 5$
(c) $y = 3x + 1$ (d) $y = 2x - 4$

6. Some equations produce curved graphs.

6. Using *x* values from ⁻3 to 3, draw the graphs of:
(a) $y = x^2 + 3$ (b) $y = x^2 - 5$
(c) $y = 9 - x^2$

7. Real-life relationships can be illustrated with a graph.

7. This table shows the relationship between the time a plumber works and his bill.

Hours worked	1	5	10
Cost (£)	40	120	220

(a) Draw a graph from the values in the table. Use 1 cm to represent 1 hour on the *x*-axis and 1 cm to represent £20 on the *y*-axis.
(b) How much will repairs cost that take:
  (i) 3 hours (ii) 6 hours?
(c) How long did repairs take which cost:
  (i) £160 (ii) £100?

8. Problems involving distance and time can be solved with graphs.

8. Mr Williams lives near a motorway junction, 100 kilometres from London. At 9.00 a.m. he leaves home and travels up the motorway at a steady speed of 60 kilometres per hour towards London. Ten minutes later, his daughter Chantal also travels on the motorway towards London at 75 kilometres per hour.
   (a) Draw a distance–time graph using 1 cm to represent 15 minutes on the time axis and 1 cm to represent 10 kilometres on the distance axis.
   (b) Estimate:
       (i)   The time at which Mr Williams arrives in London.
       (ii) The time at which Chantal Williams arrives in London.
       (iii) The time at which Chantal Williams overtakes Mr Williams.
       (iv) The distance from London at which Chantal Williams overtakes Mr Williams.

Revision exercise AS7

1. (a) (i) What is the next number in the pattern?

   28,   23,   18,   13,   … .

   (ii) Explain how you found your answer to part (i).

   (b) (i) What is the missing number in the pattern?

   3,   6,   12,   …,   48,   96.

   (ii) Explain how you found your answer to part (b) (i).

   [SEG]

2. (a) What is the next number in this sequence?

   3,   7,   11,   15,   …

   One number in the sequence is x.

   (b) (i) Write, in terms of x, the next number in the sequence.
       (ii) Write, in terms of x, the number in the sequence before x.   [SEG]

3. A number sequence is shown.

   1,   4,   9,   16,   25,   …

   (a) (i) What special name is given to the numbers in this sequence?
       (ii) What is the next number in the sequence?

Patterns of black tiles and white tiles are shown.

 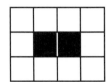 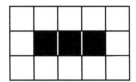

(b) The number of white tiles, w, and the number of black tiles, b, are connected by the formula

$$w = 2b + 6$$

  (i) In a pattern there are 18 black tiles.
      Use the formula to find the number of white tiles.
  (ii) In another pattern there are 136 white tiles.
      Use the formula to find the number of black tiles.

[SEG]

4. (a) Complete the table of values for the equation
         $y = 2x - 1$.

x	-1	1	3
y	-3.	1	5

(b) On a copy of the grid below draw the graph of
    $y = 2x - 1$

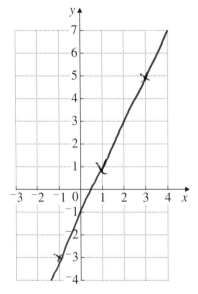

(c) **Use your graph** to estimate the value of x when $y = 2.5$

5. (a) Complete the table of values for the function
$y = x^2 - 1$.

x	-2	-1	0	1	2
$y = x^2 - 1$	3				0

(b) On graph paper, draw the graph of $y = x^2 - 1$.
(c) Find the value of y when $x = 1 \cdot 5$ [SEG]

6. A cyclist leaves town A at 9.00 am, cycles to town B, then returns to town A. The distance-time graph of the cyclist's journey is shown.

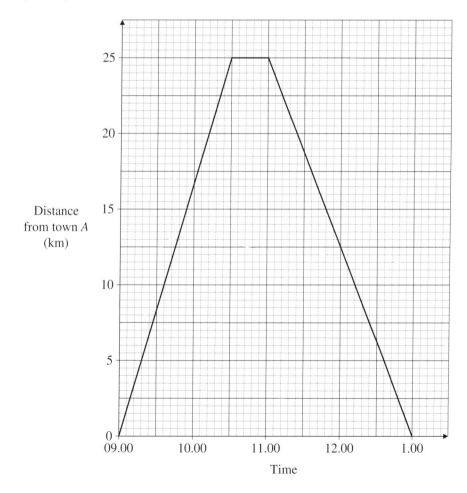

(a) What is the distance between town A and town B?
(b) How long did the cyclist stay in town B?
(c) How far was the cyclist from town B at 12.30 pm? [SEG]

AS8 SHAPE AND SPACE 4

Transformations describe how shapes change.

This unit will show you how to:

- Transform shapes using translations, reflections, rotations and enlargements
- Understand the term congruence
- Describe the symmetry of shapes and enlargements

Before you start:

MODULE 5

You should know how to...	Check in AS8
1. Use coordinates to describe position. For example,	**1.** Write down the coordinates of each point on the grid.

The point N is ⁻2 along the *x* axis and 0 up the *y* axis.

N is the point (−2, 0)

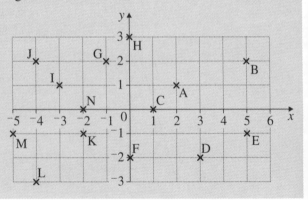

8.1 Translations

A **translation** slides a shape from one position to another without turning it.

Translations are usually shown on a square grid.

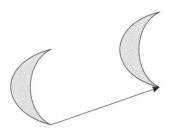

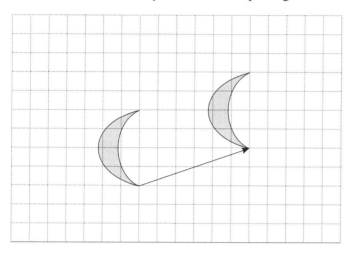

The translation of the moon shape is 6 squares to the right and 2 squares up.

Translations are often written in a vertical bracket like this: $\begin{pmatrix} +6 \\ +2 \end{pmatrix}$

The horizontal movement is always put at the top of the bracket.

Plus signs show that the movement is to the **right** or **up**.

Minus signs show that the movement is to the **left** or **down**.

Here are some more translations applied to the moon shape.

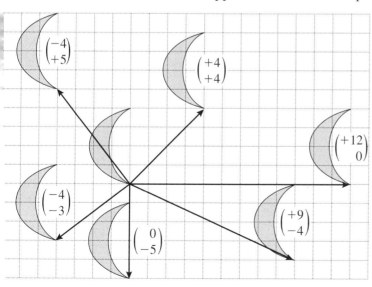

MODULE 5

Exercise 8A

1. The diagram shows a shaded triangle moved to ten new positions.

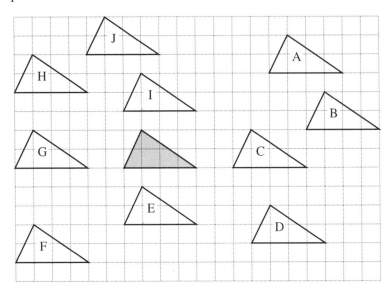

Note:

All these shapes are **congruent** to each other.

Use vertical brackets to write down the translations which move the shaded triangle to each new position.

2. The diagram shows a shaded diamond moved to ten new positions.

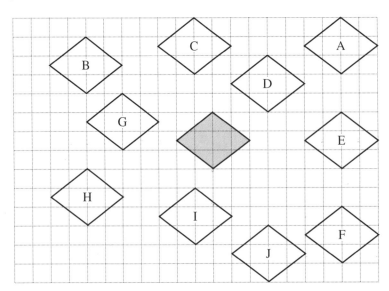

Use vertical brackets to write down the translations which move the shaded diamond to each new position.

3. Copy this triangle onto
   squared paper.

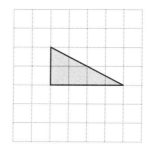

Show the new position of the triangle after each of these
translations.

(a) $\begin{pmatrix} +6 \\ +4 \end{pmatrix}$ (b) $\begin{pmatrix} -6 \\ +4 \end{pmatrix}$ (c) $\begin{pmatrix} +6 \\ -4 \end{pmatrix}$

(d) $\begin{pmatrix} -6 \\ -4 \end{pmatrix}$ (e) $\begin{pmatrix} +6 \\ 0 \end{pmatrix}$ (f) $\begin{pmatrix} -6 \\ 0 \end{pmatrix}$

(g) $\begin{pmatrix} 0 \\ +4 \end{pmatrix}$ (h) $\begin{pmatrix} 0 \\ -4 \end{pmatrix}$

4. Copy this triangle onto
   squared paper.

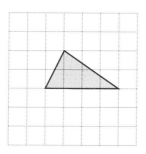

Show the new position of the triangle after each of these
translations.

(a) $\begin{pmatrix} +5 \\ +3 \end{pmatrix}$ (b) $\begin{pmatrix} -5 \\ +3 \end{pmatrix}$ (c) $\begin{pmatrix} +5 \\ -3 \end{pmatrix}$

(d) $\begin{pmatrix} -5 \\ -3 \end{pmatrix}$ (e) $\begin{pmatrix} +5 \\ 0 \end{pmatrix}$ (f) $\begin{pmatrix} -5 \\ 0 \end{pmatrix}$

(g) $\begin{pmatrix} 0 \\ +3 \end{pmatrix}$ (h) $\begin{pmatrix} 0 \\ -3 \end{pmatrix}$

MODULE 5

5.

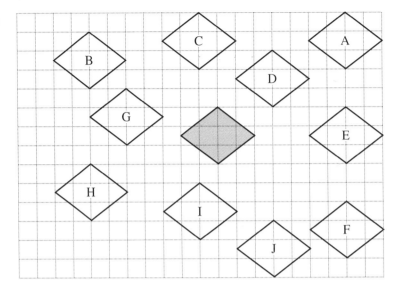

Use vertical brackets to write down the translations that move:

(a) A to B   (b) A to C   (c) A to D

(d) A to E   (e) A to F   (f) B to A

(g) B to D   (h) B to E   (i) B to I

(j) B to J   (k) C to G   (l) C to A

(m) C to E   (n) C to H   (o) C to I

(p) I to H   (q) H to I   (r) J to F

(s) G to A   (t) F to B

Which of the shapes are congruent to each other?

8.2 Reflections

A **reflection** makes an image of a shape in a mirror line.

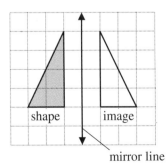

mirror line

This diagram shows some more reflections in mirror lines. The starting shapes are shaded. The starting shape is sometimes called the object.

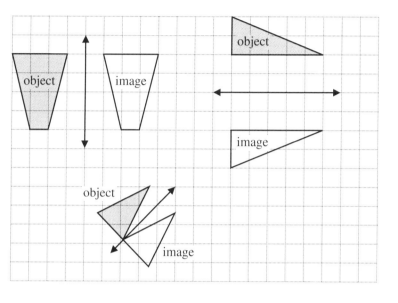

> **Note:**
> The object and image are **congruent** under a reflection.

To reflect a shape, imagine the object is drawn with wet ink. The image is the shape printed by the wet ink if the paper is folded along the mirror line.

To complete a reflection with a diagonal mirror line, turn the page to make the mirror line vertical or horizontal.

If a shape crosses the mirror line the image will also cross the mirror line.

Example

Reflect this shape in the mirror line.

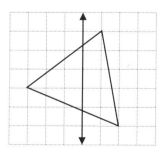

This is the completed reflection.

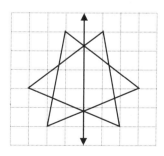

MODULE 5

Exercise 8B

Copy these diagrams onto squared paper. Reflect each shape in the mirror line.

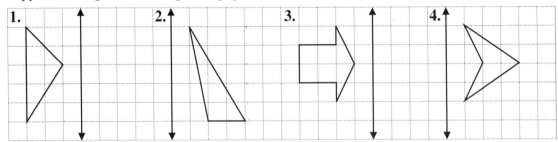

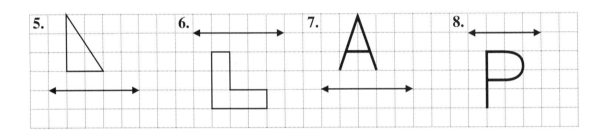

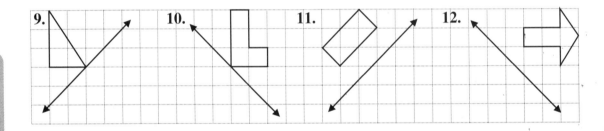

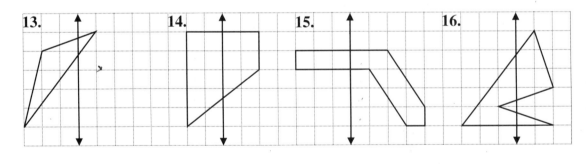

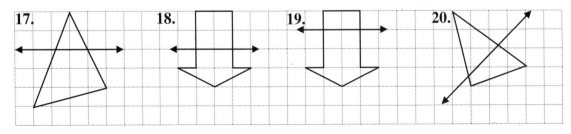

8.3 Rotations

A **rotation** moves a shape by turning it.

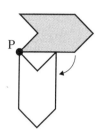

This rotation is a 90° clockwise rotation about the point P.

The point P is called the **centre of rotation**.

This diagram shows a shape rotated about a point M through anticlockwise angles of 90°, 180° and 270°.

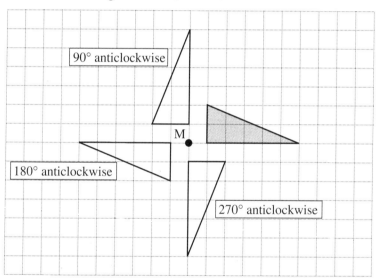

90° anticlockwise

M

180° anticlockwise

270° anticlockwise

Note:

If you rotate a shape, it is still congruent to the original shape.

Rotations can be completed using tracing paper.
This is done in three stages:

- Cover the object and the centre of rotation with tracing paper and trace it.

- Place the point of a pencil on the centre of rotation and turn the tracing paper through the required angle.

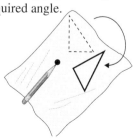

- Trace the object back onto the paper.

MODULE 5

Exercise 8C

1. Copy each diagram onto squared paper and use tracing
   paper to complete the given rotation.

   (a) 90° clockwise about P

   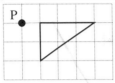

   (b) 180° clockwise about M

   (c) 90° clockwise about A

   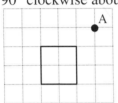

   (d) 90° anticlockwise about B

   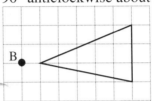

   (e) 180° anticlockwise about P

   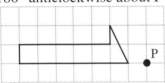

   (f) 90° anticlockwise about Q

   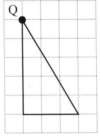

   (g) 270° clockwise about O

   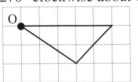

   (h) 270° anticlockwise about T

   (i) 90° clockwise about M

   (j) 90° anticlockwise about M

   (k) 90° clockwise about P

   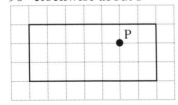

   (l) 90° anticlockwise about P

   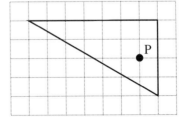

2. Look at this diagram.

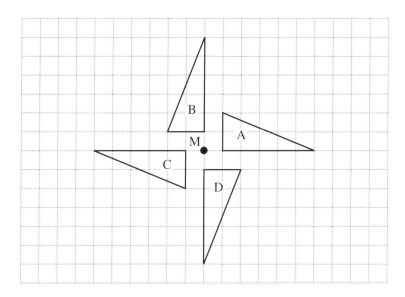

Write down the clockwise rotation about M which will move:

(a) A onto B   (b) A onto C   (c) A onto D   (d) B onto A

(e) B onto C   (f) B onto D   (g) C onto A   (h) C onto B

(i) C onto D   (j) D onto A   (k) D onto B   (l) D onto C

3. Look at this diagram.

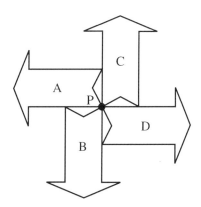

Write down the anticlockwise rotation about P which will move:

(a) A onto B   (b) A onto C   (c) A onto D   (d) B onto A

(e) B onto C   (f) B onto D   (g) C onto A   (h) C onto B

(i) C onto D   (j) D onto A   (k) D onto B   (l) D onto C

8.4 Reflectional symmetry

A shape has **reflectional symmetry** if one half of the shape reflects onto the other.

This shape has reflectional symmetry because this mirror line can be drawn on it.

The mirror line is called a **line of symmetry**.

Some shapes have several lines of symmetry.
This square has four lines of symmetry.

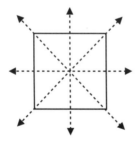

Exercise 8D

Trace each diagram onto squared paper and mark all the lines of symmetry on each shape.

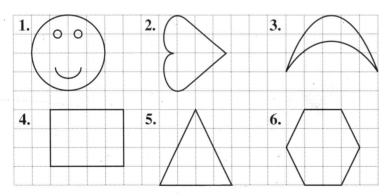

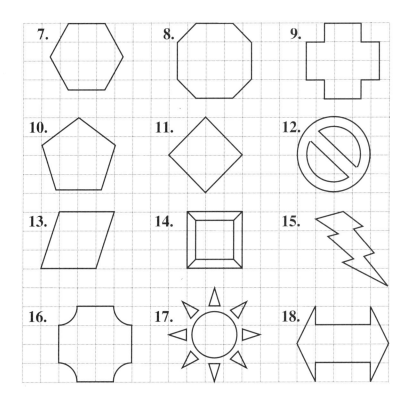

8.5 Rotational symmetry

The **order of rotational symmetry** of a shape is the number of times it fits back into its original position when it is rotated through 360°.

This shape has **rotational symmetry of order 2** because it fits back into its original position twice when it is rotated through 360°.

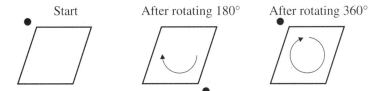

This shape has **rotational symmetry of order 4** because it fits back into its original position 4 times when it is rotated through 360°.

Exercise 8E

1. State the order of rotational symmetry of each shape.

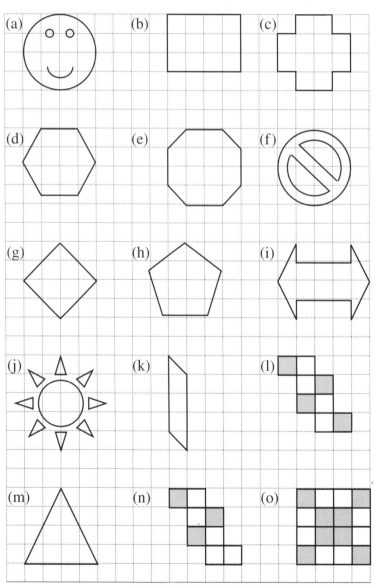

Hint:

If a shape only fits back after a full turn, it has order of rotational symmetry 1.

2. (i) Copy and complete each shape so that the arrow lines are lines of symmetry.
 (ii) State the order of rotational symmetry of each completed shape.

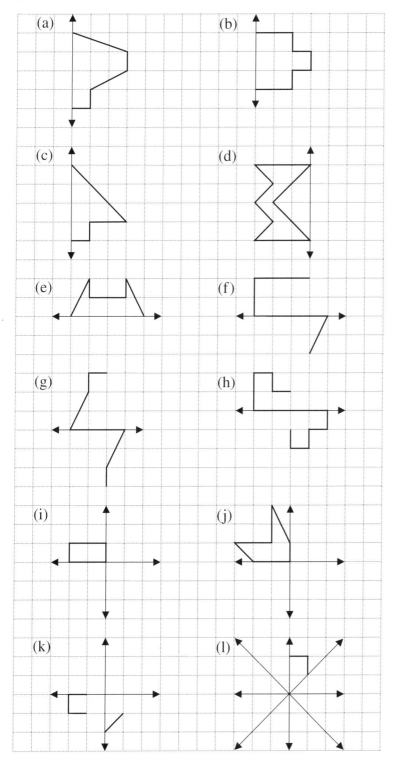

8.6 Enlargements

An **enlargement** changes the size of a shape. Enlargements are usually completed on square grids.

This shape is drawn on a 1 cm grid.   This is the shape drawn on a 2 cm grid.

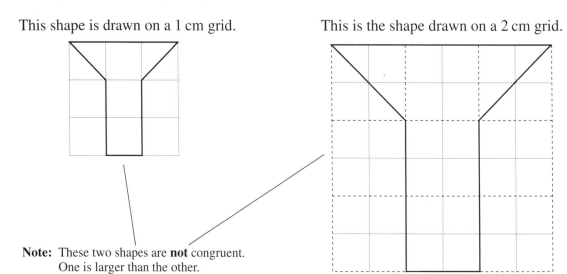

Note: These two shapes are **not** congruent. One is larger than the other.

The shape has been **enlarged with a scale factor of 2**.

Exercise 8F

1. Draw a 2 cm grid on squared paper. Use the grid to enlarge each of these shapes with a scale factor of 2.

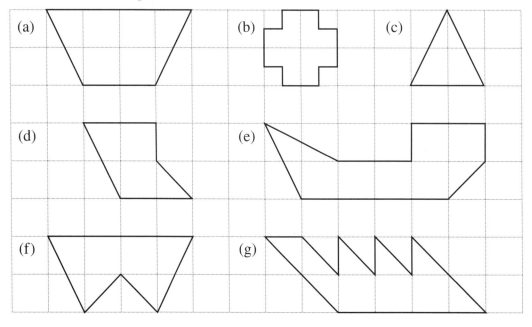

2. Draw a 3 cm grid on squared paper. Use the grid to enlarge
each of these shapes with a scale factor of 3.

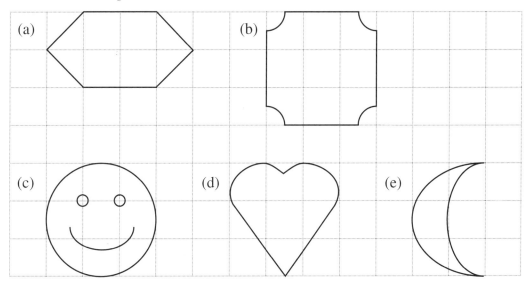

8.7 Fractional enlargements

A **fractional enlargement** makes a shape smaller.

This shape is drawn on a 2 cm grid.

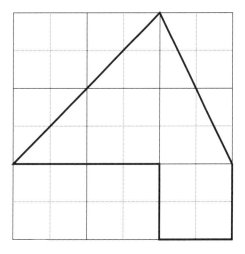

This is the shape drawn on a 1 cm grid.

The shape has been
enlarged with a scale factor of $\frac{1}{2}$.

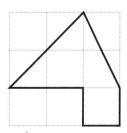

MODULE 5

Exercise 8G

1. The shapes below are drawn on a 2 cm grid. Use a 1 cm grid to enlarge each of these shapes with a scale factor of $\frac{1}{2}$.

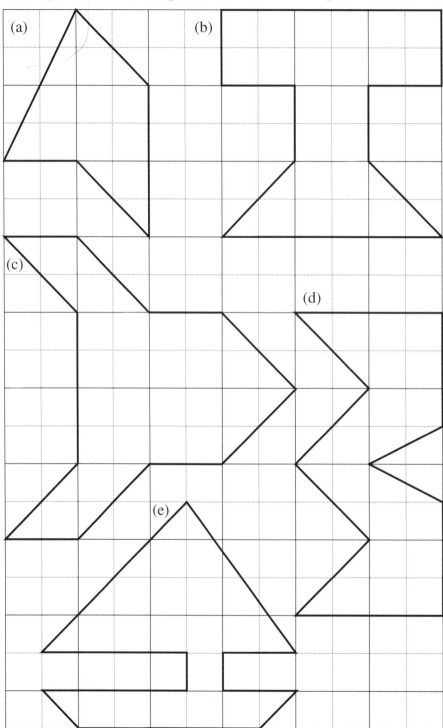

2. The shapes below are drawn on a 3 cm grid. Use a 1 cm grid
to enlarge each of these shapes with a scale factor of $\frac{1}{3}$.

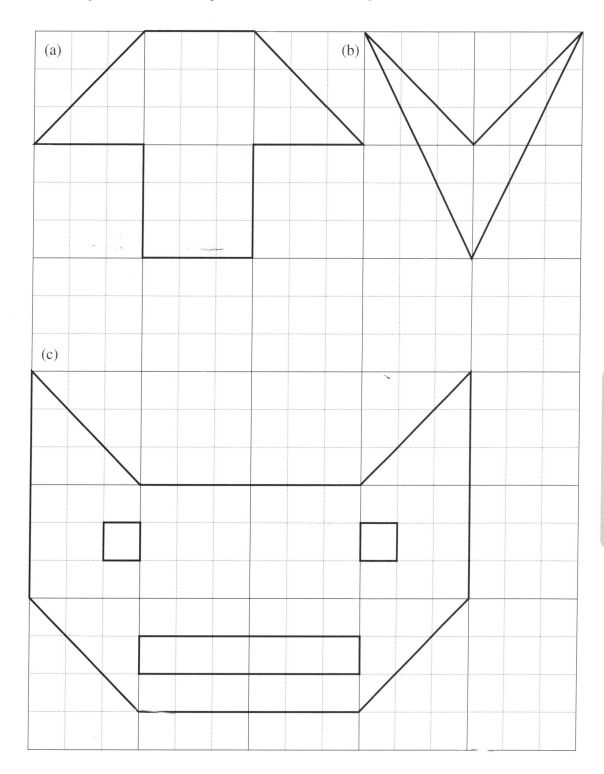

Summary

1. A translation slides a shape from one position to another without turning it.

   Translations are often written in a vertical bracket.

   The horizontal movement is always put at the top of the bracket.

   A plus sign shows that the movement is to the **right** or **up**.

   A minus sign shows that the movement is to the **left** or **down**.

Checkout AS8

1. Use vertical brackets to write down the translations which move the shaded moon to each new position.

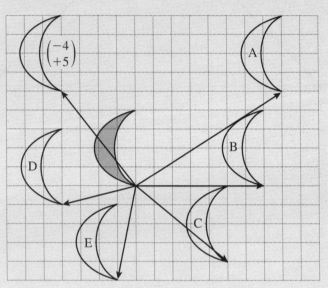

2. A **reflection** makes an image of a shape in a mirror line.

2. Copy this diagram and draw the image of each object.

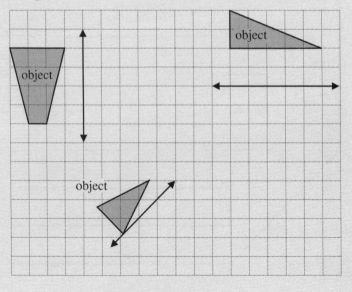

3. A **rotation** moves a shape by turning it about a point called the centre of rotation.

3. (a) Write down the anticlockwise rotations about M which move the shaded triangle to positions A, B and C.

(b) Write down the clockwise rotations about M which move the shaded triangle to positions A, B and C.

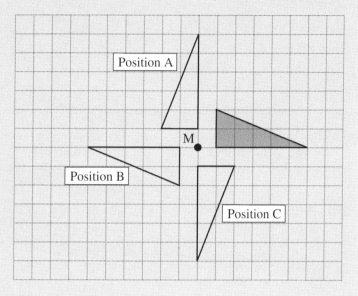

4. A shape has **reflectional symmetry** if a mirror line can be drawn which reflects one half of the shape onto the other. The mirror line is called a **line of symmetry**.

The **order of rotational symmetry** of a shape is the number of times it fits back into its original position when it is rotated through 360°.

4. (a) Copy and complete each shape so that the arrow lines are lines of symmetry.

(b) State the order of rotational symmetry of each completed shape.

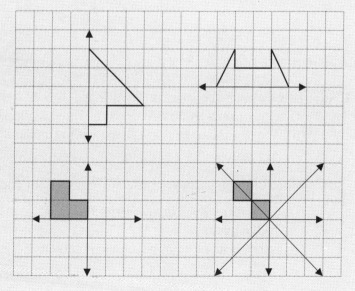

MODULE 5

5. An **enlargement** changes the size of a shape.

This means the image is not congruent to the original shape.

5. Draw a 2 cm grid on squared paper. Use the grid to enlarge this shape with a scale factor of 2.

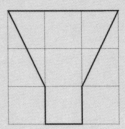

6. A **fractional enlargement** makes a shape smaller.

6. The shape below is drawn on a 2 cm grid. Use a 1 cm grid to enlarge the shape with a scale factor of $\frac{1}{2}$.

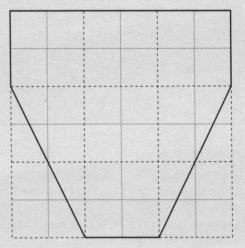

Revision exercise AS8

1. (a) This diagram shows a six-sided shape.
  (i) Copy the diagram and draw the line of symmetry.
  (ii) What is the name for a shape with six sides?

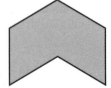

(b) Three of these shapes are used in a design for a badge.

  (i) How many lines of symmetry does this badge have?
  (ii) What is its order of rotational symmetry? [NEAB]

2. (a) The position of a point P is shown.

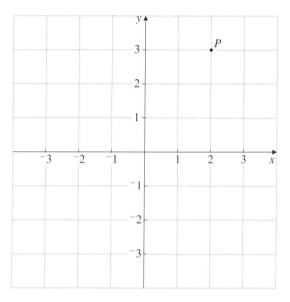

   (i) What are the co-ordinates of P?
   (ii) *P* is reflected in the *x*-axis.
        On a copy of the diagram above, mark the new
        position of *P*.
(b) The triangle below is rotated half a turn about the point *X*.
     Draw the new position of the triangle on a copy of the diagram.

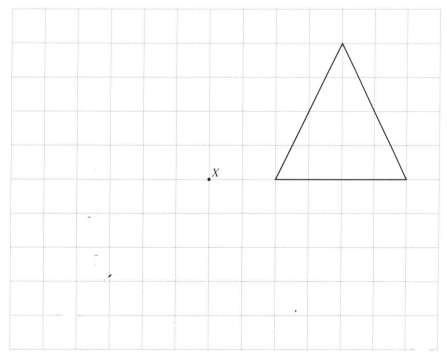

[SEG]

3. The diagram shows a rectangle *ABCD*.
The co-ordinates of *A*, *B* and *C* are given.

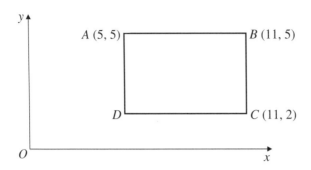

(a) Write down the co-ordinates of *D*.

(b) The rectangle has two lines of symmetry.

    (i) Draw these two lines on a copy of the diagram.

    (ii) Write down the equations of the lines of symmetry.

(c) The rectangle *ABCD* has been translated **9 units to the left and 4 units down**. Its new position is shown by the rectangle *EFGH*.

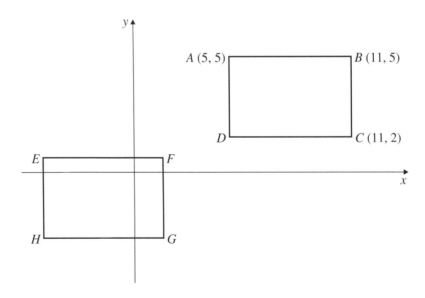

    (i) Write down the co-ordinates of *E*.

    (ii) Describe the translation that would move the rectangle back to its original position.   [NEAB]

4. 'L' shapes are made from 4 squares of side 1 cm as shown.

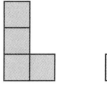

(a) (i) Two of these shapes are put together to make a rectangle.
One of the shapes is drawn on the grid below.
Copy the diagram and draw the other L shape to complete the rectangle.

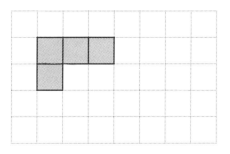

(ii) On your rectangle draw all the lines of symmetry.

(b) On a grid show how two L shapes can be put together to make a different shape with line symmetry.

(c) On a grid show how two L shapes can be put together to make a shape with rotational symmetry.

[NEAB]

5. A square is placed against a 2 by 3 rectangle as shown. The square is rotated 90° clockwise about the point A into the position shown.

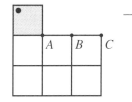 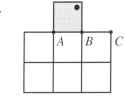

(a) On a copy of this diagram show the position of the square and the black dot corner after it is rotated by 90° about the point B.

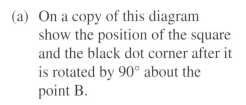

(b) On a copy of this diagram show the position of the square and the black dot at the corner after it is rotated by 180° about the point C.

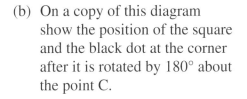

[NEAB]

AS9 SHAPE AND SPACE 5

This unit will show you how to:

- Calculate perimeters
- Find areas of shapes made from rectangles
- Calculate the area of a parallelogram
- Find the area of a triangle
- Calculate areas of compound shapes

Before you start:

You should know how to...	Check in AS9
1. Multiply decimals. For example $5 \times 4{\cdot}6$ is like $5 \times 46 \div 10$ $\quad 5 \times 46 = 230$ so $5 \times 4.6 = 23$	**1.** Work out: (a) $2 \times 3{\cdot}5$ (b) $3 \times 4{\cdot}1$ (c) $5 \times 6{\cdot}2$ (d) $3{\cdot}6 \times 10$ (e) $4 \times 3{\cdot}8$ (f) $9{\cdot}3 \times 10$ (g) $3{\cdot}4 \times 1{\cdot}2$ (h) $8{\cdot}4 \times 9{\cdot}5$
2. Divide by 2 in your head. For example $27 \div 2$ is between $26 \div 2$ and $28 \div 2$ so $27 \div 2 = 13\frac{1}{2}$ or $13{\cdot}5$	**2.** Write down the answers to: (a) $17 \div 2$ (b) $28 \div 2$ (c) $17{\cdot}4 \div 2$ (d) $35 \div 2$ (e) $41 \div 2$ (f) $27{\cdot}4 \div 2$ (g) $87{\cdot}3 \div 2$ (h) $56{\cdot}7 \div 2$

9.1 Perimeters

The distance round the outside of a shape is called its **perimeter**.

The perimeter of this rectangle is 16 cm.

You just add up the lengths: $6 + 2 + 6 + 2 = 16$

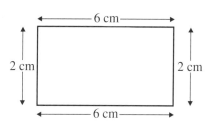

Example

Find the perimeter of this shape drawn on a 1 centimetre grid.

The diagonal of a 1 cm square is approximately 1·4 cm long.

The perimeter of the
shape $= 4 + 1·4 + 1·4 + 1 + 2 + 3 = 12·8$ cm.

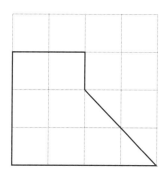

Exercise 9A

Find the perimeter of each of these shapes drawn on a 1 cm grid.

1.

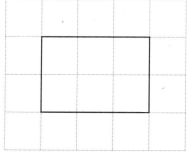

2.

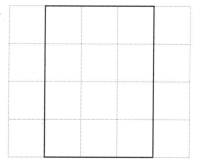

3.

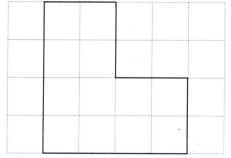

4.

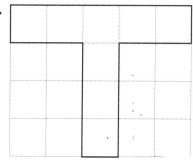

MODULE 5

5.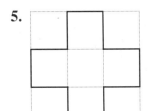

6.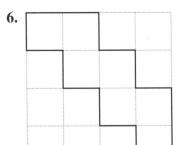

7.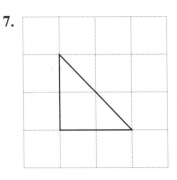

8.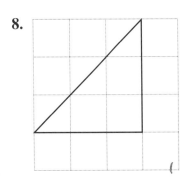

9.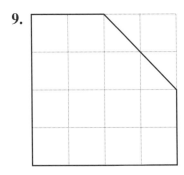

10.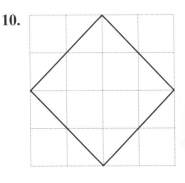

11.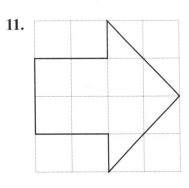

12.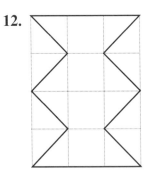

13.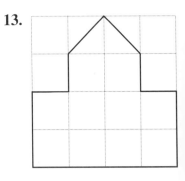

14.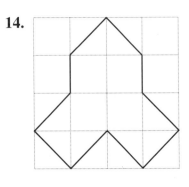

15.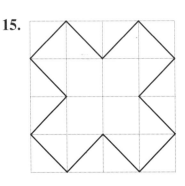

MODULE 5

9.2 Area by counting squares

The area of a shape can be measured
in square centimetres. This is a square centimetre.

Example

Find the area of this shape drawn on a 1 centimetre grid.

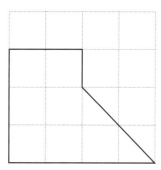

Each half square has an area of 0·5 square centimetres.

By counting squares,
the area of the shape = 7 + 0·5 + 0·5 = 8 square centimetres.

The answer is normally shortened to 8 cm².

Exercise 9B

Find the area of each of these shapes drawn on a 1 cm grid.

1.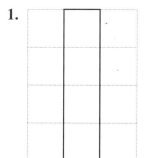

2.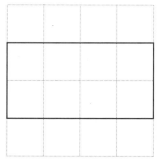

3.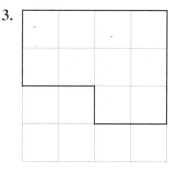

4.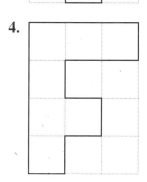

5.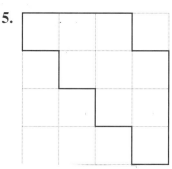

6.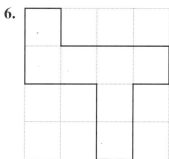

7.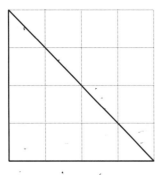

8.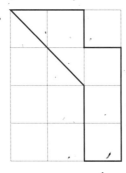

9.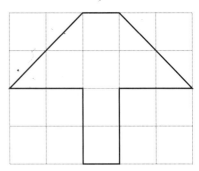

10.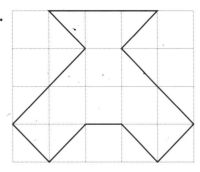

11.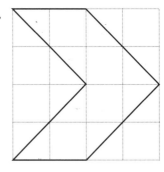

12.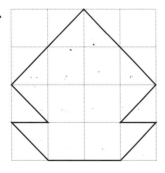

13.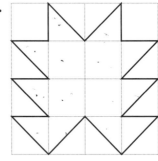

14.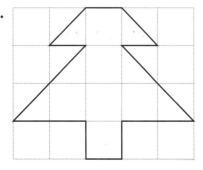

15.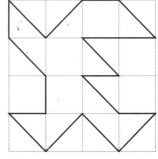

9.3 Area of a rectangle by calculation

You can find the area of this rectangle in two ways.

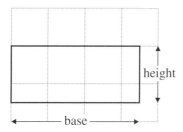

First, by counting squares:

Area = three whole squares plus four half squares plus one quarter square
   $= 3 + 0.5 + 0.5 + 0.5 + 0.5 + 0.25 = 5.25 \text{ cm}^2$

Second, by using this formula for the area of a rectangle:

Area = base × height
   $= 3.5 × 1.5 = 5.25 \text{ cm}^2$

Areas may also be calculated in square metres (m^2) or square millimetres (mm^2).

Examples

Find the area of these rectangles.

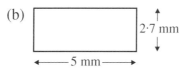

(a) Area $= 2 × 4.5 = 9 \text{ m}^2$ (b) Area $= 5 × 2.7 = 13.5 \text{ mm}^2$

Exercise 9C

Find the area of each rectangle.

1. 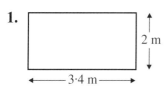   **2.** 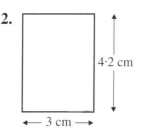   **3.**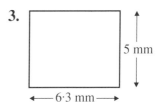

MODULE 5

4.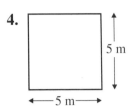

5 m

5 m

5.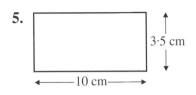

3·5 cm

10 cm

6.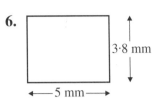

3·8 mm

5 mm

7.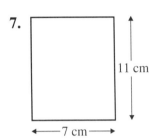

11 cm

7 cm

8.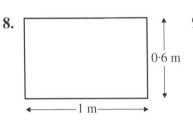

0·6 m

1 m

9.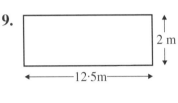

2 m

12·5m

10. Copy and complete the table for each square:

Square	Base	Height	Area
(a)	1 cm	1 cm	
(b)	10 mm	10 mm	

Remember: 1 cm = 10 mm

11. Look at your table in Question 10.
Now copy and complete:

$$1 \text{ cm}^2 = \square \text{ mm}^2$$

12. Copy and complete the table for each square:

Square	Base	Height	Area
(a)	1 m	1 m	
(b)	100 cm	100 cm	

Remember: 1 m = 100 cm

13. Look at your table in Question 12.
Now copy and complete:

$$1 \text{ m}^2 = \square \text{ cm}^2$$

9.4 Areas of shapes made from rectangles

You can find the area of a more complex shape by splitting it
into rectangles.

Example

Find the area of this shape.

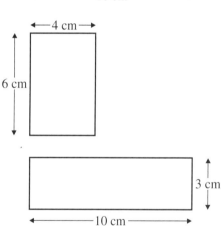

Split the shape into rectangles.

Area = $(4 \times 6) + (10 \times 3) = 24 + 30 = 54 \, \text{cm}^2$

Exercise 9D

Find the area of each shape.

1.

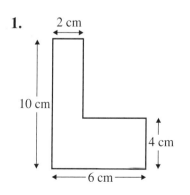

2.

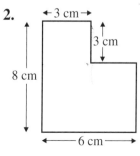

3.

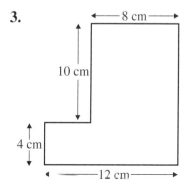

MODULE 5

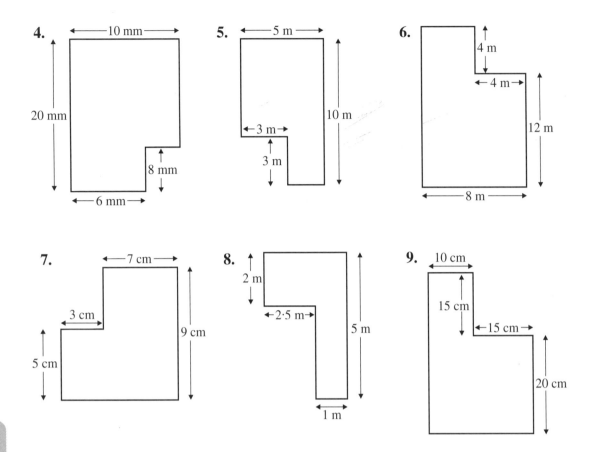

9.5 Area of a parallelogram

Any parallelogram can be changed into a rectangle with the
same height and base length.

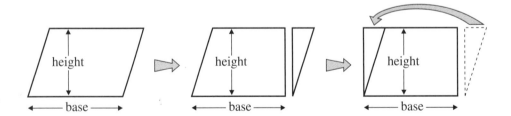

Rectangles and parallelograms have the same area formula:

Area = base × height

Remember:

It is the perpendicular
height, not the slant
height.

Example

Find the area of this parallelogram.

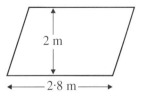

Area = base × height = 2·8 × 2 = 5·6 m²

Exercise 9E

Find the area of each parallelogram.

1.
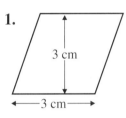

2.
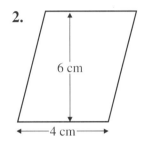

3.
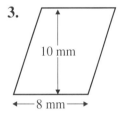

4.
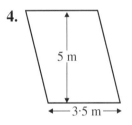

5.
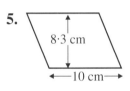

6.
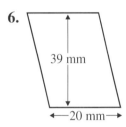

7.
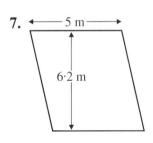

8.
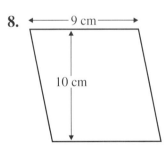

9.
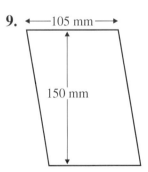

10.
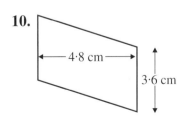

11.
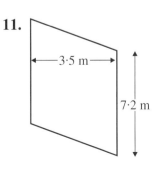

12.
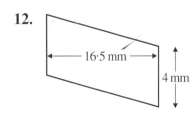

MODULE 5

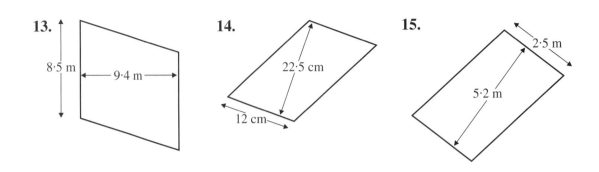

13. 8·5 m, 9·4 m

14. 22·5 cm, 12 cm

15. 2·5 m, 5·2 m

9.6 Area of a triangle

Any triangle is half of a parallelogram with the same base and height.

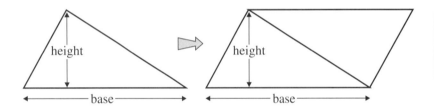

> **Remember:**
> The height is the perpendicular height.

The formula for the area of a triangle is therefore:

$$\text{Area} = \tfrac{1}{2} \text{ of (base} \times \text{height)}$$
$$= \tfrac{1}{2} \times \text{base} \times \text{height}$$

Example

Find the area of this triangle.

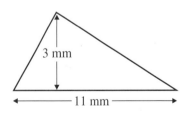

3 mm

11 mm

$$\text{Area} = \tfrac{1}{2} \times \text{base} \times \text{height} = \tfrac{1}{2} \times 11 \times 3 = \tfrac{1}{2} \times 33 = 16\cdot5 \text{ mm}^2$$

MODULE 5

Exercise 9F

Find the area of each triangle.

1.
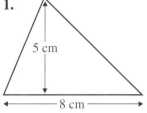
5 cm
8 cm

2.
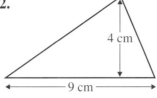
4 cm
9 cm

3.
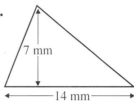
7 mm
14 mm

4.
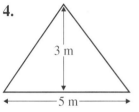
3 m
5 m

5.
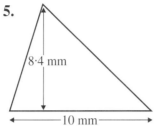
8·4 mm
10 mm

6.
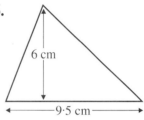
6 cm
9·5 cm

7.
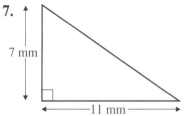
7 mm
11 mm

8.
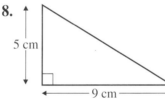
5 cm
9 cm

9.
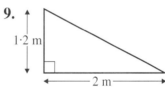
1·2 m
2 m

10.
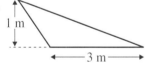
1 m
3 m

11.
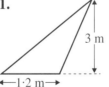
3 m
1·2 m

12.
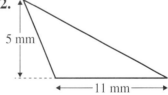
5 mm
11 mm

13.
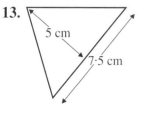
5 cm
7·5 cm

14.
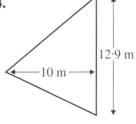
12·9 m
10 m

15.
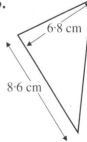
6·8 cm
8·6 cm

9.7 Area of a compound shape

A compound shape is made from two or more basic shapes.
To find the area you need to split it up into shapes you know.

Example

Find the area of this shape.

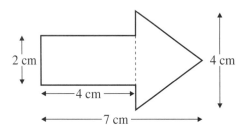

Split the shape up.

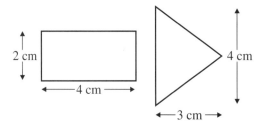

Area $= (2 \times 4) + \frac{1}{2}$ of $(3 \times 4) = 8 + 6 = 14 \text{ cm}^2$

Exercise 9G

Find the area of each shape.

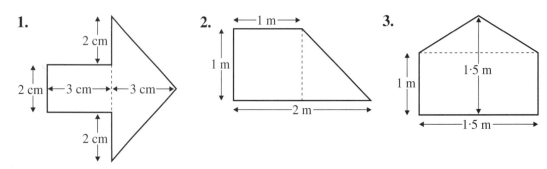

MODULE 5

4.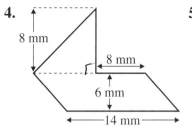

5.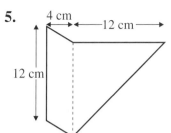

6.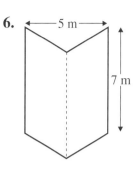

7.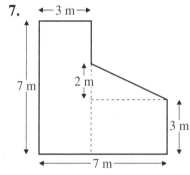

8.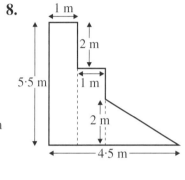

9.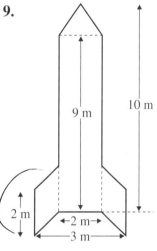

10.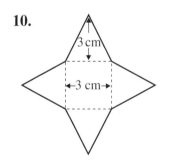

11.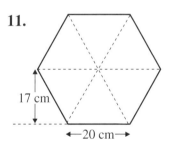

12.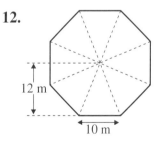

MODULE 5

13. This drawing shows a plan for a square garden. The shaded area will be a patio and the rest of the garden will be grass.

   (a) Calculate the total area of the garden.
   (b) Calculate the area of the patio.
   (c) Calculate the area of grass.

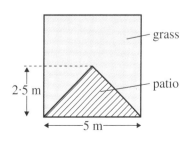

14. This drawing shows a patio door with three glass windows.
The glass in each window is 2 metres by 1·4 metres.

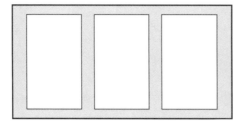

(a) Calculate the area of glass in one window.
(b) Calculate the area of glass in the door.
(c) Glass costs £2·50 a square metre. Calculate the cost of
the glass in the door.

15. Use 1 centimetre squared paper to answer this question.
(a) Rectangle A is 8 cm high. It has a perimeter of 24 cm.
Draw rectangle A.
(b) Rectangle B is 5 cm wide. It has an area of 30 cm².
Draw rectangle B.
(c) Rectangle C is 9 cm high. It has the same area as a 6 cm
square. Draw rectangle C.

Summary   Checkout AS9

1. The distance around the outside of a shape is called its **perimeter**.
The area of a shape is measured in square centimetres (cm²), square metres (m²) or square millimetres (mm²).

1. (a) Find the perimeter of this shape drawn on a 1 centimetre grid.

(b) Find the area of the shape.

2. The area of a rectangle can be found with the formula
Area = base × height

2. Find the area of these rectangles.

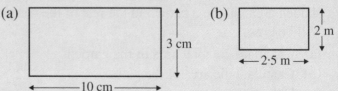

(a) 10 cm, 3 cm   (b) 2·5 m, 2 m

3. The area of some shapes can be found by dividing them into rectangles.

3. Find the area of this shape.

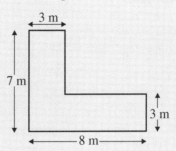

4. The area of a parallelogram can also be found with the formula

Area = base × height

4. Find the area of this parallelogram.

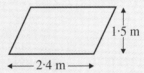

5. The area of a triangle can be be found with this formula

Area = $\frac{1}{2}$ × base × height

5. Find the area of these triangles.

(a)   (b)

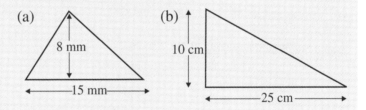

6. The area of a compound shape can be found by splitting it into basic shapes.

6. Find the area of this shape.

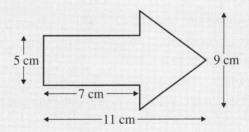

MODULE 5

Revision exercise AS9

1. This is a 1 cm grid.

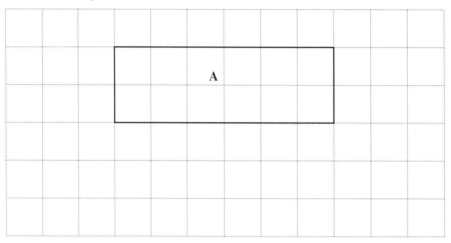

(a) What is the perimeter of rectangle *A*?

(b) On a copy of the grid, draw **two different** rectangles which have the same perimeter as rectangle *A*. Label them *B* and *C*. [NEAB]

2. A rectangle is shown.

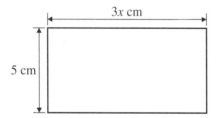

The length of the rectangle is $3x$ cm.
The width of the rectangle is 5 cm.

(a) Write down an expression for the perimeter of the rectangle.
Write your answer in its simplest form.

(b) Write down an expression for the area of the rectangle.
Write your answer in its simplest form.

(c) (i) The area of the rectangle is 105 cm².
Use your answer to part (b) to write down an equation for the area of the rectangle.

(ii) Solve your equation in part (i) and use your answer to find the **perimeter** of the rectangle. [SEG]

3. (a) The base of a triangle is 8 cm. The height is 6 cm.

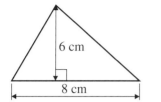

Not to scale

What is the area of the triangle?

(b) The area of a rectangle is 24 cm².

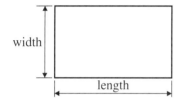

Not to scale

Write down a possible pair of values for the length and
the width of the rectangle.   [SEG]

4. A rectangle is 4 cm wide and 9 cm long.
What is the length of the side of a square with exactly the
same area?

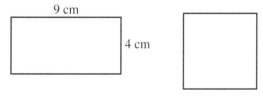

[NEAB]

5. The diagram shows a rectangle.

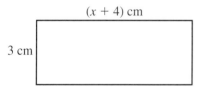

Not to scale

(a) The rectangle has width 3 cm and length $(x + 4)$ cm.
Write an expression for the area of the rectangle.
The diagram shows a right-angled triangle.

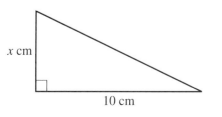

Not to scale

MODULE 5

(b) The triangle has base 10 cm and height x cm.
Write an expression for the area of the triangle.
Give your answer in its simplest form.

(c) The area of the triangle is equal to the area of the
rectangle.
By forming an equation work out the value of x. [SEG]

6. The diagram shows two shapes.

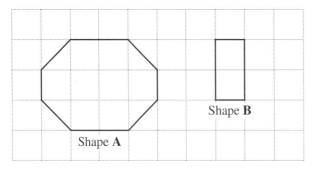

(a) Copy the diagram and draw all the lines of symmetry
on Shape **A**.
(i)   Find the area of Shape **A**.
(ii) Find the perimeter of Shape **B**.   [SEG]

7. By measuring the base and the height calculate the area of
this triangle.

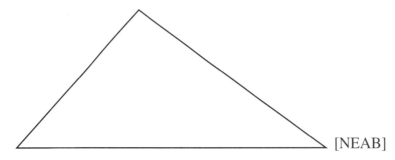

[NEAB]

AS10 SHAPE AND SPACE 6

This unit will show you how to:

- Find the radius and diameter of a circle
- Find the surface area of a cuboid
- Find the volume of a prism

Before you start:

You should know how to...	Check in AS10
1. Multiply by 3·14 For example $\quad$ 3·14 × 5 is like $\quad$ 314 × 5 = 1570 so $\quad$ 3·14 × 5 = 15·7	**1.** Find: (a) 3·14 × 10 $\qquad$ (b) 3·14 × 12 (c) 3·14 × 5·2 $\qquad$ (d) 3·14 × 5 × 5 (e) 3·14 × 8 × 8 $\qquad$ (f) 3·14 × 2 × 2

2. Sketch the net of a cuboid.
Here is a sketch of a 2 cm × 3 cm × 5 cm cuboid.

3 cm

5 cm $\quad$ 2 cm

3 cm

2 cm

2 cm

5 cm

You don't have to mark **all** the lengths.
Just the bottom lengths will do!

2. Sketch the net of a cuboid measuring:
(a) 2 cm by 1 cm by 6 cm
(b) 3 cm by 4 cm by 6 cm

10.1 The radius and diameter of a circle

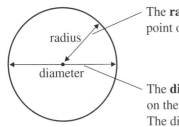

The **radius** is a line from the centre to a point on the circle.

The **diameter** is a line joining two points on the circle and passing through the centre. The diameter is twice as long as the radius.

You draw circles with a pair of compasses.

Exercise 10A

1. Draw circles with a radius of:
   (a) 5 cm   (b) 3 cm   (c) 6 cm   (d) 20 mm   (e) 45 mm

2. Draw circles with a diameter of:
   (a) 8 cm   (b) 6 cm   (c) 5 cm   (d) 110 mm   (e) 70 mm

3. Find the diameter of a circle with a radius of:
   (a) 5 cm   (b) 7 cm   (c) 2·5 cm   (d) 6·4 m   (e) 9·3 mm

4. Find the radius of a circle with a diameter of:
   (a) 20 cm   (b) 32 cm   (c) 7 cm   (d) 15 m   (e) 16·6 mm

10.2 Finding the circumference if you know the diameter or radius

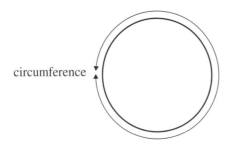

circumference

The **circumference** of a circle is the distance round the circle. It is a special name for the perimeter of a circle.

The circumference is difficult to measure accurately. If you know the radius or diameter then you can calculate the circumference.

MODULE 5

To find the circumference, the diameter is multiplied by a number close to 3.

The number 3·1 gives an approximate answer.
The number 3·14 gives a more accurate answer.
The number 3·142 gives an even more accurate answer.

The Greek letter π (pi) is used to represent all these possible multipliers. So you can write:

Circumference $= \pi \times$ diameter

or

$C = \pi d$

You will usually be told which approximation to use for π.

Example 1

Find the circumference of this circle if $\pi = 3\cdot1$.

$C = \pi d = 3\cdot1 \times 5 = 15\cdot5$ cm

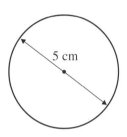

Example 2

Find the circumference of this circle if $\pi = 3\cdot14$.

The radius is 4 m, so the diameter $= 2 \times 4 = 8$ m
$C = \pi d = 3\cdot14 \times 8 = 25\cdot12$ m

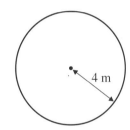

Exercise 10B

1. Find the circumference of each circle if $\pi = 3\cdot1$.

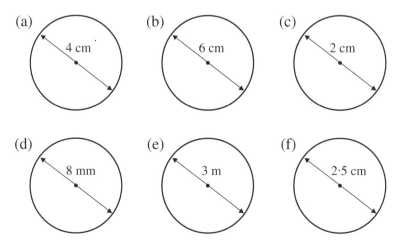

(a) 4 cm

(b) 6 cm

(c) 2 cm

(d) 8 mm

(e) 3 m

(f) 2·5 cm

MODULE 5

2. Find the circumference of each circle if $\pi = 3.14$.

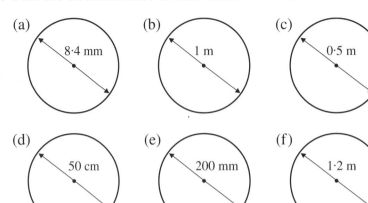

(a) 8·4 mm   (b) 1 m   (c) 0·5 m

(d) 50 cm   (e) 200 mm   (f) 1·2 m

3. Find the circumference of each circle if $\pi = 3.1$.

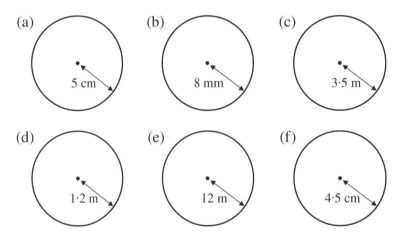

(a) 5 cm   (b) 8 mm   (c) 3·5 m

(d) 1·2 m   (e) 12 m   (f) 4·5 cm

4. Find the circumference of each circle if $\pi = 3.14$.

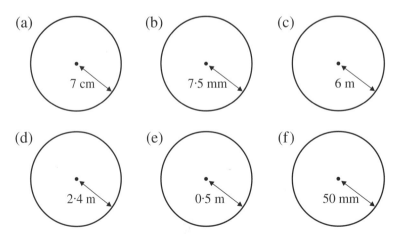

(a) 7 cm   (b) 7·5 mm   (c) 6 m

(d) 2·4 m   (e) 0·5 m   (f) 50 mm

5. The front wheel on John's bike has a diameter of 70 cm.

(a) What is the circumference of the wheel?
   Take π to be 3·14.
(b) John cycles along the road. How far will he travel each
   time the front wheel turns 10 times?

6. A ring road is to be built around the town of Inkdoor.
   It will be a circle with a diameter of 7 miles.

(a) What is the length of the ring road to the nearest mile?
   Take π to be 3·14.
(b) Salina travels all the way round the ring road at an
   average speed of 66 miles per hour.
   How long will this journey take?

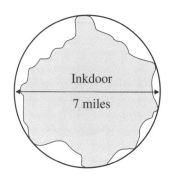

10.3 Finding the area if you know the radius

The area of a circle is found using the formula:

   Area = π × radius × radius

or

   $A = \pi r^2$

Hint:

Many people lose marks
in an exam by mixing up
the formulae for the
circumference and area.
Try to remember which
is which.

Example

Find the area of this circle. Use $\pi = 3{\cdot}14$.

$A = \pi r^2 = 3{\cdot}14 \times 4 \times 4 = 50{\cdot}24 \text{ m}^2$

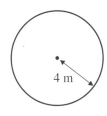

MODULE 5

Exercise 10C

1. Find the area of each circle if $\pi = 3\cdot 1$.

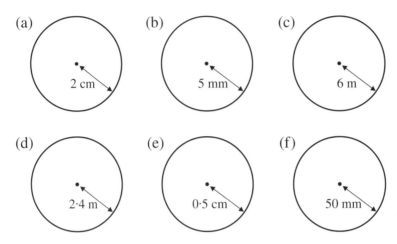

(a) 2 cm

(b) 5 mm

(c) 6 m

(d) 2·4 m

(e) 0·5 cm

(f) 50 mm

2. Find the area of each circle if $\pi = 3\cdot 14$.

(a) 1 cm

(b) 8 mm

(c) 3·5 m

(d) 1·2 m

(e) 12 m

(f) 4·5 cm

3.

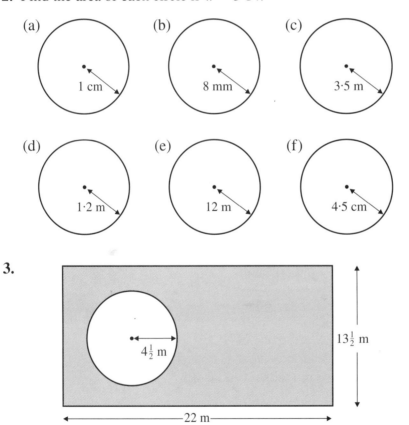

$13\frac{1}{2}$ m

$4\frac{1}{2}$ m

22 m

The diagram shows a rectangular garden measuring 22 m by $13\frac{1}{2}$ m.
There is a circular pond in the garden with a radius of $4\frac{1}{2}$ m.

(a) What is the total area of the garden?
(b) What is the area of the pond? Take π to be 3·14.
(c) The garden is to be seeded with grass.
   What area will be seeded?
(d) One box of grass seed covers 15 m².
   How many boxes will be needed?

4. A wooden door has a glass window in the form of a half circle.

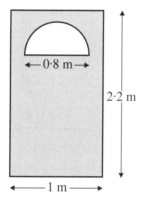

(a) Calculate the area of the door, including the window.
(b) Calculate the area of a circle with a radius of 0·4 m.
   Use $\pi = 3\cdot14$.
(c) Calculate the area of the glass in the window.
(d) The door is to be treated with wood stain.
   Calculate the area to be treated.

5. A French cheese is sold in two different boxes.
   Both boxes are cylinders.

One box has a radius of 5 cm, the other box has a radius of 10 cm. The top of both boxes is covered with a foil label.
(a) Find the area of the label on the smaller box.
   Use $\pi = 3\cdot14$.
(b) Find the area of the label on the big box. Use $\pi = 3\cdot14$.
(c) Divide the area of the big box label by the area of the small box label. What do you notice?

MODULE 5

10.4 Finding the surface area of a cuboid

This net of this cuboid shows that it has six faces.

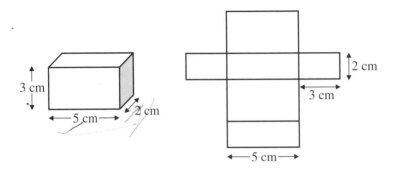

There is more about nets on page 272.

Total surface area = (2 × 3) + (2 × 3) + (3 × 5) + (3 × 5) + (2 × 5) + (2 × 5)

= 6 + 6 + 15 + 15 + 10 + 10 = 62 cm²

Exercise 10D

1. Sketch the net of each cuboid and calculate the total surface area.

(a)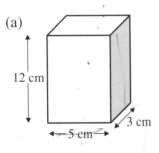

(b)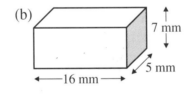

(c)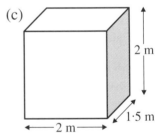

(d)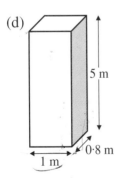

(e)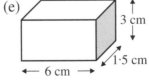

(f)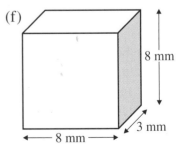

MODULE 5

2. A drinks manufacturer is considering two different cuboid-shaped containers for a new fruit juice. Both containers hold the same amount of juice.

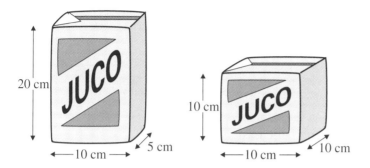

(a) Find the total surface area of the 20 cm by 10 cm by 5 cm container.
(b) Find the total surface area of the 10 cm by 10 cm by 10 cm container.

The containers are made from a special foil-covered card.
50 cm² of the card costs 1p.

(c) Find the cost of the card used in each container.

3. DJ's cat food is sold in tins like this:

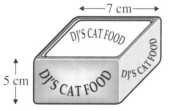

The area of the top of the tin is 56 cm². Work out the area of the label, which goes all the way round the sides of the tin.

4. A box of toy wooden bricks contains 25 cubic bricks.

(a) Find the total surface area of one brick.
(b) Find the total surface area of 25 bricks.

Painting the bricks costs 4p per 100 cm².

(c) Find the cost of painting 25 bricks.

MODULE 5

10.5 Finding volume by counting cubes

The volume of a solid is the amount of space it fills. Volume is measured in cubes. The common units are:

cubic millimetre   (mm³)
cubic centimetre   (cm³)
cubic metre   (m³)

Example

Find the volume of these solids if each cube has a volume of 1 cm³.

(a) 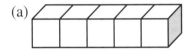   (b)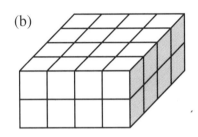

(a) Volume = 5 cm³   (b) Volume = 32 cm³

Exercise 10E

Find the volume of each solid if each cube has a volume of 1 cm³.

1. 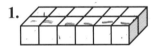   2.   3.

4. 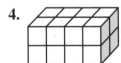   5.   6.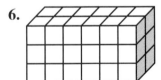

7. 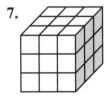   8. 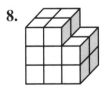   9.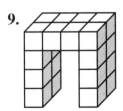

10.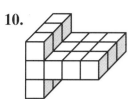

11.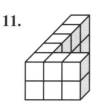

12.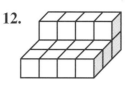

10.6 Finding the volume of a cuboid by using the formula

The volume of a cuboid can be found by using the formula:

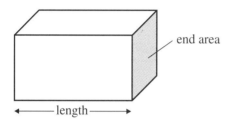

Volume = end area × length

Example

Find the volume of this cuboid.

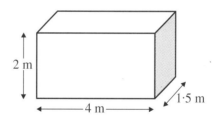

end area = 2 × 1·5 = 3 m²

volume = 3 × 4 = 12 m³

Exercise 10F

1. Find the volume of each cuboid.

(a)

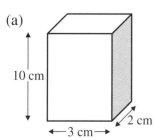

(b)

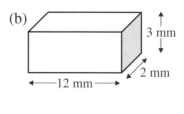

(c)

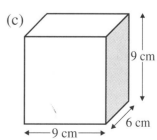

MODULE 5

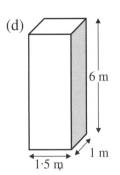

(d) 6 m, 1 m, 1·5 m

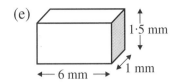

(e) 1·5 mm, 6 mm, 1 mm

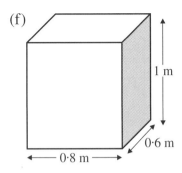

(f) 1 m, 0·8 m, 0·6 m

2. The diagram shows a matchbox measuring
5 cm by 4 cm by 2 cm.

(a) Find the volume of the matchbox.

12 of these matchboxes are packed in a carton with a
base 10 cm by 8 cm.

Find:
(b) The volume of the carton.
(c) The height of the carton.

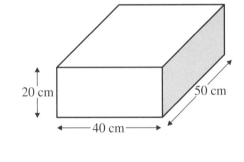

3. The fuel tank of a car is a cuboid
50 cm by 40 cm by 20 cm.

(a) Find the volume of the fuel tank.

One litre of fuel has a volume of 1 000 cm³.

(b) How many litres of fuel will the tank hold?
(c) If petrol costs 75p per litre, how much will it
cost to fill the fuel tank?

4. A packet of icing sugar is 9 cm by 6 cm by 16 cm.
(a) Find the volume of the box.
(b) The sugar in a new packet fills the box to within 1 cm
of the top. Find the volume of sugar in a new packet.
(c) Some of the sugar in a packet has been used. The sugar
in the box is now 9 cm deep. What volume of sugar has
been used?

Sweeto
Icing
Sugar

16 cm, 9 cm, 6 cm

5. (a) What is the name of the cuboid with all
edges the same?
(b) Copy and complete, for these cuboids:

Remember: 1 cm = 10 mm

Length	Width	Height	Volume
1 cm	1 cm	1 cm	
10 mm	10 mm	10 mm	

MODULE 5

6. Study your table in Question 5. Now copy and complete:

$$1 \text{ cm}^3 = \boxed{} \text{ mm}^3$$

7. Sugar cubes have a volume of 1000 mm³.
How many such cubes can be packed in a box
measuring 15 cm by 10 cm by 5 cm?

8. (a) Copy and complete the table.

Length	Width	Height	Volume
1 m	1 m	1 m	
100 cm	100 cm	100 cm	

(b) Copy and complete:

$$1 \text{ m}^3 = \boxed{} \text{ cm}^3$$

9. How many cubic millimetres make 1 m³?

Remember: 1 m = 100 cm = 1 000 mm.

10.7 Finding the volume of a prism

A **prism** is a solid with the same shape along its length.
These are all prisms:

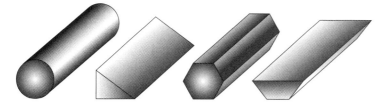

The volume of a prism can be found by using the formula:

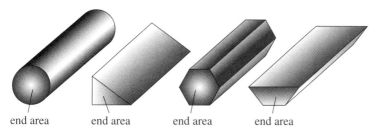

end area   end area   end area   end area

Volume = end area × length

Example

Find the volume of each prism. Use $\pi = 3\cdot14$.

(a)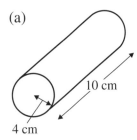

10 cm

4 cm

(b)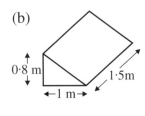

0·8 m

1 m

1·5m

(a) Volume = end area × length
 = $3\cdot14 \times 4 \times 4 \times 10$
 = $502\cdot4$ cm^3

(b) Volume = end area × length
 = $\frac{1}{2}$ of $(0\cdot8 \times 1) \times 1\cdot5$
 = $0\cdot4 \times 1\cdot5$
 = $0\cdot6$ m^3

Exercise 10G

1. Find the volume of each prism. Use $\pi = 3\cdot14$.

(a)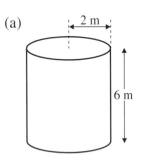

2 m

6 m

(b)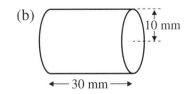

10 mm

30 mm

(c)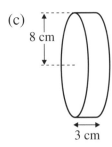

8 cm

3 cm

(d)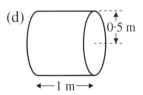

0·5 m

1 m

(e)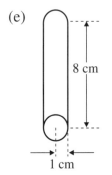

8 cm

1 cm

(f)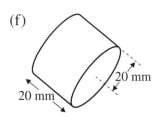

20 mm

20 mm

2. Find the volume of each prism.

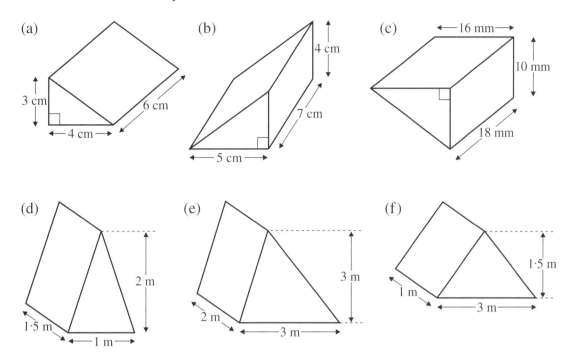

(a)

3 cm

4 cm

6 cm

(b)

4 cm

7 cm

5 cm

(c)

16 mm

10 mm

18 mm

(d)

2 m

1·5 m

1 m

(e)

3 m

2 m

3 m

(f)

1·5 m

1 m

3 m

3. This diagram shows a barn.

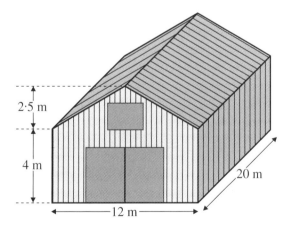

2·5 m

4 m

20 m

12 m

(a) Find the area of a rectangle 4 m by 12 m.
(b) Find the area of a triangle with a base of 12 m and
 a height of 2·5 m.
(c) Find the area of one end of the barn.
(d) Find the volume of the barn.

4. A swimming pool is in the shape of a prism like this:

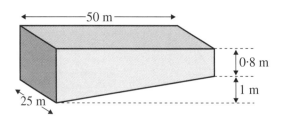

(a) Find the area of a rectangle 50 m by 0·8 m.
(b) Find the area of a triangle with a base of 50 m and a height of 1 m.
(c) The pool is filled with water to a greatest depth of 1·8 m. Find the volume of water in the pool.

5. The coffee urn in a café is a cylinder with a radius of 20 cm and a height of 50 cm.
(a) Find the volume of coffee in the urn when it is full.
(b) Each cup of coffee served has a volume of 125 cm³. How many cups of coffee can be served from a full urn?

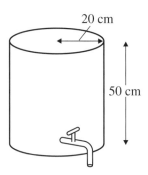

Summary

1. These words are used to describe circles.

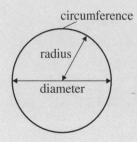

Checkout AS10

1. (a) Draw circles with a radius of:
  (i) 4 cm (ii) 25 mm
  (b) Draw circles with a diameter of:
  (i) 10 cm (ii) 120 mm

2. The circumference of a
circle can be found with
the formula

$C = \pi d$

2. (a) Use $\pi = 3\cdot1$ to find the circumference of a circle with
a radius of:
    (i) 4 cm   (ii) 25 mm
  (b) Use $\pi = 3\cdot14$ to find the circumference of a circle
with a radius of:
    (i) 10 cm   (ii) 120 mm

3. The area of a circle can be
found with the formula:

$A = \pi r^2$

3. Use $\pi = 3\cdot14$ to find the area of a circle with a radius of:
  (a) 8 cm   **(b)** 20 mm

4. The total surface area of a
cuboid can be found by
sketching its net.

4. Sketch the net of this cuboid and calculate its total surface
area.

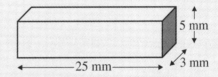

5. Volumes can be found by
counting cubes.

5. Find the volume of this solid if each cube has a volume of
1 cm³.

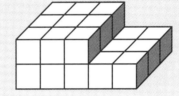

6. The volume of a cuboid can
be found using the formula
Volume = end area × length

6. Find the volume of this cuboid.

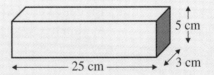

7. The volume of a prism can
also be found using the
formula
Volume = end area × length

7. Find the volume of each prism. Use $\pi = 3\cdot14$.

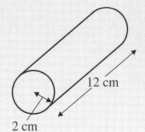
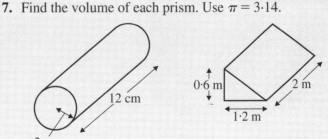

MODULE 5

Revision exercise AS10

1. This cube has edges of 3 cm.
   It is made out of centimetre cubes.

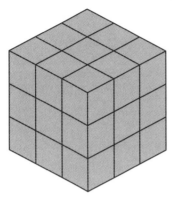

   (a) How many centimetre cubes have been used to make it?

   (b) A line of centimetre cubes through the middle is taken out.

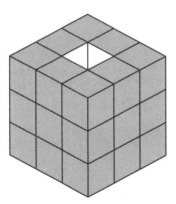

   How many centimetre cubes are left?

   (c) Two more lines of centimetre cubes are taken out.

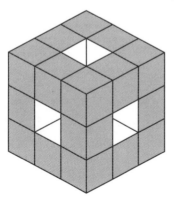

   How many cubes are left now?   [NEAB]

2. A garage has a rectangular base.

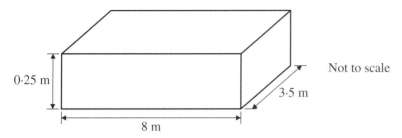

0·25 m

3·5 m

8 m

Not to scale

(a) The base is 8 metres long and 3·5 metres wide.
The depth of the base is 0·25 metres.
What is the volume of the base?

(b) A rectangular hole is dug for the base of a shed.
The volume of soil dug out is $1·2\ m^3$.
The hole is 3 m long and 2 m wide.
How deep is the hole?

(c) A circular fish pond has a radius of 2·1 m.
Calculate the area of the pond.
State your units. [SEG]

3. (a) Draw a circle of radius 5 cm.

(b) Draw a diameter on your circle. Label its ends A and B.

(c) Mark a point, P, anywhere on the circumference of
your circle. Join A to P and P to B.

(d) Use a protractor to measure the angle APB. [NEAB]

4. The plan of a rectangular pond, with a path all round it, is
drawn below.

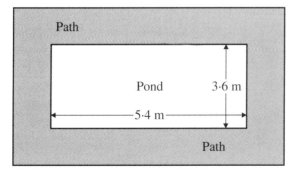

Path

Pond   3·6 m

5·4 m

Path

(a) Calculate the area of the pond, in $m^2.$

(b) The water in the pond is 0.75 m deep.
Calculate the volume of water in the pond, in m^3.

The path around the pond is 1.2 m wide.

MODULE 5

(c) Calculate the area of the path, in m².

The path is made with square slabs of side 0·6 m.

(d) How many slabs are needed? [SEG]

5. Calculate the area of a semi-circle, radius 20 cm.

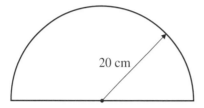

The radius of a semi-circle is 2·5 cm.

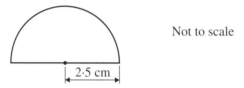

Not to scale

Calculate the area of the semi-circle. [SEG]

6. (a) A shoe box is in the shape of a cuboid.

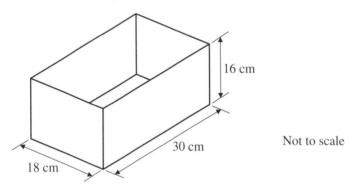

Not to scale

The box is 30 cm long, 18 cm wide and 16 cm high.
Calculate the volume of the box.
State your units.

(b) A circular table cloth has a radius of 0·75 m.
Calculate the area of the table cloth. [SEG]

7. A factory produces packets of tea.
These packets are put into cardboard boxes to be delivered
to shops.

A drawing of one cardboard box is shown below.

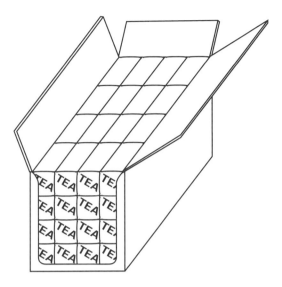

(a) How many packets of tea are there in one cardboard box?

(b) Each packet of tea measures 12 cm by 8 cm by 8 cm. Calculate the volume of one packet of tea.   [NEAB]

8. Clare makes a solid shape by joining together cubes of side 1 cm. This is her solid.

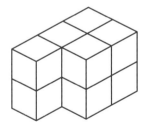

(a) Work out the volume of the solid. Remember to state the units.

(b) Before she made the solid, she had 30 cubes. What fraction of the cubes did she use?   [NEAB]

Module 5   Practice Calculator Test

1. From the list of numbers:

$$4, \quad 5, \quad 8, \quad 9, \quad 7, \quad 11, \quad 13, \quad 17$$

(a) State:
 (i)   the even numbers
 (ii) the factors of 24
 (iii) the prime numbers
 (iv) the multiples of 3

(b) Write down:
 (i)   two numbers which add up to 20
 (ii) the two numbers which have the highest product
 (6 marks)

2. Emma made these shapes with matchsticks.

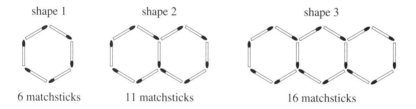

shape 1	shape 2	shape 3
6 matchsticks	11 matchsticks	16 matchsticks

(a) Draw shape 4 for Emma.
(b) (i)   Complete this table.

Shape number	1	2	3	4	5
Number of matchsticks	6	11	16		

 (ii) What pattern do you notice in the "number of matchsticks" row?
 (iii) How many matchsticks are needed to make shape 9? Explain how you can work it out **without** doing any drawings.   **(5 marks)**   [NEAB]

3. (a) A pattern of numbers is shown.

$$15, \quad 19, \quad 23, \quad 27, \quad \ldots .$$

(i)   What is the next number in the pattern?
(ii) Explain how you found your answer.

(b) A second pattern or numbers uses the rule:

> **Take four from the previous number.**

Continue this pattern by writing down the **next two** numbers in the pattern.

$$19, \quad 15, \quad 11, \quad 7, \ldots, \quad \ldots$$

(c) A third pattern of numbers uses the rule:

> **Add five to the previous number.**

What number comes before the number 33 in the pattern?   **(5 marks)**   [SEG]

4. (a) All three sides of a triangle are the same length.
   (i)   What special name is given to this type of triangle?
   (ii) What is the size of one of the angles of the triangle?

(b) A regular polygon is shown.

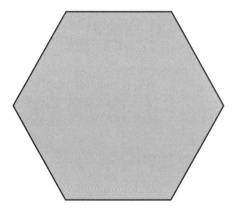

   (i)   What special name is given to this type of polygon?
   (ii) Draw all the lines of symmetry on the polygon.
   (iii) What is the order of rotational symmetry of this polygon?   **(6 marks)**   [SEG]

MODULE 5

5. The grid shows the locations of the points A, B, C, D and E.

(a) Which letter marks the point (6, 1)?

(b) Write down the co-ordinates of the point C.

Make a copy of the grid, then answer (c) and (d).

(c) Through B, draw a line which is perpendicular to the y axis.

(d) P is a point 6 cm from O. The line OP makes an angle of 60° with the x axis. Mark the position of point P on the diagram.

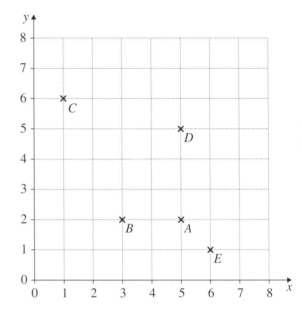

(4 marks) [NEAB]

6. Mary has some cubes of side 1 centimetre.

She makes this shape with her cubes.

Not drawn to scale

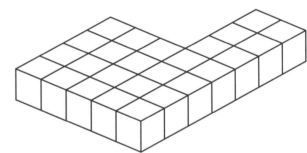

(a) What is the volume of this shape? Remember to state the units.

(b) 24 of Mary's cubes just fill this box.

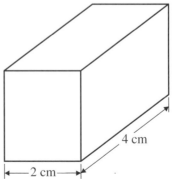

Not drawn to scale

4 cm

2 cm

What is the height of the box?

(c) On a copy of the grid below complete the full size
drawing of the box.

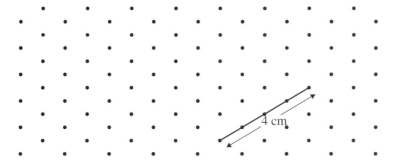

(d) Here is another box.

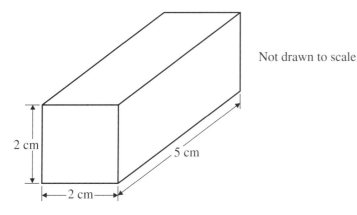

Not drawn to scale

2 cm

5 cm

2 cm

Will 24 of Mary's cubes fit into it?
Give a reason for your answer.   **(7 marks)**   [NEAB]

7. (a) *ABCD* is a quadrilateral.

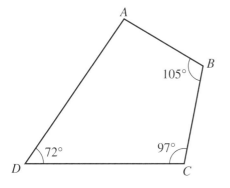

Not to scale

(b) Work out the size of angle *DAB*.   **(3 marks)**   [SEG]

8. Jenny cycles to school each day.

The graph shows her journey from home to school.

On the way she stops to talk to her friends.

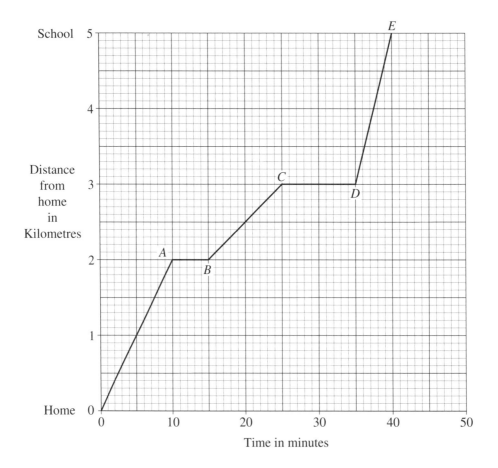

(a) How many times does she stop to talk to her friends?

(b) (i) How far does she travel in the first stage from home to *A*?

(ii) What is her average speed over the first ten minutes?
Give your answer in kilometres per hour.

(c) On which stage of the journey is her average speed the fastest? **(5 marks)** [NEAB]

9. Simplify $7a + 2b - 3a + b$ **(2 marks)**

10. A circle has diameter 12.4 cm.

    (a) Calculate the circumference of the circle.

    (b) Calculate the area of the circle.   **(5 marks)**

11. (a) Express 40 as a product of its prime factors.

    (b) Express 50 as a product of its prime factors.

    (c) Hence write down the HCF of 40 and 50.

                               (6 marks)

12. The diagram shows a regular octagon *ABCDEFGH* centre *O*.

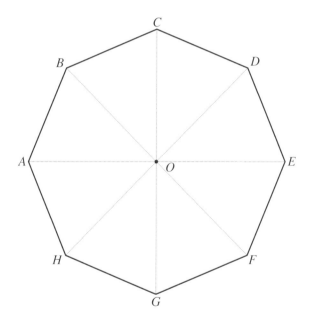

Octagon *ABCDEFGH* is rotated clockwise about centre *O*, so that *A* moves to *D*, *B* moves to *E* and so on.

    (a) Calculate the angle through which the octagon has been rotated.
        You **must** show your working.

    (b) Calculate angle *HGF*.
        You **must** show all your working.   **(5 marks)**   [SEG]

Module 5   Practice Non-calculator Test

1. Write down the following fractions in their lowest terms:

   (a) $\frac{4}{14}$ (b) $\frac{5}{50}$ **(2 marks)**

2. From the numbers   4,   6,   9,   15,   25,   27:
   write down   (a)   the square numbers
                      (b)   the cube numbers   **(2 marks)**

3. Four people can sit at a square table in a restaurant.

   When a larger group arrives, tables are moved into a line.
   For example, for 6 people two tables are needed.

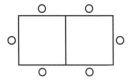

   (a) Complete this table to show the greatest number of
       people who can be seated.

Number of Tables	1	2	3	4	5
Greatest Number of People	4	6	8		

   (b) How many tables will be needed for 18 people?

   (c) There are 20 tables in a line.
       Explain how you could work out quickly the greatest
       number of people who can be seated.
                              (3 marks)   [NEAB]

4. (a) Here are the first five odd numbers:

                   1,   3,   5,   7,   9

      (i) Write down the tenth odd number.
      (ii) What is the twentieth odd number?

   (b) Here are the first four terms of a sequence:

                   21,   20,   17,   12,   …,   …

       Write down the next two terms in the sequence.
                              (4 marks)   [NEAB]

5. A sequence of numbers begins

$$2, \quad 5, \quad 8, \quad 11, \quad \ldots$$

(a) Write down the next number in this sequence.

(b) Find the nth term of this sequence. **(3 marks)** [SEG]

6. The diagram shows a pyramid on a square base.

(a) How many edges does it have?

(b) How many triangular faces does it have?

(c) The length of each edge of the pyramid
is 3 cm.
Draw a full-size net of this pyramid.

(5 marks) [SEG]

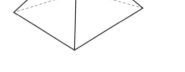

Not to scale

7. This sketch shows the plan of a garden *ABCD*.

In the garden there is a flower bed and a pond.
The centre of the pond is at *P*.
The radius of the pond is 3 metres.

(a) On a copy of the grid below complete the
accurate plan of the garden including the pond.
Use a scale of 1 cm represents 1 m.
The line *AD* has been drawn for you.

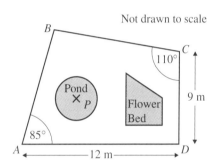

Not drawn to scale

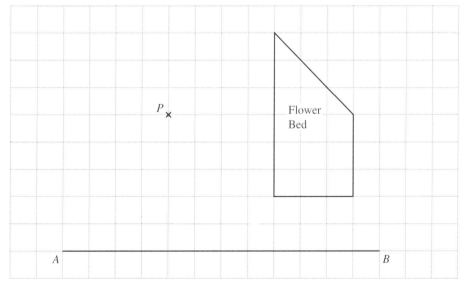

(b) What is the name given to the shape of the garden?

(c) Find the area of the real flower bed.
Remember to state the units in your answer.

(d) Find the perimeter of the real flower bed.

(8 marks) [NEAB]

8. The diagram shows a polygon, *ABCDE*.

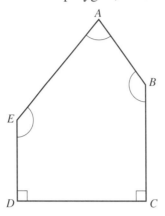

(a) Write down two lines that are parallel.

(b) Write down the line that is perpendicular to *BC*.

(c) Which **two** angles are obtuse angles?   **(3 marks)**

[NEAB]

9. (a) This diagram shows a shape with 5 sides.

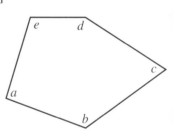

  (i) What is the mathematical name given to a shape with 5 sides?

  (ii) Explain why the shape in the diagram is **not** regular.

(b) Three of the shapes are fitted together.

  (i) The angles *a*, *b*, *c*, *d* and *e* have been marked on one of the shapes. Mark the positions of angles *a*, *b*, *c* and *e* on the other two shapes.

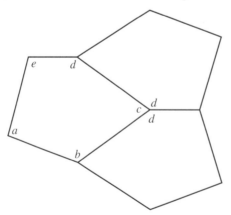

  (ii) The three angles *c*, *d* and *d* fit together exactly.
    Angle *c* is 66°.
    Calculate the size of angle *d*.   **(6 marks)**

[NEAB]

10. (a) Complete the table for $y = 3x - 1$.

x	-1	0	1	2
$y = 3x - 1$	-4	-1	2	5

(b) Draw the graph of $y = 3x - 1$ on a copy of this grid.

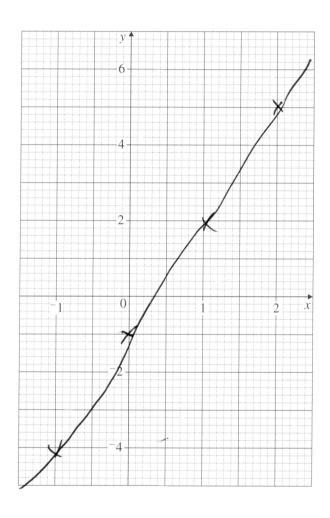

(c) Find the value of x when $y = 3$.   **(5 marks)**   [SEG]

MODULE 5

11. The scale drawing shows the location of three towns: Ayton, Beeville and Carby. Beeville is due East of Ayton.

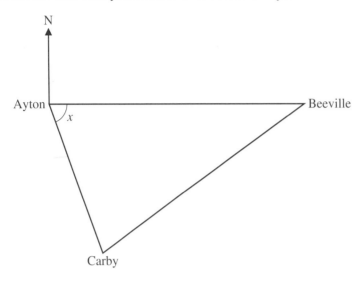

(a) Write down the 3-figure bearing of Beeville from Ayton.

(b) (i) Measure and write down the size of angle x.
(ii) Write down the 3-figure bearing of Carby from Ayton.

(c) What is the bearing of Carby from Beeville?

(5 marks)   [SEG]

12. (a) Show that the sum of two consecutive integers is an odd integer.

(b) Find the value of
(i) $\frac{1}{2} + \frac{3}{4}$
(ii) $\frac{2}{5} - \frac{1}{6}$ **(6 marks)**

13. (a) If $r = 7$ and $h = 8$,
find A when $A = 3r + 2h$

(b) Solve the equation $3x - 5 = 22$

(c) Solve the equation $5x + 7 = 3x + 4$ **(8 marks)**

COURSEWORK GUIDANCE

For your GCSE Maths you will need to produce two pieces of coursework:

1. Investigative – module 4
2. Statistical – module 2

Each piece is worth 10% of your exam mark.

This unit gives you guidance on approaching your coursework and will tell you how to get good marks for each piece.

Module 4: Investigative coursework

In your investigative coursework you will need to:

- Say how you are going to carry out the task and provide a plan of action
- Collect results for the task and consider an appropriate way to represent your results
- Write down observations you make from your diagrams or calculations
- Look at your results and write down any observations, rules or patterns – try to make a general statement
- Check out your general statements by testing further data – say if your test works or not
- Develop the task by posing your own questions and provide a conclusion to the questions posed
- Extend the task by using techniques and calculations from the content of the intermediate tier
- Make your conclusions clear and link them to the original task giving comments on your methods.

Assessing the task

Before you start, it is helpful for you to know how your work will be marked. This way you can make sure you are familiar with the sort of things which examiners are looking for.

Investigative work is marked under three headings;

1. **Making and monitoring decisions to solve problems**
2. **Communicating mathematically**
3. **Developing skills of mathematical reasoning**

Each strand assesses a different aspect of your coursework. The criteria are:

1. Making and monitoring decisions to solve problems

This strand is about deciding what needs to be done then doing it. The strand requires you to select an appropriate approach, obtain information and introduce your own questions which develop the task further.

For this strand you need to:

- solve the task by collecting information
- break down the task by solving it in a systematic way
- extend the task by introducing your own *relevant* questions
- extend the task by following through alternative approaches

2. Communicating mathematically

This strand is about communicating what you are doing using words, tables, diagrams and symbols. You should make sure your chosen presentation is accurate and relevant.

For this strand you need to:

- illustrate your information using diagrams and calculations
- interpret and explain your diagrams and calculations
- begin to use mathematical symbols to explain your work
- use mathematical symbols consistently to explain your work

3. Developing skills of mathematical reasoning

This strand is about testing, explaining and justifying what you have done. It requires you to search for patterns and provide generalisations. You should test, justify and explain any generalisations.

For this strand you need to:

- make a general statement from your results
- confirm your general statement by further testing
- make a justification for your general statement
- develop your justification further

This unit uses a series of investigative tasks to demonstrate how each of these strands can be achieved.

MODULES 2 and 4

Task 1

TRIANGLES

Patterns of triangles are made as shown in the following diagrams:

  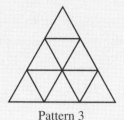

Pattern 1   Pattern 2   Pattern 3

What do you notice about the pattern number and the number of small triangles?

Investigate further.

Note:
You are reminded that any coursework submitted for your GCSE examination must be your own. If you copy from someone else then you may be disqualified from the examination.

Planning your work

A straightforward approach to this task is to continue the pattern further. You can record your results in a table and then see if you can make any generalisations.

Collecting information

A good starting point for any investigation is to collect information about the task.

You can see that:

Pattern 1 shows 1 small triangle
Pattern 2 shows 4 small triangles
Pattern 3 shows 9 small triangles

You can then extend this by considering further patterns.

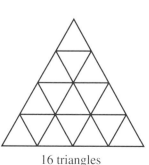

16 triangles

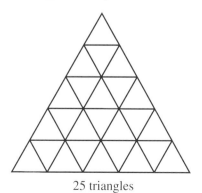
25 triangles

Moderator comment
It is a good idea not to collect too much data as this is time consuming ... aim to collect 4 or 5 items of data to start with.

MODULES 2 and 4

Drawing up tables

The information is not easy to follow so it is **always** a good idea to illustrate it in a table.

A table to show the relationship between
the pattern number and the number of triangles.

pattern number	1	2	3	4	5
no of triangles	1	4	9	16	25

It is important to give your table a title and to make it quite clear what the table is showing.

Now you try …

Using the table:

- Can you see anything special about the number of triangles?
- Ask yourself: are they odd numbers, even numbers, square numbers, triangle numbers, are they multiples, do they get bigger, do they get smaller …
- What other relationships might you look for?

Being systematic

Another important aspect to your work is to be systematic

This task shows you what that means.

Task 2

ARRANGE A LETTER

How many different ways can you arrange the letters ABCD?

Investigate further.

Note: You are reminded that any coursework submitted for your GCSE examination must be your own. If you copy from someone else then you may be disqualified from the examination.

You could haphazardly try out some different possibilities:

ABCD
BCDA
CDAB etc

You may or may not find all the arrangements this way. To be sure of finding them all you should list the arrangements systematically. To be systematic you group letters starting with A:

ABCD
ABDC
ACBD
ACDB
ADBC
ADCB

Notice the system here:
A followed by B,
then A followed by C,
then A followed by D
and so on.

Now you try …

Now see if you can systematically produce all of the arrangements starting with B (you should find six of them) then complete the other arrangements.

You should also be systematic about the way you collect your data. In Task 2, you were asked to find the arrangements of 4 letters: A, B, C and D.

To approach the whole task systematically, you should start by finding the arrangements for:

- 1 letter: A
- 2 letters: A and B
- 3 letters: A, B and C

This will give you more information about the task.

For different numbers of letters you should find:

Arrangement of different numbers of letters

number of letters	1	3	3	4
number of arrangements	1	2	6	24

You should now try and explain what your table tells you:

From my table I can …

Finding a relationship – making a generalisation

To make a generalisation, you need to find a relationship from your table of results. A useful method is to look at the differences between terms in the table.

Here is the table of results from Task 1:

A table to show the relationship between
the pattern number and the number of triangles.

pattern number	1	2	3	4	5
no of triangles	1	4	9	16	25

$$+3 \quad +5 \quad +7 \quad +9 \quad +11$$
$$+2 \quad +2 \quad +2 \quad +2$$

In this table the 'first differences' are going up in two's.

The 'second differences' are all the same … this tells you that the relationship is quadratic, so you should compare the numbers with the square numbers.

Here are some generalisations you could make:

> *From my table I notice that the number of triangles are all square numbers*

> *From my table I notice that the number of triangles are the pattern numbers squared*

A graph may help you see the relationship:

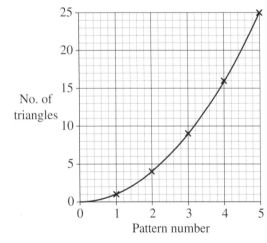

No. of triangles
Pattern number

Moderator comment
Remember that the idea is to identify some relationship from your table or graph so that there is some point in you using it in your work … a table or graph without any comment on the findings if of little use.

> *From my graph I notice that there is a quadratic relationship between the number of triangles and the pattern number*

Using algebra

You will gain marks if you can express your generalisation or rule using algebra.

The rule:

I notice that the number of triangles are the pattern numbers squared

can be written in algebra:

$t = p^2$ where t is the number of triangles and p is the pattern number

> Remember that you must explain what t and p stand for.

Testing generalisations

You need to confirm your generalisation by further testing.

From my table I notice that the number of triangles are the pattern numbers squared so that the sixth pattern will have $6^2 = 36$ triangles

You can confirm this with a diagram:

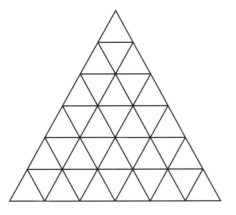

My diagram confirms the generalisation for the sixth pattern

> Always confirm your testing by providing some comment, even if your test has not worked!

Now try to use all of these ideas by following Task 3.

Now you try …

For Task 3: 'Perfect Tiles' given below:

- Collect the information for different arrangements
- Make sure you are systematic
- Draw up a table of your results.

Task 3

PERFECT TILES

Floor spacers are used to give a perfect finish when laying tiles on the kitchen floor.

Three different spacers are not used including

    L spacer
    T spacer
    + spacer

Here is a 3 × 3 arrangement of tiles

This uses   4 **L** spacers
             8 **T** spacers and
             4 **+** spacers

Investigate different arrangements of tiles.

Note:

You are reminded that any coursework submitted for your GCSE examination must be your own. If you copy from someone else then you may be disqualified from the examination.

You should be able to produce this table:

Number of spacers for different arrangement of tiles

size of square	1 × 1	2 × 2	3 × 3	4 × 4
number of L spacers	4	4	4	4
number of T spacers	0	4	8	12
number of + spacers	0	1	4	9

MODULES 2 and 4

Now you try …

What patterns do you notice from the table?

What general statements can you make?

Now test your general statements.

Generalisations for the 'Perfect Tiles' task might include:

$L = 4$ where L is the number of L spacers

$T = 4(n - 1)$ where T is the number of T spacers and
                      n is the size of the arrangement ($n \times n$)

The formula $T = 4(n - 1)$ can also be written as $T = 4n - 4$.

Test:

For a 5×5 arrangement (ie $n = 5$)

$T = 4(n - 1)$
$T = 4(5 - 1)$
$T = 4 \times 4$
$T = 16$

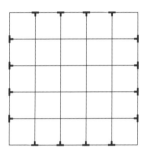

The number of T spacers is 16 so the formula works for a 5×5 arrangement.

$+ = (n - 1)^2$ where $+$ is the number of $+$ spacers and
                      n is the size of the arrangement ($n \times n$)

Test:

For a 6×6 arrangement (ie $n = 6$)

$+ = (n - 1)$
$+ = (6 - 1)$
$+ = (5)^2$
$+ = 25$

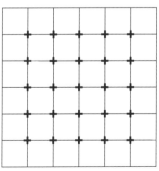

The number of $+$ spacers is 25 so the formula works for a 6×6 arrangement.

Making justifications

Once you have found the general statement and tested it then you need to justify it. You justify the statement by explaining WHY it works.

For example, here are possible justifications for the rules in task 3:

WHY is the number of L spacers always 4?

> The number of L spacers is always 4 because there are 4 corners to each arrangement.

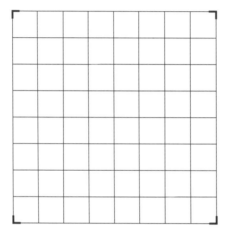

WHY are all of the T spacers multiples of 4?

> The number of T spacers are multiples of 4 because each time you add another tile to the side then you add another T spacer.

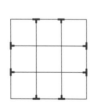 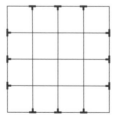

> As there are 4 sides to the arrangement then the number of T spacers will go up by 4.

WHY are all of the + spacers square numbers?

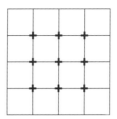

> **Now you try ...**
> Explain why the number of + spacers are **always** square numbers.

Extending the problem – investigating further

Once you have understood and explained the basic task, you should extend your work to get better marks.

To extend a task you need to pose your own questions.
This means that you must think of different ways to extend the original task.

Extending task 1: The triangle problem
You could ask and investigate:

What about different patterns?

For example, triangles

What about patterns of different shapes?

For example, squares

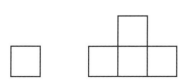 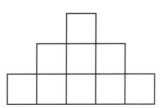

> *What about three dimensional patterns?*

For example, cubes

 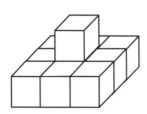 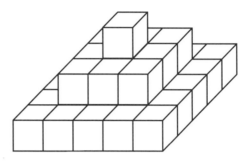

Extending task 2: 'Arrange a letter'

> *What about different numbers of letters?   For example, ABCDE*

> *What happens when:*
> - *a letter is repeated?*   *For example, AABCD*
> - *a letter is repeated more than once?*   *For example, AAABC*
> - *more than one letter is repeated?*   *For example, AAABB*

Of course, you will have to do more than just pose a question – you will have to carry out the investigation and come to a conclusion.

> **Now you try …**
> Think of some different ways to extend task 3: Perfect Tiles.
> What sort of questions might you ask?
> What other areas might you explore?

Extending task 3: 'Perfect Tiles'
You could ask:

> *What about rectangular arrangements of tiles?*

What about different shaped tiles?

For example, triangles

Consider rectangular arrangements of tiles:

> Remember to work systematically.

Number of spacers for different arrangement of tiles

size of arrangement	2 × 1	2 × 2	2 × 3	2 × 4	2 × 5
number of L spacers	4	4	4	4	4
number of T spacers	2	4	6	8	10
number of + spacers	0	1	2	3	4
number of spacers	6	9	12	15	18

Number of spacers for different arrangement of tiles

size of arrangement	3 × 1	3 × 2	3 × 3	3 × 4	3 × 5
number of L spacers	4	4	4	4	4
number of T spacers	4	6	8	10	12
number of + spacers	0	2	4	6	8
number of spacers	8	12	16	20	24

Rules for the 'Perfect Tiles' task extension might include:

$L = 4$ where L is the number of L spacers

$T = 2(x - 1) + 2(y - 1)$ where T is the number of T spacers and
     x is the length of the arrangement and
     y is the width of the arrangement

$P = (x - 1)(y - 1)$ where P is the number of + spacers and
     x is the length of the arrangement and
     y is the width of the arrangement

$N = (x + 1)(y + 1)$ where N is the number of + spacers and
     x is the length of the arrangement and
     y is the width of the arrangement

> Note that the formula $T = 2(x - 1) + 2(y - 1)$ can also be written
> $T = 2(x - 1) + 2(y - 1)$
> $T = 2x - 2 + 2y - 2$
> $T = 2x + 2y - 4$

> It is sensible to replace + by P so that P stands for the number of + spacers.

> **Moderator comment**
> If you use algebra from the Intermediate tier you will get higher marks.

MODULES 2 and 4

In this unit we have tried to give you some hints on approaching investigative coursework to gain your best possible mark.

This mathematics is often useful in investigative tasks:

- Creating tables
- Drawing and interpreting graphs
- Recognising square numbers
- Recognising triangular numbers
- Finding the *n*th term of a linear sequence

Summary

These are the grade criteria your coursework will be marked by:

Identifying information and making statements (grade E/F)

To achieve this level you must:

- solve the task by collecting information
- illustrate your information using diagrams and calculations
- make a general statement from your results

Testing general statements (grade D)

To achieve this level you must:

- break down the task by solving it in an orderly manner
- interpret and explain your diagrams and calculations
- confirm your general statement by further testing

Posing questions and justifying (grade C)

To achieve this level you must:

- extend the task by introducing your own *relevant* questions
- begin to use mathematical symbols to explain your work
- make a justification for your general statement
- provide a sophisticated justification

MODULES 2 and 4

Module 2: Statistical coursework

In your statistical coursework you will need to:

- Provide a well considered hypothesis and provide a plan of action to carry out the task
- Decide what data is needed and collect results for the task using an appropriate sample size and sampling method
- Consider the most appropriate way to represent your results and write down any observations you make
- Consider the most appropriate statistical calculations to use and interpret your findings in terms of the original hypothesis
- Develop the task by posing your own questions – you may need to collect further data to move the task on
- Extend the task by using techniques and calculations from the content of the intermediate tier
- Make your conclusions clear – always link them to the original hypothesis recognising limitations and suggesting improvements.

Assessing the task

It may be helpful for you to know how the work is marked. This way, you can make sure you are familiar with the sort of things that examiners are looking for.

Statistical work is marked under three headings:

1. **Specifying the problem and planning**
2. **Collecting, processing and representing the data**
3. **Interpreting and discussing the results**

Each strand assesses a different aspect of your coursework as follows:

1. Specifying the problem and planning
This strand is about choosing a problem and deciding what needs to be done then doing it. The strand requires you to provide clear aims, consider the collection of data, identify practical problems and explain how you might overcome them.

2. Collecting, processing and representing the data
This strand is about collecting data and using appropriate statistical techniques and calculations to process and represent the data. Diagrams should be appropriate and calculations mostly correct.

3. Interpreting and discussing the results

This strand is about commenting, summarising and interpreting your data. Your discussion should link back to the original problem and provide an evaluation of the work undertaken.

This unit uses a series of statistical tasks to demonstrate how each of these strands can be achieved.

Planning your work

Statistical coursework requires careful planning if you are to gain good marks. Before undertaking any statistical investigation, it is important that you plan your work and decide exactly what you are going to investigate – do not be too ambitious!

Before you start you should:

- decide what your investigation is about and why you have chosen it
- decide how you are going to collect the information
- explain how you intend to ensure that your data is representative
- detail any presumptions which you are making.

Getting started – setting up your hypothesis

A good starting point for any statistical task is to consider the best way to collect the data and then to write a clear hypothesis you can test.

Moderator comment
Your statistical task must always start with a 'hypothesis' where you state exactly what you are investigating and what you expect to find.

Task 1

WHAT THE PAPERS SAY

Choose a passage from two different newspapers and investigate the similarities and differences between them.

Write down a hypothesis to test.

Design and carry out a statistical experiment to test the hypothesis.

Investigate further.

Note: You are reminded that any coursework submitted for your GCSE examination must be your own. If you copy from someone else then you may be disqualified from the examination.

MODULES 2 and 4

First consider different ways to compare the newspapers:

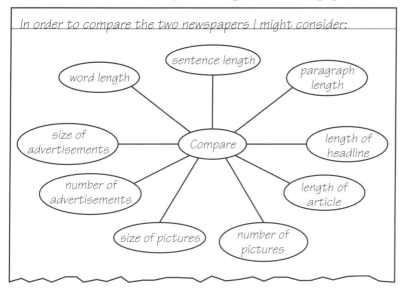

In order to compare the two newspapers I might consider:

- sentence length
- word length
- paragraph length
- size of advertisements
- Compare
- length of headline
- number of advertisements
- length of article
- size of pictures
- number of pictures

Now formulate your hypothesis.
Here are some possible hypotheses:

For my statistics coursework I am going to investigate the hypothesis that 'tabloid' papers use shorter words than 'broadsheet' newspapers.

My hypothesis is that word lengths in the tabloid newspaper will be shorter than word lengths in the broadsheet newspaper.

My hypothesis is that sentence lengths in the tabloid newspaper will be shorter than sentence lengths in the broadsheet newspaper.

My hypothesis is that the number of advertisements in the tabloid newspaper will be greater than the number of advertisements in the broadsheet newspaper.

Remember: it does not matter whether your hypotheses are true or false and you will still gain marks if your hypothesis turns out to be false.

Now you try …

See if you can add some hypotheses of your own.

Explain how you would proceed with the task.

Choosing the right sample

Once you have decided your aims and set up a hypothesis then it is important to consider how you will test your hypothesis.

Sampling techniques include;

- **Random sampling** is where each member of the population has an equally likely chance of being selected. An easy way to do this would be to give each person a number and then choose the numbers randomly, out of a hat say.
- **Systematic sampling** is the same as random sampling except that there is some system involved such as numbering each person and then choosing every 20th number.
- **Stratified sampling** is where each person is divided into some particular group or category (strata) and the sample size is proportional to the size of the group or category in the population as a whole.
- **Convenience sampling** or opportunity sampling is one which involves simply choosing the first person to come along … although this method is not particularly random!

Here are some ways you could test the hypotheses for task 1:

Moderator comment

It is important to choose an appropriate sample, give reasons for your choice and explain what steps you will take to avoid bias.

Moderator comment

You should **always** say why you choose your sampling method.

Sampling method	Reason
To investigate my hypothesis I am going to choose a similar article from each type of newspaper and count the lengths of the first 100 words.	I decided to choose similar articles because the words will be describing similar information and so will be better to make comparisons.
To investigate my hypothesis I will choose every tenth page from each type of newspaper and calculate the percentage area covered by pictures.	I decided to choose every tenth page from each type of newspaper because the types of articles vary throughout the newspaper (for example news headlines at the front and sports at the back of the paper).

Collecting primary data

If you are collecting primary data then remember:

- **Observation** involves collecting information by observation and might involve participant observation (where the observer takes part in the activity), or systematic observation (where the observation happens without anyone knowing).
- **Interviewing** involves a conversation between two or more people. Interviewing can be formal (where the questions follow a strict format) or informal (where they follow a general format but can be changed around to suit the questioning).
- **Questionnaires** are the most popular way of undertaking surveys. Good questionnaires are
  - simple, short, clear and precise,
  - attractively laid and quick to complete

  and the questions are

  - not biased or offensive
  - written in a language which is easy to understand
  - relevant to the hypothesis being investigated
  - accompanied by clear instructions on how to answer the questions.

Avoiding bias

You must be very careful to avoid any possibility of bias in your work. For example, in making comparisons it is important to ensure that you are comparing like with like.

Jean undertook task 1: 'What the papers say'.
She collected this data from two newspapers by measuring (observation).

	Tabloid	Broadsheet
Number of advertisements	3	3
Number of pages	5	3
Area of each page	100 cm^2	200 cm^2

Her hypothesis is:

The tabloid newspaper has more advertisements than the broadsheet newspaper.

Moderator comment
It is important to carefully consider the collection of reliable data. Appropriate methods of collecting primary data might include observation, interviewing, questionnaires or experiments.

Moderator comment
It is always a good idea to undertake a small scale 'dry run' to check for problems. This 'dry run' is called a pilot survey and can be used to impove your questionnaire or survey before it is undertaken.

MODULES 2 and 4

A quick glance at the table may make her claim look true: the broadsheet has 30 adverts but the tabloid has 35, which is more.

However, the sizes of the newspapers are different so Jean is not really comparing like with like.

To ensure Jean compares like with like she should take account of:

- the area of the pages
- the number of pages

and so on.

Percentage coverage per page:
Tabloid $= 35 \div 50 \times 100\% = 70\%$
Broadsheet $= 30 \div 30 \times 100\% = 100\%$

This shows that:

> *The broadsheet newspaper has more advertisements per page than the tabloid newspaper.*

Note: this still doesn't take account of the size of the adverts!

The total area of the pages is:
Tabloid $= 50 \times 1000 \text{ cm}^2 = 50\,000 \text{ cm}^2$
Broadsheet $= 30 \times 2000 \text{ cm}^2 = 60\,000 \text{ cm}^2$

So the percentage coverage is:
Tabloid $= 35 \div 50\,000 \times 100\% = 0.07\%$
Broadsheet $= 30 \div 60\,000 \times 100\% = 0.05\%$

This shows that:

> *The tabloid newspaper has more advertisements per area of coverage than the broadsheet newspaper.*

Methods and calculations

Once you have collected your data, you need to use appropriate statistical methods and calculations to process and represent your data.

You can represent the data using statistical calculations such as the mean, median, mode, range and standard deviation.

Task 2

GUESSING GAME

Dinesh asked a sample of people to estimate the length of a line and weight of a packet.

Write down a hypothesis about estimating lengths and weights and carry out your own experiment to test your hypothesis.

Investigate further.

Note: You are reminded that any coursework submitted for your GCSE examination must be your own. If you copy from someone else then you may be disqualified from the examination.

Maurice and Angela decide to explore the hypothesis that:

Students are better at estimating the length of a line than the weight of a package.

To test the hypothesis they collect data from 50 children, detailing their estimations of the length of a line and the weight of a parcel.

Here are their findings:

A table to show the estimations for the
length of a line and the weight of a parcel

	Length (cm)	Weight (g)
Mean	15.9	105.2
Median	15.5	100
Mode	14	100
Range	8.6	28
SD	1.2	2.1

Moderator comment

It is important to consider whether information on all of these statistical calculations is essential.

Note: the actual length of the line is 10 cm and the weight of the parcel is 100 g.

MODULES 2 and 4

Now you try …

Using the table:

- What do you notice about the average of the length and weight?
- What do you notice about the spread of the length and weight?
- Does the information suppose the hypothesis?

Graphical representation

The data for task 2 was sorted into different categories and represented as a table.

It may be useful to show your results using graphs and diagrams as sometimes it is easier to see trends.

Graphical representations might include stem and leaf diagrams and cumulative frequency graphs.

Once you have drawn a graph you should say what you notice from the graph:

Other statistical representations might include pie charts, bar charts, scattergraphs and histograms.

Moderator comment

You should only use appropriate diagrams and graphs.

From my representation, I can see that the estimations for the line are generally more accurate than the estimations for the weight because:

- the mean is closer to the actual value for the lengths and
- the standard deviation is smaller for the lengths

However, on closer inspection:

- the percentage error on the mean is smaller for the weights
- so the median and mode value are better averages to use for the weights

Remember to consider the possibility of bias in your data:

The percentage error for the lengths is

$$\frac{0.9}{15} \times 100 = 6\%$$

The percentage error for the weights is

$$\frac{5.2}{100} \times 100 = 5.2\%$$

MODULES 2 and 4

Using secondary data

You may use secondary data in your coursework.

Secondary data is data that is already collected for you.

Moderator comment

If you use secondary data there must be enough 'to allow sampling to take place' – about 50 pieces of data.

Task 3

GENDER DIFFERENCES IN EXAMINATIONS

The following information gives the GCSE examination results for Year 11 students at a local comprehensive school.

		%A*–C	%A*–G	APS
Art	Girls	66	94	4.7
	Boys	55	91	4.6
Business Studies	Girls	51	93	4.7
	Boys	65	95	5.0
English Language	Girls	62	93	4.9
	Boys	46	89	4.3
French	Girls	49	90	4.2
	Boys	41	88	4.1
Geography	Girls	43	88	4.1
	Boys	53	90	4.2
Mathematics	Girls	47	91	4.2
	Boys	45	89	4.2
Religious Education	Girls	56	92	4.9
	Boys	61	94	5.1
Science	Girls	48	91	4.4
	Boys	45	88	4.3

Use the data provided to write down a hypothesis to test.

Design and carry out a statistical experiment to test your hypothesis.

Investigate further.

Note:

You are reminded that any coursework submitted for your GCSE examination must be your own. If you copy from someone else then you may be disqualified from the examination.

ade explores the hypothesis that:

> *Year 11 girls do better in their GCSE examinations than boys*

ɔ test the hypothesis she decided to concentrate on the core ɪbjects and her findings are shown in the table:

A table to show the performance of Year 11
girls and boys in their GCSE examinations

		%A*–C	%A*–G	APS
English	Girls	62	93	4.9
	Boys	46	89	4.3
	All	54	91	4.6
Mathematics	Girls	47	91	4.2
	Boys	45	89	4.2
	All	46	90	4.2
Science	Girls	48	91	4.4
	Boys	45	88	4.3
	All	47	90	4.4

Now you try ...

- What do you notice about the percentages of A*–C grades?
- What do you notice about the percentages of A*–G grades?
- What do you notice about the average point scores?
- Does the information support the hypothesis?

The data has been sorted into different categories and
represented as a table.

Jade could use comparative bar charts to represent the data as it
will allow her to make comparisons more easily.

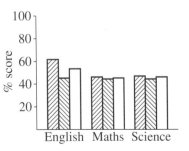
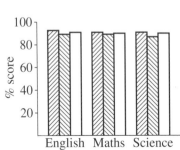
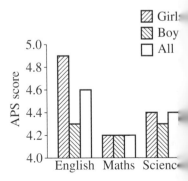

Summarising and interpreting data

Jade summarises her findings like this:

> From my graph, I can see that Year 11 girls do better in their
> GCSE examinations than boys in terms of A*–C grades,
> A*–G grades and average point scores.
>
> The performance of Year 11 girls is significantly better than boys
> in English although less so in mathematics.

Moderator comment

You should refer to your original hypothesis when you summarise your results.

Moderator comment

In your conclusion you should also suggest limitations to your investigation and explain how these might be overcome.
You may wish to discuss:

- sample size
- sampling methods
- biased data
- other difficulties

Hint:

You need to appreciate that the data is more secure if the sample size is 500 rather than 50.

Extending the task

To gain better marks in your coursework you should extend the task in light of your findings.

In your extension you should:

- Give a clear hypothesis
- Collect further data if necessary
- Present your findings using charts and diagrams as appropriate
- Summarise your findings referring to your hypothesis

Extending task 3: Gender differences in examinations

Jade extends the task by looking at the performance of individual students in combinations of different subjects.

> I am now going to extend my task by looking at the performance
> of individual students in English and mathematics. My
> hypothesis is that there will be no correlation between the two
> subjects.

She represents the data on a scattergraph:

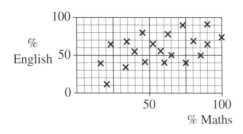

Note:
You should only draw a line of best fit on the diagram to show the correlation if you make some proper use of it (for example to calculate a students' likely English mark given their mathematics mark).

She summarises her findings:

> *From my scattergraph, I can see that there is a small amount of correlation between the performance of individual students in English and mathematics.*

Jack extends the task further:

> *I shall now look at the performance of individual students in mathematics and science. My hypothesis is that there will be a correlation between the two subjects.*

She presents the data on a scattergraph.

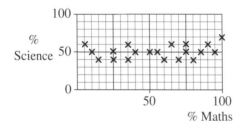

She summarises her findings:

> *From my scattergraph, I can see that there is no correlation between the performance of individual students in mathematics and science.*

Note:
The strength of the correlation could be measured using higher level statistical techniques such as Spearman's Rank Correlation.

MODULES 2 and 4

Extending task 2: The guessing game

Maurice extends 'The guessing game' like this:

> *I am now going to extend my task by looking to see whether*
> *people who are good at estimating lengths are also good at*
> *estimating weights. My hypothesis is that there will be a strong*
> *correlation between peoples' ability at estimating lengths and*
> *estimating weights.*

He draws a scattergraph:

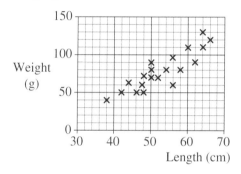

He summarises his findings:

> *From my scattergraph, I can see that there is a strong*
> *correlation between peoples' ability at estimating lengths and*
> *estimating weights.*

Using a computer

It is quite acceptable that calculations and representations are
generated by computer, as long as any such work is
accompanied by some analysis and interpretation.

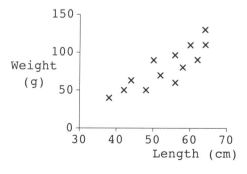

Remember:
Make sure that your
computer generated
scattergraph has labelled
axes and a title to make it
quite clear what it is
showing.

MODULES 2 and 4

> *From my computer generated scattergraph, I can see that*
> *there is a strong correlation between peoples' ability at*
> *estimating lengths and estimating weights.*

In this unit we have tried to give you some hints on approaching statistical coursework to gain your best possible mark.

This statistics is often useful in investigative tasks:

- Calculating averages (mean, median and mode)
- Finding the range
- Pie charts, bar charts, stem and leaf diagrams
- Constructing a cumulative frequency graph
- Finding the interquartile range
- Histograms
- Calculating the standard deviation
- Drawing a scattergraph and line of best fit
- Sampling techniques
- Discussing bias

Summary

These are the grade criteria your coursework will be marked by:

Foundation statistical task (grade E/F)

To achieve this level you must:

- set out reasonably clear aims and include a plan
- ensure that the sample size is of an appropriate size (about 25)
- collect data and make use of statistical techniques and calculations
    For example: pie charts, bar charts, stem and leaf diagrams, mean, median, mode and scattergraphs
- summarise and interpret some of your diagrams and calculations

Intermediate statistical task (grade C)

To achieve this level you must:

- set out clear aims and include a plan designed to meet those aims
- ensure that the sample size is of an appropriate size (about 50)
- give reasons for your choice of sample
- collect data and make use of statistical techniques and calculations

   For example: pie charts, bar charts, stem and leaf diagrams, mean, median, mode (of grouped data), scattergraphs and cumulative frequency

- summarise and correctly interpret your diagrams and calculations
- consider your strategies and how successful they were

Higher statistical task (grade A)

To achieve this level you must:

- set out clear aims for a more demanding problem
- include a plan which is specifically designed to meet those aims
- ensure that sample size is considered and limitations discussed
- collect relevant data and use statistical techniques and calculations

   For example: pie charts, bar charts, stem and leaf diagrams, mean, median, mode (of grouped data), scattergraphs, cumulative frequency, histograms and sampling techniques

- summarise and correctly interpret your diagrams and calculations
- use your results to respond to your original question
- consider your strategies, limitations and suggest possible improvements

MODULES 2 and 4

ANSWERS MODULE 1

D1 Data handling 1

Check in D1

1. (a) 3   (b) 8   (c) 16   (d) 13
2. (a) ЩН ЩН IIII   (b) ЩН I   (c) ЩН ЩН ЩН ЩН I   (d) ЩН ЩН ЩН II

Exercise 1A

1. Suitable questions might be:
   Tick one box for your gender.
   ☐ Boy   ☐ Girl
   Tick one box for your year group.
   ☐ 7 ☐ 8   ☐ 9   ☐ 10   ☐ 11   ☐ Sixth Form
   Do you consider your health before deciding what to eat for lunch?
   ☐ Yes   ☐ No

2. Suitable questions might be:
   Tick one box for your gender.
   ☐ Male   ☐ Female
   Tick one box for your age.
   ☐ 21–30   ☐ 31–40   ☐ 41–50   ☐ 51–60   ☐ over 60
   Tick one box for the number of hours of television you watch during an average day.
   ☐ less than 1   ☐ 1 to 2   ☐ 2 to 3   ☐ 3 to 4   ☐ 4 to 5   ☐ more than 5

4. Suitable questions might be:
   Do you smoke cigarettes?
   ☐ Yes   ☐ No
   If you do smoke, how many cigarettes do you smoke each day?
   ☐ 1 to 5   ☐ 6 to 10   ☐ 11 to 15   ☐ 16 to 20   ☐ more than 20
   Tick one box in each line.
   Does your mother smoke?   ☐ Yes   ☐ No
   Does your father smoke?   ☐ Yes   ☐ No

Exercise 1B

1. (a)

Number of eggs	Tally	Frequency
0	ЩН	5
1	II	2
2	ЩН I	6
3	IIII	4
4	ЩН I	6
5	II	2

   (b) bars with heights: 5, 2, 6, 4, 6, 2

2. (a)

Girls	Tally	Frequency
Yes	ЩН ЩН II	12
No	ЩН III	8

Boys	Tally	Frequency
Yes	ЩН IIII	9
No	ЩН ЩН I	11

   (b) Girls: bars with heights 12 and 8.

   Boys: bars with heights 8 and 11.

   (b) bars with heights 9, 3, 7 and 11.

3. (a)

Type of sausage	Tally	Frequency
Porkers	ЩН IIII	9
Sizzlers	III	3
Yumbos	ЩН II	7
Bangers	ЩН ЩН I	11

4. (a)

Score (Kathy)	Tally	Frequency
1	II	2
2	II	2
3	II	2
4	IIII III	8
5	IIII	5
6	IIII I	6

Score (Kyle)	Tally	Frequency
1	II	2
2	II	2
3	IIII	4
4	IIII II	7
5	IIII I	6
6	IIII	4

(b) Kathy: bars with heights 2, 2, 2, 8, 5 and 6.   Kyle: bars with heights 2, 2, 4, 7, 6 and 4.

5. (a)

Number of hours watched (Men)	Tally	Frequency
less than one hour	IIII	4
one to two hours	II	2
two to three hours	IIII III	8
three to four hours	IIII	4
more than four hours	II	2

Number of hours watched (Women)	Tally	Frequency
less than one hour	III	3
one to two hours	IIII	4
two to three hours	IIII II	7
three to four hours	IIII	4
more than four hours	II	2

(b) Men: bars with heights 4, 2, 8, 4, 2.   Women: bars with heights 3, 4, 7, 4, 2.

Checkout D1

1. Possible questions might be:
How long does it take you to travel to this supermarket?
☐ less than 5 minutes   ☐ 5 to 10 minutes   ☐ 10 to 15 minutes
☐ 15 to 20 minutes ☐ more than 20 minutes
How often do you visit this supermarket?
☐ once a day   ☐ twice a week ☐ once a week
☐ once every two weeks   ☐ once a month ☐ less than once a month
How much do you spend each time you visit this supermarket?
☐ less than £10   ☐ between £10 and £20   ☐ between £20 and £50
☐ between £50 and £100   ☐ more than £100

2. (a)

Colour of car	Tally	Frequency
white	IIII IIII	10
blue	IIII	5
red	IIII IIII	9
green	IIII I	6

(b) bars with heights 10, 5, 9, 6.

Revision exercise D1

1. (a) 12
2. (b) 15
3.

	Colour of vehicle				
	Red	Blue	Silver	White	Other
Car	III	III	III	II	III
Lorry		I			I
Bus	II	I			
Van				IIII I	

4 (a) Watched TV
(b) More boys played computer games than girls.
More girls read a book than boys.
(c)

Number of hours	Tally
0–1	
1–2	
2–3	
Above 3	

5. (a) (i) Esso   (ii) Sainsbury

6. (a) (i)

Temperature °C	Tally	Frequency
11–15	I	1
16–20	III	3
21–25	IIII IIII	9
26–30	IIII I	6
31–35	I	1

(b) Bar showing an increase in supermarket share

(ii) 7

D2 Data handling 2

Check in D2

1. (a) 15   (b) 27   (c) 28   (d) 48   (e) 106   (f) 81   (g) 169

2. (a) 30   (b) 21   (c) 72   (d) 90   (e) 12   (f) 40   (g) 30

(h) 24

3. (a) 2, 5, 6, 7, 9, 23   (b) 47, 63, 89, 105, 121   (c) 1, 2, 2, 5, 6, 6, 7, 7, 9   (d) 9, 12, 12, 15, 17, 17, 19, 21

Exercise 2A

1. (a) 4, 6   (b) 2, 6   (c) 7, 4   (d) 4, 3   (e) 4, 8   (f) 3, 3·5

   (g) 3, 3·5   (h) 6, 5·25   (i) 5, 10·7   (j) 4, 15   (k) 8, 23   (l) 1, 102·5

   (m) 3, 8   (n) 4, 16   (o) 5, 34·3

2. (a) £41   (b) £4·10

3. (a) Lisa 1, Lucy 7   (b) Lisa 7·5, Lucy 7·3

   (c) Lisa, she has a higher mean and lower range.

4. (a) Sample One 41, Sample Two 84   (b) Sample One 251·9, Sample Two 259·6

   (c) Sample Two's mean is higher, but Sample One's range is smaller and so Sample One is more consistent.

5. (a) Sally £10, Greg £20   (b) Sally £10·50, Greg £10·50

   (c) On average, they save the same amount, but Greg's savings show much more variation with a greater range.

6. (a) Alexandra 10, Emmanuel 5   (b) Alexandra 8, Emmanuel 8·5

   (c) Alexandra wins the game and can claim to be the best player, but her play is erratic as her range shows.

Exercise 2B

1. (a) 6   (b) 6   (c) 4   (d) 3   (e) 8   (f) 3·5   (g) 3·5   (h) 5

   (i) 10   (j) 15   (k) 22   (l) 102·5   (m) 8   (n) 16   (o) 34·5

2. (a) Vet 1 30 litres, Vet 2 6 litres   (b) Vet 1 35 litres, Vet 2 23 litres

   (c) Vet is more consistent.

3. (a) 20   (b) 19   (c) 14   (d) 12

4. (a) 24°C, 5°C   (b) 26°C, 10°C   (c) Eastbourne is generally hotter but more variable.

5. (a) 30, 85   (b) 29, 31   (c) Team 2

6. (a) 53·5p, 19p   (b) 61p, 19p

   (c) Tomatoes are more expensive in the South West.

Exercise 2C

1. (a) 30   (b) 22

2. (b) Kwik Bite 35, Lunch Box 46   (c) Lunch Box

Exercise 2D

1. 11   **2.** 2

3. (a) 8 and 9 (biomodal), 4   (b) 7, 2

4. (a) 5, 5   (b) 6, 4

5. (a) 36 000   (b) Summer

6. Vanilla

Exercise 2E

1. (a) 5, 4, 3, 8   (b) 25, 25, 23, 5   (c) 3, 3, 3, 3   (d) 8, 7, 7, 22
2. (a) 3   (b) 2   (c) 6   (d) 6
3. (a) ⁻1   (b) 0   (c) 1   (d) 5
4. (a) £2·25, £2·25, £2, £2·50   (b) £2·45, £1, £1, £5·75
5. (a) 126 mm, 125 mm, 125 mm, 14 mm (b) 143·8 mm, 144·5 mm, 145 mm, 11 mm
6. (a) 197°C, 197°C, 195°C, 14°C   (b) 203°C, 203·5°C, 205°C, 8°C

Exercise 2F

1. (a) 2   (b) 3   (c) between 25th and 26th values   (d) 1
(e)

Number of children	Number of houses	Number of children × Number of houses
0	14	0
1	15	15
2	18	36
3	3	9
4	0	0
Totals	50	60

(f) 1·2 children

2. (a) 2   (b) 9   (c) between 15th and 16th values   (d) 3
(e)   (f) 3·5

Number of eggs	Frequency	Number of eggs × Frequency
0	4	0
1	1	1
2	7	14
3	4	12
4	4	16
5	4	20
6	3	18
7	1	7
8	1	8
9	1	9
Totals	30	105

3. (a) 8   (b) 7   (c) between 10th and 11th values   (d) 7
(e)   (f) 7

Number correct	Frequency	Number correct × Frequency
0	0	0
1	0	0
2	0	0
3	1	3
4	1	4
5	2	10
6	3	18
7	4	28
8	5	40
9	3	27
10	1	10
Totals	20	140

4. (a) 1   (b) 5   (c) between 50th and 51st values   (d) 2
(e)   (f) 1·96

Number of tests taken	Frequency	Number of tests taken × Frequency
1	43	43
2	31	62
3	17	51
4	6	24
5	2	10
6	1	6
Totals	100	196

5. (a) 34   (b) 6   (c) 13th value   (d) 34

(e)

Number of sweets	Number of packets	Number of sweets × Number of packets
30	4	120
31	1	31
32	2	64
33	4	132
34	8	272
35	3	105
36	3	108
Totals	25	832

(f) 33·28   (g) Yes, they can use the median or mode.

Checkout D2

1. (a) 4, 3   (b) 2·25, 5   (c) 11, 5   (d) 14·6, 4

2. (a) 3   (b) 1·5   (c) 10·5   (d) 14·5

3. (a) 3   (b) 1   (c) 10   (d) 16

4. (a) 3   (b) 2   (c) 0   (d) 9

5. (a) 1   (b) 4   (c) between 25th and 26th values   (d) 2   (f) 1·66

(e)

Number of children	Number of houses	Number of children × Number of houses
0	1	0
1	23	23
2	19	38
3	6	18
4	1	4
Totals	50	83

Revision exercise D2

1. (a) (i) 4   (ii) 13·9 cm   (b) A greater spread is the size of the handspans.

2. (a) 2·5   (b) 3

3. (a) 2   (b) 31   (c) 96

4. (a) 26   (b) 2   (c) 2·1

5.

3	5	2	
2	0	1	6
1	2	5	7

Key 3|5 means 35

6.

4	1	5			
3	1	2	4	6	6	8
2	5	7	7	8	9
1	9				

Key 4|1 means 41

D3 Data handling 3

Exercise 3A

1. (a) Lisa:

Distance (miles)	Frequency
1 to 5	3
6 to 10	5
11 to 15	7
16 to 20	3
21 to 25	2

Orla:

Distance (miles)	Frequency
1 to 5	1
6 to 10	9
11 to 15	6
16 to 20	3
21 to 25	1

. (b) Lisa: bars with heights 3, 5, 7, 3, 2   Orla: bars with heights 1, 9, 6, 3, 1

(c)

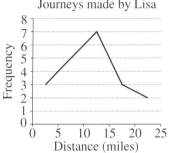

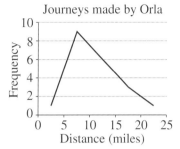

2.

Weight (kilograms)	Frequency (before)	Frequency (after)
76 to 80	1	4
81 to 85	4	4
86 to 90	6	7
91 to 95	7	12
96 to 100	8	3
101 to 105	4	0

3. (a)

Mark	Frequency (9Y)	Frequency (9Q)
0 to 2	1	0
3 to 5	2	0
6 to 8	1	4
9 to 11	5	12
12 to 14	6	10
15 to 17	12	3
18 to 20	3	1

(b) 9Y: bars with heights 1, 2, 1, 5, 6, 12, 3
9Q: bars with heights 0, 0, 4, 12, 10, 3, 1

(c)

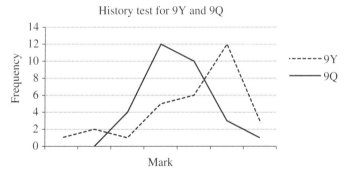

4. (a)

Age	Frequency (Day 1)	Frequency (Day 2)
0 to 4	6	1
5 to 9	8	1
10 to 14	2	1
15 to 19	2	4
20 to 24	1	2
25 to 29	1	4
30 to 34	0	4
35 to 39	0	3

(b) Day 1: bars with heights 6, 8, 2, 2, 1, 1, 0, 0
Day 2: bars with heights 1, 1, 1, 4, 2, 4, 4, 3

(c)

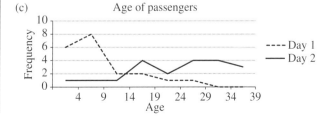

Exercise 3B

1. (a)

Pets owned	Frequency	Angle
Dog	5	50°
Cat	7	70°
Mouse	10	100°
Fish	8	80°
Hamster	6	60°
Totals	36	360°

2. (a)

Ways of coming to school	Number of pupils	Angle
Parent's car	10	120°
Friend's car	4	48°
Bus	2	24°
Walk	8	96°
Cycle	6	72°
Totals	30	360°

3. (b)

Type of spending	Frequency	Angle
Highways and planning	£14	28°
Sports and recreation	£28	56°
Environmental health	£32	64°
Housing	£27	54°
Administration	£47	94°
Emergencies	£32	64°
Totals	£180	360°

4. (b)

Expenditure	Factory A	Angle
Wages	£30	120°
Raw materials	£40	160°
Overheads	£20	80°
Totals	£90	360°

Expenditure	Factory B	Angle
Wages	£25	100°
Raw materials	£35	140°
Overheads	£30	120°
Totals	£90	360°

5. (c)

Season	Visitor 1999 (thousands)	Angle
Spring	7	63°
Summer	18	162°
Autumn	9	81°
Winter	6	54°
Totals	40	360°

Season	Visitor 2000 (thousands)	Angle
Spring	8	48°
Summer	31	186°
Autumn	14	84°
Winter	7	42°
Totals	60	360°

6. (a)

Flavour	Number of first choices (Test 1)	Angle
Strawberry	54	108°
Raspberry	47	94°
Orange	21	42°
Apple	23	46°
Pear	35	70°
Totals	180	360°

Flavour	Number of first choices (Test 2)	Angle
Strawberry	32	64°
Raspberry	44	88°
Orange	34	68°
Apple	40	80°
Pear	30	60°
Totals	180	360°

Exercise 3C

3. (a)

Brand	Votes	Percentage
Pork	5	20%
Pork with apple	10	40%
Pork with herbs	6	24%
Vegetarian	4	16%
Totals	25	100%

4. (a)

Activity	Number of first choices	Percentage
Football	30	20%
Snooker	15	10%
Table tennis	45	30%
Aerobics	60	40%
Totals	150	100%

5.

Spending idea	Votes from Year 7	Percentage
Computer for the library	48	24%
Sports equipment	84	42%
Staging for school productions	46	23%
Display boards in the school entrance	22	11%
Totals	200	100%

Spending idea	Votes from Year 7	Percentage
Computer for the library	45	25%
Sports equipment	63	35%
Staging for school productions	54	30%
Display boards in the school entrance	18	10%
Totals	180	100%

6.

Finish	Choices (pupils)	Percentage
Polished wood	6	10%
Stained wood	36	60%
Painted	18	30%
Totals	60	100%

Finish	Choices (adults)	Percentage
Polished wood	15	25%
Stained wood	24	40%
Painted	21	35%
Totals	60	100%

Exercise 3D

1. (a) 12%   (b) large   (c) 10   (d) 8   (e) bars with heights: 12, 32, 40, 16
2. (a) 135°   (b) 6 hours   (c) 3 hours   (d) 9 hours   (e) bars with heights: 6, 9, 3, 3, 3
3. (a) 78°   (b) 4°   (c) 15 mm   (d) 19·5 mm   (e) bars with heights: 20, 15, 12, 10, 14, 19·5
4. (a) 25%   (b) 60   (c) 15   (d) 18   (e) 21
  (f) bars with heights: 6, 21, 15, 18
5. (a) 80°   (b) 2   (c) 3   (d) 8   (e) bars with heights: 4, 8, 3, 2, 1
6. (a) 20%   (b) 10   (c) 5   (d) 15   (e) 50
  (f) bars with heights: 20, 5, 10, 15

Checkout D3

1. (a)

Distance miles	Frequency (Lisa)
1 to 5	7
6 to 10	7
11 to 15	4
16 to 20	2
21 to 25	0

Distance miles	Frequency (Orla)
1 to 5	5
6 to 10	5
11 to 15	5
16 to 20	1
21 to 25	4

(b) Lisa: bars with heights 7, 7, 4, 2, 0   Orla: bars with heights 5, 5, 5, 1, 4

(c)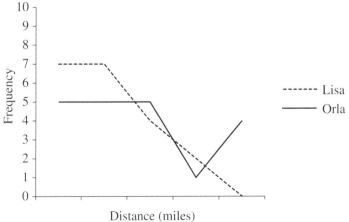

Journeys made in one week

2.

Season	Visitors (thousands)	Angle
Spring	10	60°
Summer	25	150°
Autumn	16	96°
Winter	9	54°
Totals	60	360°

3.

Topping	Votes	Percentage
Cheese and tomato	4	16%
Pepperoni and ham	12	48%
Garlic and mushroom	3	12%
Roast vegetable	6	24%
Totals	25	100%

4. (a) (i) 50%   (ii) 48   (iii) bars with heights: 20, 32, 48, 100
  (b) (i) 54°   (ii) 9°   (iii) 13   (iv) 7   (v) 9   (vi) bars with heights: 6, 5, 9, 13, 7

Revision exercise D3

1. (a) 23%   (b) 40   (c) 162°
2. (a) $\frac{1}{3}$ (b) 1836   (c) 357
3. (b) 9 to under 10   (c) Majority of area under the polygon is to the left of the 10 hour line
4. (a) Angles are 126°, 54°, 36°, 144°   (b) People rushing home from work or school   (c) (i) 240   (ii) 30
5. Angles are 170°, 120°, 70°

D5 Data handling 4

Check in D4

1. (a) rectangle (b) square   (c) square   (d) arrow

Exercise 4B

1. positively correlated   **2.** negatively correlated   **3.** positively correlated   **4.** not correlated
5. negatively correlated   **6.** positively correlated   **7.** not correlated   **8.** positively correlated
9. negatively correlated   **10.** not correlated

Exercise 4C

1. (a) coordinates at (7,0) (7,2) (8,3) (8,2) (9,3) (9,4) (10,6) (10,2) (11,5) (11,8)   (b) positive correlation
2. (a) coordinates at (1,10) (1,6) (3,8) (3,6) (4,5) (4,6) (6,4) (7,2) (10,2) (12,1)   (b) negative correlation
3. (a) coordinates at (1,9) (1,8) (2,7) (2,5) (3,6) (4,3) (4,4) (5,4) (6,2) (7,2)   (b) negative correlation
4. (a) coordinates at (24,14) (25,12) (31,18) (33,16) (35,12) (42,20) (46,22) (48,24) (51,26) (56,30)
  (b) positive correlation
5. (a) coordinates at (1,15) (1,14) (1·5,12) (1·5,13) (2,15) (2,11) (2,10) (2·5,9) (3,9) (3·5,8) (b) negative correlation

Exercise 4D

1. (a) positive
  (b) (i) 118 miles/h   (ii) 145 miles/h   (iii) 160 miles/h   (iv) 100 miles/h
  (c) (i) 1 000 cm³   (ii) 2 750 cm³   (iii) 300 cm³   (iv) 1 500 cm³

Checkout D4

2. (a) positively correlated   (b) negatively correlated   (c) not correlated
3. (a) coordinates at (4,24) (4,22) (5,20) (6,18) (6,20) (7,17) (8,19) (9,15) (10,16) (11,14)   (b) negative correlation

Revision exercise D4

1. (b) As the length of the journey increases, the cost increases.   **2.** (b) Positive correlation.
3. (b) Positive correlation.   **4.** (c) (i) 1·8 hours   (ii) Distance of 130 miles is outside the range of the other data.
5. (b) Positive correlation.   (c) All the points are close to a straight line.
6. (b) Positive correlation
7. (c) 50 miles approx   (d) 220 miles approx   (e) Most points are clustered around 50 miles.

D5 Data handling 5

Check in D5

1. (a) $\frac{2}{3}$ (b) $\frac{4}{5}$ (c) $\frac{1}{5}$ (d) $\frac{2}{3}$ (e) $\frac{1}{5}$ (f) $\frac{1}{3}$
2. (a) 0·25   (b) 0·4   (c) 0·625   (d) 0·16
3. (a) 25%   (b) 75%   (c) 50%   (d) 40%   (e) 12·5%   (f) 9%

Exercise 5A

1. (a) $\frac{1}{2}$, 0·5, 50%   (b) $\frac{1}{2}$, 0·5, 50%
2. (a) $\frac{1}{6}$, 0·167, 16·7%   (b) $\frac{1}{2}$, 0·5, 50%   (c) $\frac{2}{3}$, 0·667, 66·7%   (d) $\frac{1}{3}$, 0·333, 33·3%
3. (a) $\frac{1}{5}$, 0·2, 20%   (b) $\frac{3}{10}$, 0·3, 30%   (c) $\frac{1}{2}$, 0·5, 50%   (d) $\frac{1}{2}$, 0·5, 50%
4. (a) $\frac{3}{10}$, 0·3, 30%   (b) $\frac{1}{10}$, 0·1, 10%   (c) $\frac{2}{5}$, 0·4, 40%   (d) $\frac{3}{10}$, 0·3, 30%   (e) $\frac{1}{2}$, 0·5, 50%
5. (a) $\frac{1}{4}$, 0·25, 25%   (b) $\frac{3}{4}$, 0·75, 75%
6. (a) $\frac{7}{15}$, 0·467, 46·7%   (b) $\frac{8}{15}$, 0·533, 53·3%   (c) $\frac{1}{10}$, 0·1, 10%   (d) $\frac{1}{6}$, 0·167, 16·7%
7. (a) $\frac{1}{4}$, 0·25, 25%   (b) $\frac{2}{5}$, 0·4, 40%   (c) $\frac{7}{20}$, 0,35, 35%   (d) $\frac{3}{5}$, 0·6, 60%
8. (a) $\frac{3}{5}$, 0·6, 60%   (b) $\frac{9}{25}$, 0·36, 36%   (c) $\frac{1}{25}$, 0·04, 4%   (d) $\frac{16}{25}$, 0·64, 64%
9. (a) $\frac{1}{2}$, 0·5, 50%   (b) $\frac{1}{13}$, 0·077, 7·7%   (c) $\frac{1}{26}$, 0·038, 3·8%   (d) $\frac{1}{4}$, 0·25, 25%   (e) $\frac{1}{52}$, 0·019, 1·9%
10. (a) $\frac{1}{5}$, 0·2, 20%   (b) $\frac{3}{10}$, 0·3, 30%   (c) $\frac{1}{10}$, 0·1, 10%   (d) $\frac{2}{5}$, 0·4, 40%
11. (a) $\frac{1}{15}$, 0·067, 6·7%   (b) $\frac{1}{3}$, 0·333, 33·3%   (c) $\frac{1}{5}$, 0·2, 20%   (d) $\frac{11}{15}$, 0·733, 73·3%
12. (a) $\frac{1}{4}$, 0·25, 25%   (b) $\frac{1}{20}$, 0·05, 5%   (c) $\frac{3}{5}$, 0·6, 60%   (d) $\frac{4}{5}$, 0·8, 80%

Exercise 5B

1. $\frac{4}{5}$ 2. 0·35   3. (a) 1   (b) $\frac{3}{4}$ (c) 0
4. $\frac{7}{8}$ 5. 25%   6. 88%   7. 0·02   8. 78%
9. (a) 1   (b) 55%   (c) 0
10. $\frac{23}{30}$ 11. $\frac{4}{9}$ 12. 40%   13. 0·45   14. 0·2   15. 0·3

Exercise 5C

1. (a) $\frac{3}{10}$ (b) $\frac{7}{10}$ 2. (a) $\frac{1}{10}$ 3. (a) $\frac{3}{8}$ (b) $\frac{1}{8}$ (c) $\frac{1}{2}$
4. (a) $\frac{1}{5}$ (b) $\frac{4}{5}$ 5. (a) 0·1   6. (a) 0·8   (b) 0·2
7. (a) 70%   8. (a) 40%

Exercise 5D

1. (a) cheese with white bread, cheese with wholemeal bread, ham with white bread, ham with wholemeal bread, chicken with white bread, chicken with wholemeal bread, prawns with white bread, prawns with wholemeal bread
   (b) 8   (c) $\frac{1}{8}$

2. (a) red top with red skirt, red top with white skirt, red top with gold skirt, blue top with red skirt, blue top with white skirt, blue top with gold skirt, black top with red skirt, black top with white skirt, black top with gold skirt, silver top with red skirt, silver top with white skirt, silver top with gold skirt
   (b) 12   (c) $\frac{1}{6}$

3. (a)

	R	R	W
R	RR	RR	RW
R	RR	RR	RW
R	WR	WR	WW

   (b) 4
   (c) (i) $\frac{4}{9}$ (ii) $\frac{1}{9}$ (iii) $\frac{4}{9}$

5. (a)

+	1	2	3	4
1	2	3	4	5
2	3	4	5	6
3	4	5	6	7
4	5	6	7	8

   (b) 4
   (c) $\frac{1}{4}$
   (d) (i) $\frac{1}{16}$ (ii) $\frac{1}{8}$ (iii)

6. (a)

+	1	3	5	7
2	3	5	7	9
4	5	7	9	11
6	7	9	11	13
8	9	11	13	15

   (b) 2
   (c) $\frac{1}{8}$
   (d) (i) $\frac{1}{16}$ (ii)

7. (a)

+	1	2	3	4	5	6
1	2	3	4	5	6	7
2	3	4	5	6	7	8
3	4	5	6	7	8	9
4	5	6	7	8	9	10
5	6	7	8	9	10	11
6	7	8	9	10	11	12

(b) 6
(c) $\frac{1}{6}$
(d) (i) $\frac{1}{18}$ (ii) $\frac{5}{36}$ (iii) $\frac{1}{9}$ (iv) $\frac{1}{9}$ (v) 0
(vi) $\frac{1}{2}$

Checkout D5

1. (a) $\frac{1}{5}$ (b) $\frac{1}{10}$ (c) $\frac{2}{5}$ (d) $\frac{3}{5}$
2. (a) 0·4   (b) 0   (c) 1
3. (a) $\frac{1}{5}$ (b) $\frac{4}{5}$
4. (a)

	P	P	R
P	PP	PP	PR
R	RP	RP	RR
R	RP	RP	RR

(b) 2   (c) (i) $\frac{2}{9}$ (ii) $\frac{2}{9}$ (iii) $\frac{5}{9}$

Revision exercise D5

1. (a) $\frac{3}{10}$ (b) $\frac{1}{2}$ **2.** (a) $\frac{1}{20}$ (b) $\frac{7}{20}$ (c) $\frac{13}{20}$
3. (a) $\frac{1}{4}$ (b) $\frac{3}{8}$
(c) 2 and 3 have two chances each out of 8 being of landed upon, the other numbers only have one chance.
4. 0·7   **5.** (a) $\frac{3}{8}$ (b) $\frac{1}{8}$ (c) 0.75
6. (a) $\frac{1}{2}$ (b) $\frac{4}{11}$
(c) (i) 0.4   (ii) less black counters than yellow or green, equal number of yellow and green counters.

Module 1 Calculator paper

1. (a) 1   (b) 3, 4   (c) 0   **2.** 16 cm   **3.** (a) 531   (b) 354.1   (c) 115 000 or 115 437
4. 140°, 120°, 68°, 32°
5. (b) As a child wins more at one game, they will have less wins at the other game–negative correlation.

Module 1 Non-calculator paper

1. (a) $5\frac{1}{2}$ (b) 1 hour   (c) 5 symbols   **2.** $\frac{4}{7}$ **3.** Frequencies; 12, 7, 6, 3, 2
4. (a) $\frac{5}{19}$ (b) 0.75
5.

6	3		
5			
4	1	9	
3	4	6	
2	6	5	7

Key 6|3 means 6·3

f the following items were on sale which would you buy?

(b) For example:

	Tally
Sandwiches	IIII IIII I
Pizzas	IIII II
Soup	IIII
Jack Potatoes	IIII I
Salad	I

ANSWERS MODULE 3

N1 Number 1

Exercise 1A

1. (a) 40 (b) 5 (c) 800 (d) 3 (e) 0 (f) 200 (g) 3 000
   (h) 20 (i) 4 (j) 6 000 (k) 0 (l) 8 (m) 300 (n) 70
   (o) 2 000 (p) 1 (q) 60 (r) 900 (s) 3 000 (t) 0
2. 300, 40, 8   3. 900, 0, 3   4. 2 000, 600, 50, 8   5. 7 000, 100, 90, 0
6. 3 000, 500, 20, 7   7. 1 000, 400, 10, 1   8. 8 000, 0, 0, 6   9. 10 000, 2 000, 400, 60, 7
10. (a) 258, 285, 528, 582, 825, 852   (b) 258, 285, 528, 582, 825, 852
11. (a) 379, 397, 739, 793, 937, 973   (b) 379, 397, 739, 793, 937, 973
12. (a) 1 046, 1 064, 1 406, 1 460, 1 604, 1 640, 4 016, 4 061, 4 106, 4 160, 4 601, 4 610, 6 014, 6 041, 6 104, 6 140, 6 401, 6 410
    (b) 1 046, 1 064, 1 406, 1 460, 1 604, 1 640, 4 016, 4 061, 4 106, 4 160, 4 601, 4 610, 6 014, 6 041, 6 104, 6 140, 6 401, 6 410

Exercise 1B

1. (a) 374 (b) 211 (c) 548 (d) 609 (e) 760 (f) 125 (g) 3 715
   (h) 6 419 (i) 14 990 (j) 17 845 (k) 24 519 (l) 48 660 (m) 86 886 (n) 68 068
   (o) 92 003 (p) 212 113 (q) 318 716 (r) 608 339 (s) 580 297 (t) 600 404
2. (a) three hundred and fifty-eight   (b) two hundred and seventeen
   (c) six hundred and seventy-seven   (d) four hundred and sixty-nine
   (e) one hundred and eleven   (f) two thousand five hundred and nineteen
   (g) six thousand and eighty-five   (h) nine thousand eight hundred and one
   (i) seven thousand four hundred and forty-two   (j) five thousand six hundred and thirteen
   (k) fifteen thousand seven hundred and twenty-three   (l) eighteen thousand four hundred and fifty-nine
   (m) thirty-four thousand and ninety-eight   (n) sixty-seven thousand one hundred and twelve
   (o) ten thousand one hundred and eleven
   (p) two hundred and thirty-one thousand two hundred and fourteen
   (q) six hundred and sixteen thousand two hundred and seventy
   (r) one hundred and nine thousand seven hundred and ten
   (s) one hundred thousand
   (t) eight hundred and fifty-seven thousand two hundred and forty-three
3. Californian Redwood: three hundred and sixty-six feet
   Douglas Fir: three hundred and two feet
   Noble Fir: two hundred and seventy-eight feet
   Giant Sequoia: two hundred and seventy-two feet
   Ponderosa Pine: two hundred and twenty-three feet
   Cedar: two hundred and nineteen feet
   Sitka Spruce: two hundred and sixteen feet
   Western Larch: one hundred and seventy-seven feet
   Hemlock: one hundred and sixty-three feet
   Beech: one hundred and sixty-one feet
   Black Cottonwood: one hundred and forty-seven feet
4. Mercury; three thousand and thirty-two miles
   Pluto: three thousand seven hundred miles
   Mars: four thousand two hundred and seventeen miles
   Venus: seven thousand five hundred and twenty-one miles
   Earth: seven thousand nine hundred and sixty-two miles
   Neptune: thirty thousand eight hundred miles
   Uranus: thirty-two thousand two hundred miles
   Saturn: seventy-four thousand six hundred miles
   Jupiter: eighty-eight thousand seven hundred miles
   Sun: eight hundred and sixty-five thousand five hundred miles

Exercise 1C

1. (a) 10   (b) 20   (c) 10   (d) 30   (e) 30   (f) 20   (g) 40
   (h) 50   (i) 50   (j) 60   (k) 50   (l) 60   (m) 80   (n) 70
   (o) 80   (p) 90   (q) 100   (r) 100   (s) 60   (t) 90
2. (a) 260   (b) 250   (c) 260   (d) 320   (e) 490   (f) 140   (g) 140
   (h) 130   (i) 800   (j) 970   (k) 310   (l) 310   (m) 300   (n) 210
   (o) 220   (p) 590   (q) 600   (r) 790   (s) 900   (t) 1 000
3. 54, 52, 65, 69
4. (a) 75, 76, 77, 78, 79, 80, 81, 82, 83, 84   (b) 125, 126, 127, 128, 129, 130, 131, 132, 133, 134
   (c) 295, 296, 297, 298, 299, 300, 301, 302, 303, 304   (d) 355, 356, 357, 358, 359, 360, 361, 362, 363, 364
   (e) 995, 996, 997, 998, 999, 1 000, 1 001, 1 002, 1 003, 1 004

Exercise 1D

1. (a) 300   (b) 600   (c) 900   (d) 500   (e) 400   (f) 500   (g) 800
   (h) 700   (i) 800   (j) 600   (k) 200   (l) 300   (m) 300   (n) 800
   (o) 700   (p) 700   (q) 500   (r) 600   (s) 900   (t) 1 000
2. (a) 1 000   (b) 1 400   (c) 1 400   (d) 1 300   (e) 1 300   (f) 1 600   (g) 3 400
   (h) 4 300   (i) 4 400   (j) 8 100   (k) 5 000   (l) 5 100   (m) 5 100   (n) 3 800
   (o) 3 900   (p) 3 000   (q) 8 000   (r) 9 000   (s) 8 900   (t) 13 000
3. 518, 549, 650, 660
4. (a) 150 to 249   (b) 450 to 549   (c) 750 to 849
   (d) 2 850 to 2 949   (e) 55 550 to 55 649
5. Greenland 840 000 square miles   New Guinea 316 900 square miles
   Borneo 287 000 square miles   Madagascar 227 000 square miles
   Baffin (Canada) 183 800 square miles   Sumatra 182 900 square miles
   Honshu (Japan) 88 900 square miles   Great Britain 88 800 square miles
   Victoria (Canada) 82 100 square miles   Ellesmere (Canada) 81 900 square miles

Exercise 1E

1. (a) 4 000   (b) 2 000   (c) 2 000   (d) 1 000   (e) 2 000   (f) 6 000   (g) 6 000
   (h) 6 000   (i) 5 000   (j) 8 000   (k) 8 000   (l) 6 000   (m) 3 000   (n) 8 000
   (o) 7 000   (p) 7 000   (q) 9 000   (r) 10 000   (s) 10 000   (t) 10 000
2. (a) 11 000   (b) 18 000   (c) 20 000   (d) 12 000   (e) 16 000   (f) 25 000   (g) 60 000
   (h) 24 000   (i) 32 000   (j) 22 000   (k) 45 000   (l) 26 000   (m) 501 000   (n) 235 000
   (o) 568 000   (p) 234 000   (q) 350 000   (r) 500 000   (s) 1 000 000   (t) 950 000
3. (a) 5 500 to 6 499   (b) 4 500 to 5 499
   (c) 18 500 to 19 499   (d) 54 500 to 55 499
4. Wimbledon 10 000   Southampton 15 000   Coventry 23 000   Blackburn 28 000
   Sheffield Wednesday 34 000   Middlesbrough 35 000   Newcastle 37 000   Arsenal 38 000
   Everton 39 000   Manchester United 55 000

Exercise 1F

1. 20   2. 20   3. 40   4. 40   5. 60   6. 80   7. 70
8. 90   9. 90   10. 100   11. 100   12. 200   13. 200   14. 300
15. 300   16. 400   17. 500   18. 400   19. 700   20. 700   21. 1 000
22. 2 000   23. 4 000   24. 5 000   25. 7 000   26. 8 000   27. 8 000   28. 6 000
29. 20 000   30. 10 000

Exercise 1G

1. (a) 10   (b) 8   (c) 8   (d) 15   (e) 9   (f) 11   (g) 7
   (h) 15   (i) 10   (j) 13   (k) 12   (l) 12   (m) 16   (n) 13
   (o) 10   (p) 13   (q) 18   (r) 16   (s) 17   (t) 14   (u) 10
   (v) 12   (w) 14   (x) 11   (y) 14
2. (a) 13   (b) 17   (c) 15   (d) 19   (e) 14   (f) 18   (g) 16
   (h) 20   (i) 12   (j) 15   (k) 19   (l) 17   (m) 19   (n) 17
   (o) 18   (p) 16   (q) 18   (r) 18   (s) 19   (t) 20   (u) 15
   (v) 14   (w) 13   (x) 17   (y) 14

3. (a) 30 (b) 40 (c) 50 (d) 70 (e) 80 (f) 60 (g) 50
(h) 80 (i) 90 (j) 110 (k) 110 (l) 140 (m) 130 (n) 130
(o) 100 (p) 110 (q) 150 (r) 170 (s) 140 (t) 130 (u) 160
(v) 120 (w) 90 (x) 150 (y) 120

4. (a) 57 (b) 55 (c) 48 (d) 99 (e) 105 (f) 93 (g) 121
(h) 106 (i) 158 (j) 117 (k) 87 (l) 132 (m) 136 (n) 106
(o) 165 (p) 83 (q) 88 (r) 115 (s) 116 (t) 123 (u) 119
(v) 187 (w) 74 (x) 111

5. (a) 31 (b) 46 (c) 29 (d) 33 (e) 69 (f) 52 (g) 47
(h) 95 (i) 76 (j) 89 (k) 101 (l) 106 (m) 107 (n) 115
(o) 133 (p) 138 (q) 162 (r) 124 (s) 121 (t) 198 (u) 187
(v) 175 (w) 193 (x) 207 (y) 201

6. (a) 137 (b) 143 (c) 166 (d) 126 (e) 177 (f) 128 (g) 98
(h) 159 (i) 148 (j) 139 (k) 139 (l) 108 (m) 60 (n) 63
(o) 103 (p) 75 (q) 71 (r) 97 (s) 134 (t) 136 (u) 132
(v) 164 (w) 127 (x) 198

Exercise 1H

1. (a) 29 (b) 37 (c) 78 (d) 78 (e) 100 (f) 63 (g) 73
(h) 82 (i) 56 (j) 64 (k) 28 (l) 34 (m) 44 (n) 85
(o) 90 (p) 82 (q) 38 (r) 34 (s) 63 (t) 75 (u) 118
(v) 123 (w) 161 (x) 147 (y) 165

2. (a) 132p (b) 103p (c) 123p (d) 145p (e) 142p (f) 160p (g) 155p
(h) 90p (i) 110p (j) 220p (k) 285p (l) 310p (m) 200p (n) 210p
(o) 195p (p) 420p

3.

Saved this week	Total so far
£12	£12
£17	£29
£9	£38
£22	£60
£35	£95
£5	£100
£16	£116
£17	£133
£24	£157
£18	£175
£6	£181
£11	£192
£23	£215

4.

By end of month	Days passed
January	31
February	59
March	90
April	120
May	151
June	181
July	212
August	243
September	273
October	304
November	334
December	365

Exercise 1I

1. (a) 3 (b) 6 (c) 3 (d) 6 (e) 5 (f) 9 (g) 9
(h) 8 (i) 6 (j) 7 (k) 5 (l) 7 (m) 2 (n) 6
(o) 8 (p) 9 (q) 8 (r) 8 (s) 7 (t) 7 (u) 9
(v) 6 (w) 9 (x) 6 (y) 7

2. (a) 22 (b) 42 (c) 63 (d) 82 (e) 41 (f) 40 (g) 22
(h) 84 (i) 31 (j) 54 (k) 55 (l) 43 (m) 121 (n) 152
(o) 183 (p) 233 (q) 60 (r) 83 (s) 80 (t) 21 (u) 44
(v) 51 (w) 72 (x) 73 (y) 90

3. (a) 25 (b) 17 (c) 36 (d) 29 (e) 48 (f) 36 (g) 53
(h) 12 (i) 14 (j) 45 (k) 57 (l) 47 (m) 19 (n) 17
(o) 24 (p) 23 (q) 27 (r) 15 (s) 45 (t) 15 (u) 39
(v) 61 (w) 16 (x) 63 (y) 38

4. (a) 33   (b) 13   (c) 52   (d) 24   (e) 33   (f) 21   (g) 41
(h) 22   (i) 31   (j) 61   (k) 41   (l) 40   (m) 12   (n) 27
(o) 41   (p) 20   (q) 31   (r) 11   (s) 34   (t) 46   (u) 42
(v) 44   (w) 64   (x) 55   (y) 45

5. (a) 17   (b) 39   (c) 19   (d) 26   (e) 78   (f) 58   (g) 78
(h) 68   (i) 47   (j) 39   (k) 29   (l) 79   (m) 27   (n) 68
(o) 67   (p) 28   (q) 39   (r) 27   (s) 46   (t) 55   (u) 85
(v) 55   (w) 25   (x) 74   (y) 52

6. (a) 19   (b) 59   (c) 28   (d) 69   (e) 27   (f) 28   (g) 29
(h) 47   (i) 78   (j) 6   (k) 7   (l) 59   (m) 78   (n) 38
(o) 35   (p) 25   (q) 29   (r) 37   (s) 67   (t) 27   (u) 25
(v) 54   (w) 36   (x) 29   (y) 56

7.

Time passed between checks	Time left
18 mins	222 mins
25 mins	197 mins
23 mins	174 mins
31 mins	143 mins
42 mins	101 mins
17 mins	84 mins
56 mins	28 mins
28 mins	0 mins

8.

Time (mins)	Temp (°C)	Temp fall (°C)
0	176	–
5	155	21
10	138	17
15	124	14
20	112	12
25	98	14
30	96	2
35	95	1
40	81	14
45	64	17
50	43	21
55	31	12
60	29	2

Exercise 1J

1. (a) 79   (b) 99   (c) 99   (d) 97   (e) 196   (f) 687   (g) 779
(h) 877   (i) 956   (j) 777   (k) 549   (l) 339   (m) 888   (n) 289
(o) 938   (p) 845   (q) 398   (r) 888   (s) 799   (t) 979   (u) 899
(v) 989   (w) 159   (x) 388   (y) 189

2. (a) 70   (b) 94   (c) 65   (d) 54   (e) 80   (f) 380   (g) 683
(h) 860   (i) 691   (j) 225   (k) 328   (l) 507   (m) 449   (n) 510
(o) 469   (p) 529   (q) 817   (r) 919   (s) 1 012   (t) 439   (u) 365
(v) 876   (w) 655   (x) 439   (y) 919

3. (a) 112   (b) 122   (c) 100   (d) 120   (e) 123   (f) 205   (g) 311
(h) 607   (i) 265   (j) 325   (k) 1 222   (l) 432   (m) 471   (n) 330
(o) 531   (p) 731   (q) 932   (r) 901   (s) 903   (t) 920   (u) 1 245
(v) 1 285   (w) 1 676   (x) 1 150   (y) 1 000

4. (a) 170   (b) 112   (c) 579   (d) 215   (e) 965

5. (a) £105   (b) £113   (c) £198   (d) £145   (e) £212

Exercise 1K

1. (a) 31   (b) 24   (c) 24   (d) 52   (e) 44   (f) 111   (g) 114
(h) 222   (i) 511   (j) 322   (k) 220   (l) 122   (m) 311   (n) 336
(o) 321   (p) 320   (q) 202   (r) 543   (s) 402   (t) 320   (u) 105
(v) 236   (w) 542   (x) 636   (y) 111

2. (a) 317   (b) 236   (c) 158   (d) 119   (e) 108   (f) 428   (g) 333
(h) 218   (i) 514   (j) 444   (k) 208   (l) 118   (m) 706   (n) 308
(o) 113   (p) 145   (q) 73   (r) 571   (s) 281   (t) 50   (u) 420
(v) 11   (w) 94   (x) 178   (y) 265

ANSWERS MODULE 3

3.
(a)	155	(b)	327	(c)	179	(d)	263		
(h)	255	(i)	169	(j)	89	(k)	275		
(o)	388	(p)	199	(q)	147	(r)	479		
(v)	178	(w)	339	(x)	329	(y)	541		

(a) 155 (b) 327 (c) 179 (d) 263 (e) 263 (f) 465 (g) 167
(h) 255 (i) 169 (j) 89 (k) 275 (l) 89 (m) 137 (n) 198
(o) 388 (p) 199 (q) 147 (r) 479 (s) 199 (t) 98 (u) 619
(v) 178 (w) 339 (x) 329 (y) 541

4.

Runner	Time behind winner
1st	–
2nd	+8 mins
3rd	+14 mins
4th	+18 mins
5th	+20 mins
6th	+23 mins
7th	+25 mins
8th	+28 mins
9th	+31 mins
10th	+36 mins
11th	+39 mins
12th	+42 mins
13th	+46 mins
14th	+50 mins
15th	+57 mins
16th	+63 mins
17th	+70 mins
18th	+74 mins
19th	+76 mins
20th	+79 mins

Exercise 1L

1. (a) $^-8°C, ^-7°C, ^-6°C, 2°C, 5°C, 7°C$
   (b) $^-7°C, ^-3°C, ^-2°C, ^-1°C, 0°C, 1°C, 5°C, 6°C$
   (c) $0°C, 3°C, 4°C, 4°C, 5°C, 6°C, 7°C, 8°C, 9°C, 9°C$
   (d) $^-4°C, ^-3°C, ^-2°C, ^-1°C, 0°C, 1°C, 2°C, 3°C, 4°C, 5°C$
   (e) $^-50°C, ^-40°C, ^-30°C, ^-20°C, ^-10°C, 0°C, 10°C, 30°C, 40°C, 50°C$
   (f) $^-20°C, ^-19°C, ^-17°C, ^-13°C, ^-9°C, ^-7°C, ^-6°C, 8°C, 11°C, 11°C$
   (g) $^-73°C, ^-56°C, ^-29°C, ^-17°C, ^-16°C, 21°C, 32°C, 43°C, 65°C, 81°C$
   (h) $0°C, 34°C, 39°C, 55°C, 65°C, 67°C, 76°C, 82°C, 90°C, 93°C$
2. $58°C, 56·7°C, 53·1°C, 46°C, ^-45°C, ^-58·3°C, ^-68°C, ^-88·3°C$

Exercise 1M

1.	(a) 13°C	(b) $^-3°C$	(c) 3°C	(d) $^-13°C$
2.	(a) 5°C	(b) $^-1°C$	(c) 1°C	(d) $^-5°C$
3.	(a) 11°C	(b) $^-3°C$	(c) 3°C	(d) $^-11°C$
4.	(a) 11°C	(b) 7°C	(c) $^-7°C$	(d) $^-11°C$
5.	(a) 11°C	(b) $^-9°C$	(c) 9°C	(d) $^-11°C$
6.	(a) 11°C	(b) $^-1°C$	(c) 1°C	(d) $^-11°C$
7.	(a) 17°C	(b) 5°C	(c) $^-5°C$	(d) $^-17°C$
8.	(a) 21°C	(b) 5°C	(c) $^-5°C$	(d) $^-21°C$
9.	(a) 12°C	(b) 6°C	(c) $^-6°C$	(d) $^-12°C$
10.	(a) 20°C	(b) 10°C	(c) $^-10°C$	(d) $^-20°C$
11.	(a) 19°C	(b) $^-5°C$	(c) 5°C	(d) $^-19°C$
12.	(a) 20°C	(b) 0°C	(c) 0°C	(d) $^-20°C$
13.	(a) 14°C	(b) 0°C	(c) 0°C	(d) $^-14°C$
14.	(a) 18°C	(b) 10°C	(c) $^-10°C$	(d) $^-18°C$

15. (a) 30°C   (b) ⁻10°C   (c) 10°C   (d) ⁻30°C
16. (a) 30°C   (b) 10°C   (c) ⁻10°C   (d) ⁻30°C
17. (a) 27°C   (b) 9°C   (c) ⁻9°C   (d) ⁻27°C
18. (a) 40°C   (b) ⁻10°C   (c) 10°C   (d) ⁻40°C
19. (a) 20°C   (b) 6°C   (c) ⁻6°C   (d) ⁻20°C
20. (a) 54°C   (b) 8°C   (c) ⁻8°C   (d) ⁻54°C

Exercise 1N

1. (a) 9   (b) ⁻1   (c) ⁻1   (d) 1   (e) ⁻9   (f) ⁻9
2. (a) 12   (b) ⁻2   (c) ⁻2   (d) 2   (e) ⁻12   (f) ⁻12
3. (a) 10   (b) 6   (c) 6   (d) ⁻6   (e) ⁻10   (f) ⁻10
4. (a) 12   (b) ⁻6   (c) ⁻6   (d) 6   (e) ⁻12   (f) ⁻12
5. (a) 15   (b) ⁻3   (c) ⁻3   (d) 3   (e) ⁻15   (f) ⁻15
6. (a) 16   (b) 4   (c) 4   (d) ⁻4   (e) ⁻16   (f) ⁻16
7. (a) 8   (b) 2   (c) 2   (d) ⁻2   (e) ⁻8   (f) ⁻8
8. (a) 7   (b) 5   (c) 5   (d) ⁻5   (e) ⁻7   (f) ⁻7
9. (a) 17   (b) ⁻3   (c) ⁻3   (d) 3   (e) ⁻17   (f) ⁻17
10. (a) 7   (b) 3   (c) 3   (d) ⁻3   (e) ⁻7   (f) ⁻7
11. (a) 14   (b) 8   (c) 8   (d) ⁻8   (e) ⁻14   (f) ⁻14
12. (a) 21   (b) ⁻7   (c) ⁻7   (d) 7   (e) ⁻21   (f) ⁻21

Exercise 1O

1. (a) 15   (b) 5   (c) 5   (d) 15   (e) ⁻5   (f) ⁻15   (g) ⁻15   (h) ⁻5
2. (a) 1   (b) ⁻1   (c) 1   (d) ⁻1   (e) ⁻13   (f) 13   (g) 13   (h) ⁻13
3. (a) ⁻7   (b) 7   (c) 7   (d) ⁻1   (e) ⁻1   (f) 1   (g) ⁻7   (h) 1
4. (a) 12   (b) 0   (c) 0   (d) ⁻12   (e) 0   (f) ⁻12   (g) 12   (h) 0
5. (a) 12   (b) 8   (c) 8   (d) 12   (e) ⁻8   (f) ⁻12   (g) ⁻12   (h) ⁻8
6. (a) ⁻7   (b) 7   (c) ⁻7   (d) 7   (e) ⁻9   (f) 9   (g) 9   (h) ⁻9
7. (a) ⁻10   (b) 10   (c) 10   (d) ⁻4   (e) ⁻4   (f) 4   (g) ⁻10   (h) 4
8. (a) 19   (b) ⁻1   (c) 1   (d) ⁻19   (e) 1   (f) ⁻19   (g) 19   (h) ⁻1
9. (a) 13   (b) 5   (c) 5   (d) 13   (e) ⁻5   (f) ⁻13   (g) ⁻13   (h) ⁻5
10. (a) 1   (b) ⁻1   (c) 1   (d) ⁻1   (e) ⁻3   (f) 3   (g) 3   (h) ⁻3
11. (a) ⁻19   (b) 19   (c) 19   (d) ⁻13   (e) ⁻13   (f) 13   (g) ⁻19   (h) 13
12. (a) 18   (b) 0   (c) 0   (d) ⁻18   (e) 0   (f) ⁻18   (g) 18   (h) 0

Exercise 1P

1. £740   2. £1 910   3. £39   4. £1 040   5. £675   6. 0   7. £100
8. £17   9. £200   10. £370   11. ⁻£150   12. ⁻£1   13. ⁻£196   14. ⁻£100

Exercise 1Q

1. 10.30   2. (a) 11.45   (b) 2 hours 4 minutes   3. 1 hour 39 minutes   4. (a) 29 minutes   (b) 16.23

Checkout N1

1. (a) 70   (b) 800
2. (a) 3 994   (b) seven thousand eight hundred and forty-three
3. (a) (i) 80   (ii) 100   (iii) 230
   (b) (i) 700   (ii) 400   (iii) 2 500
   (c) (i) 4 000   (ii) 23 000   (iii) 45 000
4. (a) 40   (b) 40   (c) 300   (d) 600   (e) 2 000   (f) 2 000
5. (a) 14   (b) 17   (c) 110   (d) 95   (e) 56   (f) 62   (g) 38
   (h) 62   (i) 6   (j) 43   (k) 15   (l) 41   (m) 28   (n) 17
6. (a) 658   (b) 397   (c) 123   (d) 1 000   (e) 32
   (f) 311   (g) 317   (h) 571   (i) 275   (j) 199
7. ⁻4°C, ⁻3°C, ⁻2°C, ⁻1°C, 0°C, 1°C, 2°C, 3°C, 4°C, 7°C
8. (a) 23°C   (b) 7°C   (c) ⁻7°C   (d) ⁻23°C
9. (a) 17   (b) ⁻5   (c) ⁻5   (d) 5   (e) ⁻17   (f) ⁻17
10. (a) ⁻10   (b) 10   (c) 10   (d) ⁻4
    (e) ⁻4   (f) 4   (g) ⁻10   (h) 4

Revision exercise N1

1. (a) (i) 7580   (ii) 7600   (b)   seven thousand five hundred and eighty-two
2. (a)   six hundred   (b)   twenty   (c)   fifty-nine thousand one hundred and fifty
3. 15, 11, 9, 8, 2, ⁻5, ⁻10, ⁻17
4. (a)   2 hours and 5 minutes   (b)   6 pounds
5. £268·07 overdrawn
6. £34·63
7. (a)   30 minutes   (b)   9.15   (c)   4 hours 45 minutes
8. 132, 34, 17, ⁻11, ⁻21
9. (a)   423   (b)   432   (c)   324
10. (a)   (i) 10 125   (ii) 1086   (b)   2700
11. 219, 115, 81, 52, 41, 17
12. 10.15 pm
13. £74·62
14. (a)   4.10 pm   (b)   1610   (c)   9.30 pm

N2 Number 2

Check in N2

1. (a) 6   (b) 60   (c) 600   (d) 7 000   (e) 700   (f) 70   (g) 400
    (h) 10   (i) zero

Exercise 2A

1. (a) 60   (b) 70   (c) 110   (d) 230   (e) 320   (f) 450   (g) 800
    (h) 610   (i) 560   (j) 980   (k) 1 120   (l) 1 720   (m) 4 510   (n) 3 900
    (o) 9 160   (p) 2 060   (q) 1 010   (r) 9 030   (s) 7 000   (t) 3 410
2. (a) 80   (b) 240   (c) 330   (d) 720   (e) 1 000   (f) 1 440
3. (a) 50   (b) 130   (c) 220   (d) 350   (e) 700   (f) 1 000

Exercise 2B

1. (a) 600   (b) 700   (c) 1 100   (d) 2 300   (e) 3 200   (f) 4 500   (g) 8 000
    (h) 6 100   (i) 5 600   (j) 9 800   (k) 11 200   (l) 17 200   (m) 45 100   (n) 39 000
    (o) 91 600   (p) 20 600   (q) 10 100   (r) 90 300   (s) 70 000   (t) 34 100
2. (a) 300   (b) 900   (c) 2 000   (d) 4 500   (e) 60 000   (f) 49 900
3. (a) 200   (b) 3 800   (c) 2 700   (d) 8 000   (e) 7 600   (f) 10 000

Exercise 2C

1. (a) 6 000   (b) 7 000   (c) 11 000   (d) 23 000   (e) 32 000   (f) 45 000   (g) 80 000
    (h) 61 000   (i) 56 000   (j) 98 000   (k) 112 000   (l) 172 000   (m) 451 000   (n) 390 000
    (o) 916 000   (p) 206 000   (q) 101 000   (r) 903 000   (s) 700 000   (t) 341 000
2. (a) 4 000   (b) 19 000   (c) 27 000   (d) 83 000   (e) 100 000   (f) 153 000
3. (a) 5 000   (b) 13 000   (c) 22 000   (d) 35 000   (e) 70 000   (f) 100 000

Exercise 2D

1. (a) 7   (b) 8   (c) 12   (d) 32   (e) 21   (f) 61   (g) 80
    (h) 51   (i) 65   (j) 89   (k) 125   (l) 127   (m) 451   (n) 290
    (o) 903   (p) 120   (q) 303   (r) 200   (s) 500   (t) 410
2. (a) £1   (b) £90   (c) £1 000   (d) £4 500   (e) £26 780   (f) £187 834
3. (a) 6 centimetres   (b) 17 centimetres   (c) 23 centimetres
    (d) 30 centimetres   (e) 50 centimetres   (f) 75 centimetres

Exercise 2E

1. (a) 7   (b) 6   (c) 12   (d) 13   (e) 25   (f) 26   (g) 8
    (h) 31   (i) 75   (j) 18   (k) 12   (l) 127   (m) 87   (n) 29
    (o) 193   (p) 128   (q) 133   (r) 200   (s) 550   (t) 2 419

2. (a) 3 metres   (b) 9 metres   (c) 6 metres
   (d) 45 metres   (e) 78 metres   (f) 67 metres

3. (a) £2   (b) £4   (c) £10   (d) £30   (e) £25   (f) £87

4. (a) 466p   (b) 580p   (c) 166p   (d) 477p   (e) 584p   (f) 294p   (g) 191p
   (h) 36p   (i) 306p   (j) 382p   (k) 362p   (l) 14p

Exercise 2F

1. (a) 7   (b) 4   (c) 12   (d) 32   (e) 21   (f) 49   (g) 18
   (h) 512   (i) 165   (j) 890   (k) 125   (l) 270   (m) 1 450   (n) 2 900
   (o) 5 030   (p) 6 200   (q) 3 435   (r) 52 430   (s) 5 367   (t) 41 321

2. (a) 1 litre   (b) 9 litres   (c) 10 litres
   (d) 5 litres   (e) 27 litres   (f) 78 litres

3. (a) 6 kilometres   (b) 8 kilometres   (c) 10 kilometres
   (d) 31 kilometres   (e) 55 kilometres   (f) 170 kilometres

Exercise 2G

1. (a) 6   (b) 12   (c) 20   (d) 12   (e) 9   (f) 16   (g) 15
   (h) 10   (i) 24   (j) 21   (k) 16   (l) 30   (m) 28   (n) 24
   (o) 40   (p) 32   (q) 14   (r) 8   (s) 30   (t) 20   (u) 40
   (v) 45   (w) 18   (x) 4   (y) 50

2. (a) 45   (b) 49   (c) 36   (d) 54   (e) 80   (f) 63   (g) 64
   (h) 81   (i) 70   (j) 100   (k) 48   (l) 72   (m) 90   (n) 63
   (o) 72   (p) 60   (q) 56   (r) 42   (s) 18   (t) 27   (u) 35
   (v) 36   (w) 56   (x) 42   (y) 25

3. (a) 150   (b) 160   (c) 180   (d) 200   (e) 180   (f) 240   (g) 270
   (h) 360   (i) 210   (j) 250   (k) 180   (l) 480   (m) 300   (n) 320
   (o) 400   (p) 120   (q) 240   (r) 240   (s) 350   (t) 490   (u) 540
   (v) 160   (w) 90   (x) 80

4. (a) 3 600   (b) 3 000   (c) 3 600   (d) 4 500   (e) 4 200   (f) 1 400   (g) 1 200
   (h) 1 500   (i) 2 100   (j) 1 800   (k) 1 000   (l) 2 700   (m) 2 800   (n) 4 800
   (o) 3 200   (p) 5 400   (q) 3 600   (r) 3 500   (s) 6 300   (t) 6 400   (u) 7 200
   (v) 8 100   (w) 5 600   (x) 4 200   (y) 1 800

5. (a) 27 000   (b) 24 000   (c) 20 000   (d) 18 000   (e) 8 000   (f) 35 000   (g) 36 000
   (h) 49 000   (i) 32 000   (j) 45 000   (k) 25 000   (l) 36 000   (m) 56 000   (n) 35 000
   (o) 54 000   (p) 9 000   (q) 16 000   (r) 10 000   (s) 63 000   (t) 42 000   (u) 40 000
   (v) 12 000   (w) 64 000   (x) 56 000   (y) 72 000

6. (a) 1 200   (b) 1 600   (c) 3 000   (d) 2 800   (e) 2 400   (f) 1 200   (g) 1 800
   (h) 1 800   (i) 800   (j) 1 400   (k) 3 000   (l) 2 800   (m) 4 200   (n) 4 000
   (o) 4 800   (p) 21 000   (q) 6 000   (r) 24 000   (s) 48 000   (t) 63 000   (u) 20 000
   (v) 15 000   (w) 36 000   (x) 36 000   (y) 72 000

Exercise 2H

1. (a) 60   (b) 42   (c) 78   (d) 32   (e) 51   (f) 56   (g) 96
   (h) 72   (i) 64   (j) 75   (k) 100   (l) 120   (m) 156   (n) 54
   (o) 280   (p) 112   (q) 279   (r) 336   (s) 294   (t) 264   (u) 216
   (v) 234   (w) 602   (x) 330   (y) 315

2. (a) £108   (b) £180   (c) £207   (d) £270   (e) £324

3. (a) 600 kg   (b) 800 kg   (c) 14 000 kg   (d) 2 400 kg   (e) 5 600 kg

4. (a) £80   (b) £96   (c) £160   (d) £216   (e) £408

Exercise 2I

1. (a) 7   (b) 4   (c) 6   (d) 9   (e) 7   (f) 3   (g) 3
   (h) 2   (i) 4   (j) 9   (k) 10   (l) 7   (m) 7   (n) 9
   (o) 5   (p) 9   (q) 6   (r) 6   (s) 6   (t) 7   (u) 7
   (v) 8   (w) 6   (x) 5   (y) 9

2. (a) 5 r 1   (b) 4 r 2   (c) 5 r 3   (d) 4 r 1   (e) 5 r 3   (f) 5 r 1   (g) 5 r 3
   (h) 2 r 5   (i) 1 r 6   (j) 1 r 2   (k) 10 r 1   (l) 8 r 2   (m) 8 r 2   (n) 8 r 3
   (o) 4 r 5   (p) 9 r 2   (q) 3 r 4   (r) 8 r 1   (s) 9 r 3   (t) 6 r 2   (u) 4 r 6
   (v) 9 r 3   (w) 9 r 3   (x) 8 r 3   (y) 10 r 8

3. (a) 9   (b) 10   (c) 8   (d) 10   (e) 11
4. (a) 4   (b) 6   (c) 6   (d) 9   (e) 10

Exercise 2J

1. (a) 8	(b) 2	(c) 6	(d) 4	(e) 3	(f) 10	(g) 2
(h) 3	(i) 8	(j) 5	(k) 5	(l) 2	(m) 6	(n) 7
(o) 5	(p) 4	(q) 5	(r) 9	(s) 7	(t) 3	(u) 2
(v) 5	(w) 7	(x) 8	(y) 6			
2. (a) 2	(b) 3	(c) 6	(d) 5	(e) 4	(f) 9	(g) 2
(h) 3	(i) 4	(j) 8	(k) 8	(l) 6	(m) 8	(n) 3
(o) 4	(p) 7	(q) 7	(r) 3	(s) 7	(t) 9	(u) 9
(v) 6	(w) 9	(x) 6				
3. (a) 5	(b) 4	(c) 6	(d) 9	(e) 2	(f) 4	(g) 8
(h) 8	(i) 6	(j) 3	(k) 8	(l) 7	(m) 2	(n) 9
(o) 7	(p) 5	(q) 6	(r) 4	(s) 9	(t) 5	(u) 6
4. (a) 30	(b) 60	(c) 70	(d) 120	(e) 40	(f) 80	(g) 600
(h) 700	(i) 400	(j) 400	(k) 500	(l) 500	(m) 400	(n) 700
(o) 900	(p) 400	(q) 6 000	(r) 600	(s) 7 000	(t) 50	(u) 90
(v) 90	(w) 80	(x) 600	(y) 8 000			

Exercise 2K

1. (a) 468	(b) 696	(c) 8 048	(d) 69	(e) 8 604	(f) 225	(g) 144
(h) 310	(i) 141	(j) 336	(k) 512	(l) 235	(m) 588	(n) 783
(o) 344	(p) 726	(q) 1 705	(r) 1 242	(s) 924	(t) 4 581	(u) 2 070
(v) 4 504	(w) 3 282	(x) 2 916	(y) 5 192			
2. (a) 1 300	(b) 2 040	(c) 1 800	(d) 2 280	(e) 1 760	(f) 2 880	(g) 2 010
(h) 3 650	(i) 7 040	(j) 1 560	(k) 2 240	(l) 3 180	(m) 4 270	(n) 7 470
(o) 2 800	(p) 1 710	(q) 9 240	(r) 28 350	(s) 20 640	(t) 18 180	(u) 18 600
(v) 32 200	(w) 20 790	(x) 62 720	(y) 41 130			
3. (a) 84	(b) 161	(c) 280	(d) 266	(e) 364		
4. (a) £1 530	(b) £2 070	(c) £3 420	(d) £6 480	(e) £8 820		

Exercise 2L

1. (a) 884	(b) 2 880	(c) 1 272	(d) 1 504	(e) 2 408	(f) 1 932	(g) 1 288
(h) 2 268	(i) 1 044	(j) 3 230	(k) 1 357	(l) 1 672	(m) 1 904	(n) 4 675
(o) 3 042	(p) 2 025	(q) 2 916	(r) 4 992	(s) 5 568	(t) 2 295	(u) 2 613
(v) 2 052	(w) 4 930	(x) 7 200	(y) 3 770			
2. (a) 9 594	(b) 12 386	(c) 39 831	(d) 27 315	(e) 26 280	(f) 14 835	(g) 14 944
(h) 47 806	(i) 35 478	(j) 39 566	(k) 60 265	(l) 41 440	(m) 23 785	(n) 49 610
(o) 23 592	(p) 59 508	(q) 30 282	(r) 19 125	(s) 27 775	(t) 49 166	(u) 48 068
(v) 27 824	(w) 65 100	(x) 82 302	(y) 53 976			
3. (a) £1 476	(b) £1 722	(c) £2 091	(d) £2 583	(e) £3 198		
4. (a) 2 025 kg	(b) 3 600 kg	(c) 6 480 kg	(d) 26 370 kg	(e) 38 475 kg		

Exercise 2M

1. (a) 51	(b) 72	(c) 46	(d) 52	(e) 57	(f) 73	(g) 88
(h) 58	(i) 40	(j) 24	(k) 94	(l) 99	(m) 42	(n) 76
(o) 44	(p) 87	(q) 87	(r) 96	(s) 65	(t) 25	(u) 29
(v) 82	(w) 77	(x) 65	(y) 64			
2. (a) 68 r 1	(b) 66 r 2	(c) 30 r 4	(d) 29 r 3	(e) 61 r 1	(f) 17 r 1	(g) 39 r 1
(h) 28 r 2	(i) 17 r 5	(j) 19 r 5	(k) 15 r 5	(l) 18 r 3	(m) 20 r 5	(n) 32 r 3
(o) 23 r 3	(p) 50 r 2	(q) 97 r 1	(r) 92 r 1	(s) 39 r 2	(t) 80 r 2	(u) 55 r 5
(v) 41 r 2	(w) 46 r 2	(x) 60 r 3	(y) 46 r 7			
3. (a) 13	(b) 18	(c) 25	(d) 43	(e) 52		

4. (a) 45 boxes, 1 left over   (b) 73 boxes, 2 left over   (c) 50 boxes, 5 left over
(d) 79 boxes, 1 left over   (e) 83 boxes, 4 left over

Exercise 2N

1. (a) 15 (b) 26 (c) 15 (d) 24 (e) 64 (f) 25 (g) 16
   (h) 15 (i) 16 (j) 42 (k) 22 (l) 32 (m) 20 (n) 15
   (o) 26 (p) 21 (q) 24 (r) 15 (s) 14 (t) 22 (u) 23
   (v) 12 (w) 21 (x) 25 (y) 13
2. (a) 11 r 3 (b) 14 r 5 (c) 15 r 5 (d) 22 r 6 (e) 17 r 1 (f) 12 r 2 (g) 24 r 5
   (h) 22 r 3 (i) 16 r 1 (j) 20 r 5 (k) 16 r 16 (l) 17 r 5 (m) 15 r 5 (n) 22 r 10
   (o) 31 r 11 (p) 12 r 6 (q) 16 r 9 (r) 40 r 3 (s) 30 r 10 (t) 41 r 5 (u) 21 r 8
   (v) 23 r 20 (w) 32 r 18 (x) 43 r 10 (y) 14 r 31
3. (a) 32 (b) 33 (c) 41 (d) 73 (e) 81
4. (a) 2 bars, 2p change (b) 5 bars, 5p change (c) 6 bars, 48p change
   (d) 9 bars, 9p change (e) 16 bars, 6p change

Exercise 2O

1. (a) 3 : 1 (b) 3 : 4 (c) 5 : 3 (d) 5 : 4 (e) 7 : 8 (f) 7 : 3
2. (a) 1 : 5 (b) 2 : 3 (c) 1 : 7 (d) 3 : 5 (e) 1 : 9 (f) 2 : 7 (g) 3 : 10
   (h) 1 : 3 (i) 5 : 7 (j) 4 : 5 (k) 1 : 6 (l) 5 : 9 (m) 6 : 7 (n) 3 : 8
   (o) 2 : 5 (p) 1 : 4 (q) 2 : 9 (r) 3 : 4 (s) 3 : 5 (t) 4 : 7 (u) 1 : 4 : 6
   (v) 5 : 6 : 7 (w) 5 : 8 : 2 (x) 7 : 8 : 5 (y) 2 : 3 : 4
3. (a) 1 : 4 (b) 2 : 5 (c) 4 : 5 (d) 1 : 20 (e) 9 : 20 (f) 8 : 25 (g) 9 : 50
   (h) 3 : 4 (i) 33 : 50 (j) 99 : 100
4. (a) 1 : 2 (b) 13 : 20 (c) 2 : 3 (d) 1 : 2 (e) 2 : 3 (f) 2 : 5 (g) 3 : 4
   (h) 3 : 7 (i) 1 : 5 (j) 2 : 5
5. 1 : 4   6. 1 : 7   7. 1 : 2   8. 3 : 5   9. 4 : 5   10. 20 : 17

Exercise 2P

1. (a) 400 g, 300 g, 320 g (b) 600 g, 450 g, 480 g (c) 800 g, 600 g, 640 g
   (d) 100 g, 75 g, 80 g (e) 300 g, 225 g, 240 g
2. (a) 6 litres, 4 litres (b) 12 litres, 8 litres (c) 15 litres, 10 litres
   (d) 30 litres, 20 litres (e) 21 litres, 14 litres
3. (a) 200 (b) 240 (c) 100 (d) 380 (e) 268
4. (a) £24 (b) £48 (c) £36 (d) £2·40 (e) £7·20
5. (a) 240 miles (b) 360 miles (c) 6 miles (d) 90 miles (e) 72 miles
6. (a) 24 cm (b) 36 cm (c) 18 cm (d) 0·5 cm (e) 5 cm
7. (a) 1 600 (b) 2 400 (c) 160 (d) 480 (e) 2 240
8. (a) 16, 24, 800 g (b) 24, 36, 1 200 g (c) 2, 3, 100 g
   (d) 6, 9, 300 g (e) 14, 21, 700 g
9. (a) 32, 1 600 g (b) 2, 100 g (c) 4, 200 g
   (d) 16, 800 g (e) 12, 600 g
10. (a) £96, £24 (b) £8, £2 (c) £24, £6 (d) £48, £12 (e) £72, £18

Exercise 2Q

1. (a) 3, 21 (b) 9, 15 (c) 18, 6 (d) 4, 20 (e) 10, 14
2. (a) 48, 24 (b) 18, 54 (c) 45, 27 (d) 56, 16 (e) 32, 40
3. (a) 63, 7 (b) 42, 28 (c) 10, 60 (d) 30, 40 (e) 21, 49
4. (a) 80, 40 (b) 72, 48 (c) 20, 100 (d) 84, 36 (e) 108, 12
5. (a) 88, 11 (b) 77, 22 (c) 90, 9 (d) 45, 54 (e) 33, 66
6. (a) 35, 7 (b) 36, 6 (c) 31·5, 10·5 (d) 30, 12 (e) 24, 18
7. (a) 112, 16 (b) 40, 88 (c) 60, 68 (d) 48, 80 (e) 62, 66
8. (a) 5, 10, 25 (b) 8, 16, 16 (c) 8, 12, 20 (d) 4, 8, 28 (e) 10, 10, 20
9. (a) 72, 120, 168 (b) 40, 140, 180 (c) 40, 120, 200
   (d) 300, 45, 15 (e) 72, 90, 198
10. (a) 84, 210, 336 (b) 35, 280, 315 (c) 30, 60, 540
    (d) 147, 168, 315 (e) 270, 216, 144
11. 48 g   12. £200, £250   13. £9
14. 600 g, 150 g, 150 g   15. 150 litres, 90 litres, 60 litres

Exercise 2R

1. (a) 5   (b) 3   (c) 9   (d) 7   (e) 10
2. (a) 17   (b) 43   (c) 284
3. 22

Exercise 2S

1. (a) 25   (b) 3   (c) 9   (d) 7   (e) 10
2. (a) 17   (b) 43   (c) 284
3. 22

Checkout N2

1. (a) 230   (b) 360
2. (a) 1 700   (b) 3 000
3. (a) 7 000   (b) 49 000
4. (a) 5   (b) 56
5. (a) 4   (b) 35
6. (a) 3   (b) 78
7. (a) 42   (b) 72   (c) 200   (d) 63 000
   (e) 115   (f) 336   (g) 6   (h) 7
8. (a) 5 r 1   (b) 9 r 2   (c) 8   (d) 9   (e) 750   (f) 900
   (g) 1 185   (h) 41 454   (i) 125   (j) 81 r 2   (k) 27   (l) 45 r 6
9. (a) 1, 2, 4, 8, 16, 32   (b) 1, 2, 3, 4, 5, 6, 10, 12, 15, 20, 30, 60
10. (a) 1 : 4   (b) 5 : 4 : 3
11. 14 litres
12. (a) £4, £20   (b) £10, £12, £2

Revision exercise N2

1. (a) (i) 4   (ii) 8   (b) (i) six hundred   (ii) six thousand
2. (a) fifty   (b) two thousand
3. (a) 7329   (b) two-tenths
4. (a) 153   (b) 150
5. 220, 165, 110, 28   6. £513   7. £12·75
8. (a) 4367   (b) (i) 2938   (ii) 746   (c) 690   (d) twenty
9. 8843   10. 518   11. £28   12. $\frac{8}{25}$ 13. 3   14. 12
15. (a) (i) 33   (ii) 1   (b) (i) 1   (ii) 2
16. (a) 3290   (b) 7
17. 56p

N3 Number 3

Check in N3

1. (a) 1324   (b) 432   (c) 1019   (d) 656   (e) 865
2. (a) 411   (b) 220   (c) 596   (d) 167   (e) 729

Exercise 3A

1. (a) 2·1   (b) 3·1   (c) 5·7   (d) 1·8   (e) 4·6   (f) 3·2
   (g) 6·5   (h) 7·1   (i) 9·8   (j) 8·9
3. (a) 5·8 cm   (b) 6·3 cm   (c) 2·9 cm   (d) 4·4 cm   (e) 8·1 cm   (f) 9·7 cm
   (g) 7·9 cm   (h) 5·2 cm   (i) 10·5 cm   (j) 12·6 cm   (k) 4 cm 9 mm   (l) 9 cm 5 mm
   (m) 10 cm 3 mm   (n) 8 cm 3 mm   (o) 9 cm 1 mm   (p) 1 cm 9 mm   (q) 3 cm 8 mm
   (r) 8 cm 6 mm   (s) 12 cm 4 mm   (t) 13 cm 3 mm

Exercise 3B

1. 1·1, 1·7, 1·9, 2·3, 2·4   2. 2·7, 3·1, 3·8, 4·0, 4·3
3. 2·6, 4·5, 5·4, 6·2, 6·8, 8·6   4. 1·9, 3·5, 5·3, 6·7, 7·6, 9·1
5. 12·0, 12·0, 12·2, 12·4, 12·8, 13·3, 13·5, 13·7   6. 1·1, 1·7, 2·5, 2·6, 2·9, 3·0, 3·6, 4·3, 4·4, 6·2

7. 2·6, 4·6, 4·9, 5·6, 7·3, 7·3, 8·0, 8·1, 8·2, 9·1   **8.** 0·7, 0·9, 1·5, 1·7, 2·1, 2·2, 2·6, 3·0, 3·4, 3·5
9. 0·3, 1·5, 2·9, 3·0, 3·8, 5·1, 6·7, 7·6, 8·3, 9·2   **10.** 13·0, 13·2, 13·3, 14·3, 14·5, 14·6, 15·0, 15·1, 15·6, 18·0, 18·2, 19·4
11. 22·0, 22·1, 22·4, 22·5, 22·8, 22·9, 23·0, 23·0, 23·6, 23·6, 23·8, 23·8
12. 40·1, 41·0, 42·6, 43·4, 43·5, 43·8, 44·3, 44·7, 45·3, 46·2, 47·4, 48·3

Exercise 3C

1. (a) 2·48   (b) 3·56   (c) 3·73   (d) 4·19   (e) 7·01   (f) 6·19
(g) 4·07   (h) 8·55   (i) 9·83   (j) 3·08
3. (a) 3·38 m   (b) 2·30 m   (c) 2·03 m   (d) 2·09 m   (e) 4·01 m   (f) 4·87 m
(g) 5·06 m   (h) 3·50 m   (i) 1·05 m   (j) 4·96 m   (k) 4 m 92 cm   (l) 3 m 51 cm
(m) 1 m 99 cm   (n) 2 m 60 cm   (o) 2 m 6 cm   (p) 2 m 45 cm   (q) 4 m 9 cm   (r) 3 m 10 cm
(s) 3 m 1 cm   (t) 2 m 11 cm

Exercise 3D

1. 2·23, 2·32, 3·02, 3·14, 3·20, 3·41   **2.** 1·21, 1·34, 1·43, 1·55, 1·84, 1·91
3. 4·04, 4·12, 4·13, 4·22, 4·31, 4·44   **4.** 5·02, 5·06, 5·12, 5·21, 5·63, 5·82
5. 4·02, 4·52, 5·50, 6·03, 6·21, 7·25   **6.** 9·01, 9·03, 9·03, 9·04, 9·10, 9·33
7. 10·09, 10·68, 10·99, 11·99, 12·21, 12·34, 12·35, 13·52   **8.** 3·05, 4·5, 5·16, 5·2, 6·34, 6·7
9. 0·01, 0·09, 0·1, 0·13, 0·3, 0·9   **10.** 9·0, 9·03, 9·19, 9·2, 9·29, 9·3
11. 12·37, 12·37, 12·4, 12·4, 12·45, 12·5, 12·8, 12·89, 12·9, 12·98
12. 32·05, 32·06, 32·2, 32·27, 32·5, 32·56, 32·6, 32·65, 32·7, 32·72

Exercise 3E

1. (a) $5 + \frac{3}{10}$ (b) $4 + \frac{8}{10} + \frac{5}{100}$ (c) $2 + \frac{7}{10} + \frac{9}{100}$
(d) $6 + \frac{6}{10} + \frac{1}{100}$ (e) $6 + \frac{1}{10} + \frac{6}{100}$ (f) $1 + \frac{6}{10} + \frac{6}{100} + \frac{4}{1\,000}$
(g) $\frac{9}{10} + \frac{3}{100} + \frac{2}{1\,000}$ (h) $9 + \frac{3}{1\,000}$ (i) $8 + \frac{7}{100} + \frac{2}{1\,000}$
(j) $5 + \frac{3}{10} + \frac{2}{1\,000}$ (k) $20 + 6 + \frac{2}{10} + \frac{5}{100}$ (l) $30 + 1 + \frac{3}{10} + \frac{2}{100} + \frac{5}{1\,000}$
(m) $200 + 30 + 1 + \frac{4}{10}$ (n) $300 + 40 + 5 + \frac{6}{10} + \frac{7}{100}$ (o) $30 + 4 + \frac{7}{100} + \frac{5}{1\,000}$
(p) $10 + 2 + \frac{3}{10} + \frac{4}{100} + \frac{6}{1\,000}$ (q) $20 + 3 + \frac{7}{10} + \frac{6}{100} + \frac{1}{1\,000}$ (r) $90 + 7 + \frac{3}{100} + \frac{5}{1\,000}$
(s) $30 + 9 + \frac{1}{100} + \frac{2}{1\,000}$ (t) $9 + \frac{2}{1\,000}$ (u) $9 + \frac{2}{10} + \frac{1}{1\,000}$
(v) $10 + 9 + \frac{4}{10} + \frac{5}{100} + \frac{7}{1\,000}$ (w) $20 + 5 + \frac{6}{10} + \frac{5}{100} + \frac{8}{1\,000}$ (x) $60 + 7 + \frac{5}{100} + \frac{4}{1\,000}$
(y) $30 + 3 + \frac{3}{10} + \frac{3}{100} + \frac{3}{1\,000}$
2. (a) 3·7   (b) 7·3   (c) 6·35   (d) 7·06   (e) 27·316   (f) 31·501
(g) 40·368   (h) 45·079   (i) 60·007   (j) 75·403   (k) 148·657   (l) 305·07
(m) 580·501   (n) 111·111   (o) 37·203   (p) 657·036   (q) 7 257·863   (r) 5 203·506
(s) 6 000·006   (t) 500·302   (u) 189·067   (v) 2 220·222   (w) 3 105·062   (x) 7 206·755

Exercise 3F

1. (a) 1, 2, 2, 2, 2   (b) 3, 4, 4, 4, 3   (c) 7, 9, 5, 5, 6, 3   (d) 4, 5, 2, 9, 8, 7
(e) 12, 13, 12, 14, 12, 13, 12, 14   (f) 16, 12, 18, 15, 15, 13, 13, 15, 19, 18, 15, 13
(g) 22, 24, 23, 24, 22, 23, 23, 23, 24, 23, 22, 24   (h) 45, 44, 43, 46, 41, 40, 44, 48, 45, 47, 44, 43
2. A, D, F, G, H or J

Exercise 3G

1. (a) 2·3, 2·3, 3·4, 3·1, 3·3, 3·1   (b) 1·6, 1·2, 1·3, 1·4, 2·0, 1·9   (c) 4·2, 5·0, 4·4, 4·1, 4·4, 4·1
(d) 5·1, 5·6, 5·8, 6·0, 5·2, 5·2   (e) 6·1, 7·3, 4·5, 4·2, 5·6, 7·0   (f) 9·0, 9·8, 9·1, 9·1, 9·1, 9·4
(g) 12·2, 12·4, 12·0, 10·7, 12·3, 13·5, 11·0, 10·1   (h) 3·1, 4·5, 6·7, 6·3, 5·2, 6·0
2. A, C, D, F, G, H, I or J

Exercise 3H

1. (a) 2·33, 2·24, 3·40, 3·10, 3·24, 3·50   (b) 1·51, 1·28, 1·33, 1·49, 1·92, 1·85
(c) 4·23, 4·13, 4·37, 4·15, 4·35, 4·40   (d) 5·02, 5·16, 5·20, 5·11, 6·00, 5·12
(e) 6·40, 7·53, 4·66, 4·60, 5·55, 6·53   (f) 9·94, 9·40, 9·10, 10·00, 9·31, 9·14
(g) 12·01, 12·32, 11·90, 10·61, 12·31, 13·06, 10·93, 10·39   (h) 3·06, 4·52, 7·00, 6·99, 5·11, 5·22, 8·00, 4·46
2. A, B, D, G, I or J

Exercise 3I

1. (a) 0·7 (b) 0·8 (c) 0·9 (d) 0·8 (e) 0·7 (f) 0·6 (g) 0·6 (h) 0·6 (i) 0·4
(j) 0·9 (k) 0·9 (l) 0·8 (m) 1·0 (n) 1·0 (o) 0·8 (p) 1·3 (q) 1·5 (r) 2·5
(s) 2·4 (t) 3·9 (u) 2·7 (v) 4·0 (w) 2·0 (x) 6·0 (y) 3·2
2. (a) 1·1 (b) 1·3 (c) 1·6 (d) 1·3 (e) 1·1 (f) 1·2 (g) 1·2 (h) 1·4 (i) 1·1
(j) 1·1 (k) 1·3 (l) 1·6 (m) 1·8 (n) 1·5 (o) 1·6 (p) 2·2 (q) 3·4 (r) 2·2
(s) 4·4 (t) 5·7 (u) 3·0 (v) 7·0 (w) 3·1 (x) 4·7 (y) 5·2
3. (a) 8·2 (b) 10·6 (c) 3·9 (d) 13·5 (e) 3·6 (f) 6·9 (g) 3·8 (h) 4·8 (i) 10·4
(j) 12·6 (k) 10·0 (l) 9·7 (m) 7·7 (n) 14·4 (o) 13·5 (p) 12·5 (q) 6·3 (r) 16·2
(s) 6·0 (t) 8·0 (u) 15·9 (v) 11·7 (w) 8·8 (x) 18·0 (y) 15·9
4. (a) 11·0 (b) 14·2 (c) 8·3 (d) 9·1 (e) 6·2 (f) 3·3 (g) 11·1 (h) 3·5 (i) 6·3
(j) 7·2 (k) 5·5 (l) 6·1 (m) 8·1 (n) 8·4 (o) 5·7 (p) 6·4 (q) 6·0 (r) 10·6
(s) 9·6 (t) 14·8 (u) 9·4 (v) 15·4 (w) 11·6 (x) 18·1 (y) 17·1
5. (a) 0·34 (b) 2·65 (c) 1·76 (d) 1·94 (e) 3·82 (f) 0·94 (g) 1·85 (h) 5·85 (i) 7·76
(j) 3·94 (k) 1·65 (l) 2·59 (m) 1·89 (n) 3·79 (o) 2·99 (p) 1·51 (q) 3·64 (r) 5·84
(s) 4·82 (t) 8·96 (u) 1·38 (v) 2·04 (w) 4·56 (x) 9·00 (y) 5·08

Exercise 3J

1. (a) 10·9 (b) 20·1 (c) 15·1 (d) 21·3 (e) 17·5 (f) 24·1 (g) 17·3
(h) 10·3 (i) 12·5 (j) 18·8 (k) 22·5 (l) 9·5 (m) 13·3 (n) 24·4
(o) 10·3 (p) 11·2 (q) 11·5 (r) 11·3 (s) 19·8 (t) 7·7 (u) 12·0
(v) 10·5 (w) 56·1 (x) 29·2 (y) 28·2
2. (a) 7·99 (b) 13·57 (c) 17·79 (d) 4·99 (e) 17·89 (f) 10·91 (g) 14·73
(h) 8·85 (i) 10·85 (j) 11·82 (k) 14·07 (l) 9·68 (m) 18·07 (n) 21·08
(o) 23·18 (p) 3·1 (q) 7·23 (r) 6·56 (s) 6·6 (t) 10·07 (u) 20·32
(v) 26 (w) 26·5 (x) 91·11 (y) 165·83
3. (a) 11·5 (b) 25·1 (c) 25 (d) 27·8 (e) 31·2 (f) 37 (g) 27·7
(h) 18·6 (i) 10·59 (j) 14·68 (k) 12·55 (l) 18·87 (m) 17·78 (n) 14·54
(o) 24·64 (p) 110·415 (q) 64·037 (r) 9 (s) 37·74 (t) 70·05 (u) 29·89
(v) 87·246 (w) 89·86 (x) 45·447 (y) 139·812
4. £3·75, £2·89 and £2·86

Exercise 3K

1. (a) 0·7 (b) 0·7 (c) 0·1 (d) 0 (e) 0·2 (f) 0·4 (g) 0·1 (h) 0·1 (i) 0·3
(j) 0·4 (k) 2·5 (l) 4·1 (m) 3·2 (n) 2·3 (o) 5·4 (p) 1·2 (q) 3·4 (r) 4·2
(s) 4·0 (t) 5·2 (u) 5·3 (v) 3·2 (w) 3·6 (x) 2·0 (y) 4·8
2. (a) 0·9 (b) 0·8 (c) 0·8 (d) 0·8 (e) 0·8 (f) 0·8 (g) 0·7 (h) 0·7 (i) 0·7
(j) 0·6 (k) 0·6 (l) 0·5 (m) 0·9 (n) 0·5 (o) 0·7 (p) 0·9 (q) 0·7 (r) 0·6
(s) 0·3 (t) 0·7 (u) 0·4 (v) 0·6 (w) 0·2 (x) 0·4 (y) 0·8
3. (a) 6·6 (b) 4·6 (c) 0·5 (d) 5·4 (e) ⁻2·2 (f) 4 (g) 6·4 (h) 0·8 (i) 2·1
(j) 3·6 (k) 3·7 (l) 1·9 (m) 1·5 (n) 1·7 (o) 1·7 (p) 3·9 (q) 1·6 (r) 2·4
(s) 1·9 (t) 4·8 (u) 2·7 (v) 1·8 (w) 1·4 (x) 0·9 (y) 0·8

Exercise 3L

1. (a) 11·1 (b) 23·1 (c) 22·7 (d) 24·2 (e) 14 (f) 20·9 (g) 42·7 (h) 34·9 (i) 10·8
(j) 62·6 (k) 29·2 (l) 15·5 (m) 36·2 (n) 35·1 (o) 8·2 (p) 3·9 (q) 26·8 (r) 48·9
(s) 57·6 (t) 18·8 (u) 26·9 (v) 64·8 (w) 66·7 (x) 27·8 (y) 49·8
2. (a) 21·22 (b) 45·42 (c) 35·24 (d) 33·02 (e) 22·22 (f) 23·17 (g) 11·05 (h) 12·27 (i) 51·05
(j) 12·18 (k) 12·51 (l) 42·81 (m) 46·28 (n) 20·91 (o) 72·51 (p) 5·35 (q) 8·72 (r) 5·22
(s) 16·31 (t) 6·24 (u) 48·62 (v) 2·83 (w) 32·66 (x) 28·25 (y) 48·47
3. (a) 62·62 (b) 57·75 (c) 24·79 (d) 66·81 (e) 41·91 (f) 13·25 (g) 25·54 (h) 34·05 (i) 72·13
(j) 11·13 (k) 0·78 (l) 6·75 (m) 10·83 (n) 46·27 (o) 13·88 (p) 35·85 (q) 25·64 (r) 8·38
(s) 38·76 (t) 15·76 (u) 7·47 (v) 8·19 (w) 66·44 (x) 85·33 (y) 28·53
4. £21·49, £12·70, £32·01, £12·66, £10·51, £23·01, £10·61, £13·91, £20·01, £14·31

Checkout N3

1. (a) (i) 7 tenths (ii) 4 units (c) 3 tenths
(b) (i) 3·5 cm (ii) 6·8 cm
(c) (i) 4 cm 3 mm (ii) 9 cm 9 mm (d) 2·4, 2·9, 3·0, 3·2, 3·4, 3·5, 3·8, 4·2

2. (a) (i) 9 hundredths   (ii) 8 tenths   (iii) 7 hundredths
    (b) (i) 3·54 m   (ii) 6·83 m
    (c) (i) 4 m 78 cm   (ii) 13 m 65 cm
3. (a) 6·08, 6·09, 6·25, 6·28, 6·30, 6·31, 6·42, 6·80   (b) 5·04, 5·05, 5·4, 5·5, 5·55, 5·6, 5·65, 5·7
4. (a) (i) 2 thousandths   (ii) 6 thousandths   (iii) 7 hundredths
    (b) (i) 3·237   (ii) 25·736
5. (a) 7·048, 7·401, 7·421, 7·423, 7·427, 7·435
    (b) 8·049, 8·059, 8·488, 8·5, 8·55, 8·63, 8·653, 8·76
6. (a) 13   (b) 14   (c) 4
7. (a) 5·6   (b) 8·8   (c) 7·0
8. (a) 6·78   (b) 7·05   (c) 13·00
9. (a) 1·1   (b) 3·9   (c) 1·15   (d) 0·79   (e) 7·9   (f) 4·38   (g) 0·6
    (h) 1·1   (i) 4·5   (j) 0·8
10. (a) 12·4   (b) 23·36   (c) 84·34   (d) 53·16   (e) 11·2   (f) 28·8   (g) 65·65   (h) 53·55

Revision exercise N3

1. (a) 3047   (b) 5·09, 5·1, 5·32, 5·8   (d) 6·64
2. (a) 142 cm   (b) 3
3. (a) 21   (b) 17p
4. (a) 42, 9, 4   (b) 8·4
5. (a) £1·64   (b) £1, 50p, 10p, 2p, 2p
6. (a) £2·45   (b) £17·15
7. (a) 40, 2, 3   (b) 8
8. £400
9. £240
10. £1200
11. (a) 37·5   (b) 20·4
12. (a) 9p   (b) £16·20

N4 Number 4

Check in N4

1. (a) 238   (b) 115   (c) 816   (d) 1 404   (e) 4 991   (f) 24 840
2. (a) 24   (b) 87   (c) 72   (d) 25   (e) 13

Exercise 4A

1. (a) 560   (b) 4 530   (c) 2 730   (d) 7 030   (e) 1 020   (f) 45   (g) 87
    (h) 193   (i) 541   (j) 789   (k) 72·3   (l) 52·7   (m) 232·1   (n) 305·6
    (o) 216·7   (p) 6·7   (q) 3·45   (r) 2·05   (s) 5·28   (t) 2·23   (u) 0·2
    (v) 0·345   (w) 0·52   (x) 0·674   (y) 0·054 2
2. (a) 20 mm   (b) 60 mm   (c) 80 mm   (d) 10 mm   (e) 20 mm   (f) 26 mm   (g) 74 mm
    (h) 59 mm   (i) 43 mm   (j) 35 mm   (k) 158 mm   (l) 249 mm   (m) 355 mm   (n) 896 mm
    (o) 289 mm   (p) 25·6 mm   (q) 53·7 mm   (r) 70·5 mm   (s) 90·8 mm   (t) 67·5 mm   (u) 9 mm
    (v) 7 mm   (w) 1 mm   (x) 2 mm   (y) 3·5 mm

Exercise 4B

1. (a) 700   (b) 600   (c) 5 700   (d) 12 300   (e) 34 700   (f) 450   (g) 780
    (h) 340   (i) 1 870   (j) 2 730   (k) 567   (l) 731   (m) 1 956   (n) 83
    (o) 3 451   (p) 53·7   (q) 34·7   (r) 52·4   (s) 56·4   (t) 23·1   (u) 3·2
    (v) 7·61   (w) 9·32   (x) 7·25   (y) 0·15
2. (a) 200 cm   (b) 500 cm   (c) 300 cm   (d) 400 cm   (e) 100 cm   (f) 150 cm   (g) 170 cm
    (h) 250 cm   (i) 890 cm   (j) 760 cm   (k) 1 530 cm   (l) 2 950 cm   (m) 3 280 cm   (n) 2 750 cm
    (o) 3 410 cm   (p) 564 cm   (q) 925 cm   (r) 863 cm   (s) 934 cm   (t) 731 cm   (u) 25 cm
    (v) 37 cm   (w) 83 cm   (x) 62 cm   (y) 77 cm

Exercise 4C

1. (a) 5 000 (b) 9 000 (c) 67 000 (d) 453 000 (e) 217 000 (f) 3 500
   (g) 9 800 (h) 5 400 (i) 17 700 (j) 47 300 (k) 5 680 (l) 7 510
   (m) 19 760 (n) 930 (o) 38 510 (p) 437 (q) 347 (r) 724
   (s) 594 (t) 271 (u) 52·3 (v) 96·1 (w) 97·2 (x) 81·5
   (y) 0·5
2. (a) 4 000 ml (b) 1 500 ml (c) 1 700 ml (d) 15 300 ml (e) 27 500 ml (f) 9 340 ml
   (g) 7 310 ml (h) 250 ml (i) 373 ml (j) 6 258 ml
3. (a) 5 000 m (b) 2 400 m (c) 4 500 m (d) 12 500 m (e) 18 400 m (f) 45 900 m
   (g) 7 450 m (h) 526 m (i) 573 m (j) 9 456 m
4. (a) 9 000 g (b) 6 400 g (c) 3 200 g (d) 14 700 g (e) 14 800 g (f) 32 800 g
   (g) 6 330 g (h) 585 g (i) 843 g (j) 7 540 g

Exercise 4D

1. (a) 7 (b) 25 (c) 34 (d) 25 (e) 456 (f) 2·3 (g) 6·7
   (h) 12·3 (i) 45·6 (j) 27·1 (k) 4·56 (l) 3·47 (m) 6·59 (n) 9·99
   (o) 5·62 (p) 0·47 (q) 0·903 (r) 0·617 (s) 0·81 (t) 0·76
   (u) 0·032 (v) 0·09 (w) 0·009 (x) 0·053 (y) 0·005 3
2. (a) 20 cm (b) 60 cm (c) 50 cm (d) 10 cm (e) 6 cm (f) 26 cm (g) 74 cm
   (h) 59 cm (i) 43 cm (j) 35 cm (k) 15·8 cm (l) 24·9 cm (m) 35·5 cm (n) 89·6 cm
   (o) 28·9 cm (p) 2·56 cm (q) 5·37 cm (r) 7·05 cm (s) 9·08 cm (t) 6·75 cm

Exercise 4E

1. (a) 7 (b) 25 (c) 34 (d) 25 (e) 456 (f) 2·3 (g) 6·7
   (h) 12·3 (i) 45·6 (j) 27·1 (k) 4·56 (l) 3·47 (m) 6·59 (n) 9·99
   (o) 5·62 (p) 0·247 (q) 0·193 (r) 0·261 7 (s) 0·081 (t) 0·076 (u) 0·003 2
   (v) 0·009 (w) 0·000 9 (x) 0·005 3 (y) 0·000 53
2. (a) 2 m (b) 6 m (c) 5 m (d) 1 m (e) 0·6 m (f) 2·6 m (g) 7·4 m
   (h) 5·9 m (i) 4·3 m (j) 3·5 m (k) 1·58 m (l) 2·49 m (m) 3·55 m (n) 8·96 m
   (o) 2·89 m (p) 0·256 m (q) 0·537 m (r) 0·705 m (s) 0·908 m (t) 0·675 m

Exercise 4F

1. (a) 5 (b) 9 (c) 3·5 (d) 9·8 (e) 5·4 (f) 17·7
   (g) 47·3 (h) 5·68 (i) 7·55 (j) 9·374 (k) 3·856 (l) 0·437
   (m) 0·271 (n) 0·052 3 (o) 0·096 1 (p) 0·009 72 (q) 0·008 1 (r) 0·005 7
   (s) 0·009 (t) 0·011 (u) 0·000 5 (v) 0·001 9 (w) 0·000 17 (x) 0·000 05
   (y) 0·003 142
2. (a) 0·4 litres (b) 0·15 litres (c) 0·17 litres (d) 0·053 litres (e) 0·025 litres
   (f) 0·075 litres (g) 0·75 litres (h) 0·25 litres (i) 0·5 litres (j) 1·25 litres
3. (a) 0·5 km (b) 0·24 km (c) 3·5 km (d) 12·7 km (e) 18·45 km (f) 45·9 km
   (g) 7·457 km (h) 5·269 km (i) 0·573 5 km (j) 1·456 8 km
4. (a) 0·9 kg (b) 0·64 kg (c) 0·32 kg (d) 0·147 kg (e) 0·148 kg (f) 1·328 kg
   (g) 1·633 kg (h) 2·585 kg (i) 3·843 kg (j) 7·5 kg

Exercise 4G

1. (a) 1 (b) 0·8 (c) 0·9 (d) 3 (e) 1·4 (f) 4 (g) 1·8
   (h) 1·2 (i) 1 (j) 0·6 (k) 3·2 (l) 1·6 (m) 4·5 (n) 4·8
   (o) 2·4 (p) 6·3 (q) 0·8 (r) 0·1 (s) 0·9 (t) 1·5
2. (a) 0·18 (b) 0·05 (c) 0·42 (d) 0·24 (e) 0·36 (f) 0·35 (g) 0·27
   (h) 0·64 (i) 0·49 (j) 0·04 (k) 0·03 (l) 0·36 (m) 0·72 (n) 0·28
   (o) 0·56 (p) 0·81 (q) 0·02 (r) 0·06 (s) 0·54 (t) 0·07
3. (a) 0·25 (b) 0·12 (c) 0·24 (d) 0·16 (e) 0·18 (f) 0·27 (g) 0·28
   (h) 0·4 (i) 0·14 (j) 0·15 (k) 0·12 (l) 0·09 (m) 0·04 (n) 0·05
   (o) 0·06 (p) 0·3 (q) 0·07 (r) 0·08 (s) 0·08 (t) 0·2
4. (a) 0·016 (b) 0·018 (c) 0·004 (d) 0·032 (e) 0·036 (f) 0·003 (g) 0·006
   (h) 0·42 (i) 0·064 (j) 0·054 (k) 0·056 (l) 0·009 (m) 0·048 (n) 0·01
   (o) 0·045 (p) 0·063 (q) 0·072 (r) 0·049 (s) 0·021 (t) 0·024

5. (a) 3·6 (b) 4·4 (c) 4·4 (d) 4·5 (e) 3·9 (f) 0·24 (g) 0·55
(h) 0·64 (i) 0·63 (j) 0·82 (k) 0·64 (l) 0·88 (m) 0·55 (n) 0·84
(o) 0·99 (p) 0·024 (q) 0·055 (r) 0·186 (s) 0·168 (t) 0·06
6. (a) £3·60 (b) £6 (c) £3·60 (d) £4·80 (e) £8·80 (f) £3·75

Exercise 4H

1. (a) 31·5 (b) 44·8 (c) 19·5 (d) 41 (e) 28·2 (f) 99 (g) 65·2
(h) 203·7 (i) 207 (j) 195·6
2. (a) 26 (b) 35·15 (c) 63·42 (d) 25·5 (e) 42·88 (f) 42·48 (g) 31·2
(h) 26·31 (i) 41·85 (j) 14·7
3. (a) 228 (b) 576 (c) 486 (d) 135 (e) 342 (f) 144·4 (g) 258
(h) 280·2 (i) 604·8 (j) 365·5
4. (a) 2·72 (b) 2·25 (c) 3·96 (d) 5·85 (e) 9·5 (f) 34·276 (g) 8·442
(h) 14·025 (i) 2·25 (j) 30·672
5. (a) £25·68 (b) £42·80 (c) £171·20 (d) £66·77 (e) £121·55
6. (a) £130·20 (b) £4 947·60
7. (a) 305·4 hours (b) £158·81
8. (a) £34·80 (b) £8·52 (c) £208·80 (d) £18·18 (e) £57·70

Exercise 4I

1. (a) 3·2 (b) 1·3 (c) 2·7 (d) 8·1 (e) 1·6 (f) 2·7 (g) 5·8
(h) 5·3 (i) 5·7 (j) 4·8 (k) 0·56 (l) 0·58 (m) 1·24 (n) 0·15
(o) 0·84 (p) 1·25 (q) 5·41 (r) 3·05 (s) 2·24 (t) 1·37
2. (a) 3·5 (b) 3·75 (c) 3·25 (d) 4·4 (e) 10·5 (f) 16·75 (g) 3·6
(h) 18·5 (i) 8·25 (j) 4·5 (k) 34·5 (l) 25·2 (m) 56·5 (n) 0·75
(o) 0·8 (p) 0·5 (q) 0·25 (r) 1·125 (s) 0·875 (t) 1·625
3. (a) £3 091·75 (b) £1 545·88 (c) £2 473·40 (d) £6 183·50 (e) £1 236·70

Exercise 4J

1. (a) 5·$\dot{3}$ (b) 2·$\dot{3}$ (c) 2·$\dot{7}$ (d) 45·$\dot{3}$ (e) 45·$\dot{6}$ (f) 3·8$\dot{3}$ (g) 4·1$\dot{6}$
(h) 13·$\dot{6}$ (i) 1·$\dot{3}$ (j) 3·$\dot{4}$ (k) 0·5$\dot{4}$ (l) 0·7$\dot{8}$ (m) 4·1$\dot{6}$ (n) 1·0$\dot{3}$
(o) 0·40$\dot{3}$ (p) 0·11$\dot{6}$ (q) 0·07$\dot{3}$ (r) 0·03$\dot{1}$ (s) 0·0$\dot{6}$ (t) 0·1$\dot{3}$
2. (a) £4·67 (b) £5·67 (c) £6·17 (d) £5·13 (e) £4·93

Exercise 4K

1. (a) 5·55, 5·6 (b) 1 363·23, 1 363·2 (c) 98·61, 98·6 (d) 1·295, 1·3
(e) 254·4, 254·4 (f) 68·25, 68·3 (g) 1 628·66, 1 628·7 (h) 41·134, 41·1
(i) 222·08, 222·1 (j) 1 214·35, 1 214·4 (k) 282·44, 282·4 (l) 443·94, 443·9
(m) 108·36, 108·4 (n) 26·124 8, 26·1 (o) 447·372, 447·4 (p) 42·704, 42·7
(q) 422·475, 422·5 (r) 1 294·98, 1 295·0 (s) 3 441·62, 3 441·6 (t) 5 068·413, 5 068·4
2. (a) £5·82 (b) £3·67 (c) £2·71 (d) £7·02 (e) £3·14 (f) £1·36 (g) £1·91
(h) £5·74 (i) £2·44 (j) £2·30 (k) £1·25 (l) £2·48
3. (a) £297 (b) £63
4. (a) £22·90 (b) £17·40 (c) £11·45 (d) £4·12 (e) £21·53

Exercise 4L

1. (a) 3·2 (b) 5·6 (c) 15·2 (d) 38·2 (e) 20·7 (f) 1·9 (g) 0·5
(h) 3·5 (i) 1·5 (j) 4·4 (k) 16·7 (l) 58·2 (m) 27·2 (n) 62·8
(o) 76·9 (p) 1·9 (q) 0·2 (r) 7·2 (s) 10·7 (t) 0·2
2. (a) £14·49 (b) £12·21 (c) £10·79 (d) £11·31 (e) £9·87
3. (a) £4·67 (b) £8
4. (a) 95 000 m (b) 1583·$\dot{3}$m (c) 26·3$\dot{8}$m

Exercise 4M

1. (a) 16·1 km (b) 6·44 km (c) 40·3 km (d) 13·7 km
2. 191 kg **3.** 13·7 litres **4.** (a) 142 cm (b) 1·42 m
5. (a) 846 gallons (b) Bad estimate
6. 76·3 kg

Checkout N4

1. (a) 134·5   (b) 2·5   (c) 10·34
2 (a) 34 mm   (b) 138 mm   (c) 96 mm
3. (a) 1 345   (b) 25·3   (c) 103·4
4. (a) 342 cm   (b) 1 308 cm   (c) 967 cm
5. (a) 13 450   (b) 253   (c) 1 532·4
6. (a) 3 420 ml   (b) 3 108 ml   (c) 350 ml
7. (a) (i) 1·34   (ii) 2·5   (iii) 0·134
    (b) (i) 4·5 cm   (ii) 12·7 cm   (iii) 0·6 cm
8. (a) (i) 1·348   (ii) 0·253   (iii) 0·014
    (b) (i) 3·42 m   (ii) 0·35 m   (iii) 1·96 m
9. (a) (i) 1·345   (ii) 0·253   (iii) 0·001 5
    (b) (i) 1·342 litres   (ii) 0·31 litres   (iii) 0·035 litres
10. (a) (i) 1·5   (ii) 1·2   (iii) 0·12   (iv) 0·03
     (v) 4·8   (vi) 9·9   (vii) 0·36   (viii) 0·096
    (b) (i) 33·6   (ii) 21·15   (iii) 2·25   (iv) 13·632
11. (a) 0·9   (b) 0·84   (c) 3·06   (d) 0·16
    (e) 5·75   (f) 1·875
12. (a) 5·$\dot{6}$ (b) 0·0$\dot{6}$ (c) 1·3$\dot{8}$ (d) 0·201 $\dot{6}$
13. (a) (i) 219·6   (ii) 2·8   (iii) 1 484·2   (iv) 73·3
     (v) 0·8   (vi) 2·6   (vii) 4·9   (viii) 0·3
    (b) (i) 4·52   (ii) 54·52   (iii) 8·20   (iv) 10·78
     (v) 2·63   (vi) 0·19   (vii) 5·69   (viii) 1·14

Revision exercise N4

1. £1·19, £2·24, £5·99   **2.** 5·26   **3.** 34p   **4.** £20·92   **5.** 5·58   **6.** 0·787
7. £3·52   **8.** (a) 50 years   (b) 2·4 metres
9. (a) 70   (b) 8·75 gallons   (c) £11·25
10. (a) 62·4 kg   (b) 10%   (c) 118·8 pounds   **11.** 28·0
12. (a) 14   (b) 48p   (c) 20p, 20p, 5p, 2p, 1p   **13.** £11·96, £9·98, 87p, £11·22, £34·03
14. (a) 2400 g   (b) 4·8 g   (c) 450 mm
15. (a) £3·45   (b) £31·05   (c) £18·95   (d) notes £10, £5, coins £2, £1, 50p, 20p, 20p, 5p

N5 Number 5

Check in N5

1. (a) $\frac{1}{2}$ (b) $\frac{1}{4}$ (c) $\frac{1}{5}$ (d) $\frac{3}{5}$ (e) $\frac{1}{4}$ (f) $\frac{1}{4}$
2. (a) 24   (b) 63   (c) 42   (d) 45   (e) 6   (f) 8   (g) 8   (h) 9

Exercise 5A

1. (a) $\frac{3}{4}$ (b) $\frac{1}{6}$ (c) $\frac{5}{8}$ (d) $\frac{1}{3}$ (e) $\frac{3}{7}$ (f) $\frac{4}{5}$
    (g) $\frac{5}{6}$ (h) $\frac{5}{9}$ (i) $\frac{7}{15}$ (j) $\frac{7}{10}$
2. (a) $\frac{13}{19}$ (b) $\frac{15}{19}$ (c) $\frac{6}{19}$ (d) $\frac{12}{19}$ (e) $\frac{3}{19}$ (f) $\frac{3}{19}$ (g) $\frac{4}{19}$
3. (a) $\frac{2}{7}$ (b) $\frac{1}{3}$ (c) $\frac{1}{4}$ (d) $\frac{3}{4}$ (e) $\frac{1}{2}$
4. (a) $\frac{3}{10}$ (b) $\frac{2}{5}$ (c) $\frac{2}{7}$ (d) $\frac{3}{8}$ (e) $\frac{3}{7}$

Exercise 5B

1. (a) $2\frac{2}{5}$ (b) $1\frac{3}{4}$ (c) $1\frac{4}{5}$ (d) $1\frac{1}{3}$ (e) $2\frac{1}{2}$ (f) 2   (g) $1\frac{1}{6}$ (h) $1\frac{1}{7}$ (i) $1\frac{2}{3}$
    (j) $1\frac{2}{7}$ (k) $1\frac{1}{12}$ (l) $6\frac{1}{3}$ (m) 3   (n) $7\frac{1}{4}$ (o) 9   (p) $6\frac{3}{5}$ (q) $5\frac{1}{2}$ (r) $2\frac{1}{4}$
    (s) $1\frac{2}{13}$ (t) $1\frac{1}{99}$ (u) $1\frac{1}{5}$ (v) $1\frac{4}{17}$ (w) $2\frac{3}{4}$ (x) $9\frac{1}{2}$ (y) $4\frac{1}{4}$
2. (a) $\frac{3}{2}$ (b) $\frac{7}{3}$ (c) $\frac{5}{4}$ (d) $\frac{7}{5}$ (e) $\frac{13}{6}$ (f) $\frac{11}{7}$ (g) $\frac{9}{8}$ (h) $\frac{17}{12}$ (i) $\frac{18}{13}$
    (j) $\frac{29}{4}$ (k) $\frac{13}{2}$ (l) $\frac{11}{3}$ (m) $\frac{11}{4}$ (n) $\frac{11}{5}$ (o) $\frac{17}{6}$ (p) $\frac{15}{7}$ (q) $\frac{13}{8}$ (r) $\frac{43}{12}$
    (s) $\frac{35}{17}$ (t) $\frac{26}{7}$ (u) $\frac{19}{2}$ (v) $\frac{22}{3}$ (w) $\frac{27}{4}$ (x) $\frac{9}{5}$ (y) $\frac{23}{6}$

Exercise 5C

1. $\frac{3}{10}$ 2. $\frac{1}{5}$ 3. $\frac{3}{4}$ 4. $\frac{9}{10}$ 5. $\frac{4}{5}$ 6. $\frac{1}{20}$ 7. $\frac{9}{20}$ 8. $\frac{1}{25}$ 9. $\frac{3}{25}$
10. $\frac{6}{25}$ 11. $\frac{3}{5}$ 12. $\frac{1}{50}$ 13. $\frac{11}{50}$ 14. $\frac{49}{50}$ 15. $\frac{7}{20}$ 16. $\frac{18}{25}$ 17. $\frac{19}{20}$ 18. $\frac{13}{20}$
19. $\frac{17}{100}$ 20. $\frac{21}{50}$ 21. $\frac{3}{25}$ 22. $\frac{7}{50}$ 23. $\frac{4}{25}$ 24. $\frac{99}{100}$ 25. $\frac{3}{20}$

Exercise 5D

1. (a) 70 (b) 200 (c) 300 (d) 300 (e) 16 (f) 18 (g) 38 (h) 5 (i) 120
   (j) 18 (k) 27 (l) 140 (m) 180 (n) 18 (o) 102 (p) 156 (q) 4 (r) 4
   (s) 20 (t) 81 (u) 18 (v) 176 (w) 273 (x) 33 (y) 33
2. (a) 3·1 (b) 13·6 (c) 10·12 (d) 71·12 (e) 61·41 (f) 161·28 (g) 36
   (h) 6·65 (i) 228·6 (j) 568·4 (k) 120·6 (l) 1·35 (m) 14 (n) 42
   (o) 24·5 (p) 17·325 (q) 7 (r) 7·75 (s) 16·272 (t) 17·4 (u) 33·6
   (v) 12 (w) 3·6 (x) 2·1 (y) 4·890 6
3. (a) £12, £68 (b) £9, £51 (c) £4·50, £25·50 (d) £10·50, £59·50
   (e) £6·75, £38·25 (f) £7·20, £40·80 (g) £2·70, £15·30 (h) 72p, £4·08
4. (a) £112, £752 (b) £140, £940 (c) £210, £1 410 (d) £87·50, £587·50
   (e) £131·25, £881·25 (f) £56. £376 (g) £568·75, £3 818·75 (h) £68·25, £458·25

Exercise 5E

1. (a) 0·5, 50% (b) 0·25, 25% (c) 0·75, 75% (d) 0·6, 60% (e) 0·7, 70% (f) 0·55, 55%
   (g) 0·12, 12% (h) 0·54, 54% (i) 0·2, 20% (j) 0·9, 90% (k) 0·15, 15% (l) 0·72, 72%
   (m) 0·02, 2% (n) 0·4, 40% (o) 0·1, 10% (p) 0·45, 45% (q) 0·68, 68% (r) 0·86, 86%
   (s) 0·35, 35% (t) 0·84, 84% (u) 0·22, 22% (v) 0·65, 65% (w) 0·44, 44% (x) 0·98, 98%
   (y) 0·96, 96%
2. (a) £40 (b) £36 (c) £50 (d) 33·3% (e) 41·6%

Exercise 5F

1. (a) 50% (b) 75% (c) 25% (d) 40% (e) 60% (f) 15% (g) 28% (h) 80%
   (i) 50% (j) 30% (k) 70% (l) 75% (m) 25% (n) 55% (o) 80% (p) 52%
   (q) 60% (r) 70% (s) 95% (t) 34% (u) 45% (v) 7% (w) 16% (x) 84%
   (y) 80%
2. 15%, 30%, 60%, 75%, 40%, 70%, 50%, 62·5%, 87·5%, 95%
3. (a) 25% (b) 50% (c) 20% (d) 45% (e) 60% (f) 75% (g) 80% (h) 85%
   (i) 65% (j) 95%
4.

Cash saving	% saving
£2·50	20%
£0·54	15%
£2·90	25%
£0·60	12·5%
£2·43	45%

5. (a) £1·80 (b) £0·18 (c) 10% (d) 18 (e) $\frac{1}{5}$

Exercise 5G

1. (a) £10·12 (b) £4·07 (c) £5·50 (d) £10·79 (e) £10·04
2. (a) £108·18 (b) £1·05 (c) £792·00 (d) £286 (e) £156·00 (f) £37·98
3. (a) £24·00 (b) £8·40 (c) £14·08 (d) 36p (e) £10·39
4. (a) £58·43 (b) £1·09 (c) £204·80 (d) £31·90 (e) £138·67 (f) £2·15

Checkout N5

1. (a) $\frac{3}{5}$ (b) $\frac{3}{4}$
2. (a) (i) $8\frac{1}{2}$ (ii) $5\frac{1}{3}$ (iii) $2\frac{1}{4}$ (b) (i) $\frac{7}{2}$ (ii) $\frac{11}{4}$ (iii) $\frac{23}{3}$
3. (a) $\frac{1}{5}$ (b) $\frac{3}{4}$ (c) $\frac{9}{25}$
4. (a) 200   (b) 4   (c) 21   (d) 221   (e) £3·50   (f) £6·30
5. (a) 0·75, 75%   (b) 0·8, 80%   (c) 0·15, 15%   (d) 0·92, 92%
6. (a) (i) 50%   (ii) 48%   (iii) 60%   (b) 30%

Revision exercise N5

1. (c) $\frac{1}{3}$
2. (a) £6   (b) £126
3. (a) 50   (b) 20%
4. £184
5. (a) £60·03 [or £60·02]   (b) £403·03 [or £403·02]
6. (a) $\frac{2}{5}$ (b) 60%
7. (a) 120   (b) 60   (c) 20%
8. (a) 1 800   (b) 120   (c) 18
9. (a) (i) 136   (ii) $\frac{2}{5}$ (b) $\frac{2}{9}$
10. (a) 25   (b) 75%
11. (a) £487·50   (b) £484·70
12. 44·4%
13. (a) £3·50   (b) £73·50

Module 3 Practice calculator test

1. £159·60, £13·00, £35·60, £208·20
2. (a) £5·44
   (b) £14·56
   (c) £10; £2, £2, 50p, 5p, 1p
3. 30·2
4. (a) £40   (b) £24
5. (a) £88   (b) £31 350
6. 4 hours 59 minutes
7. (a) £6·66   (b) £7·59

Module 3 Practice non-calculator test

1. (a) 4, 18, 22   (b) 0·1
2. (a) £14·82   (b) £10, £2, £2, 50p, 20p, 10p, 2p
3. (a) $\frac{3}{10}$ (b) 0·75   (c) 25   (d) ± 7 (e) 0·0016
4. (a) (i) 360   (ii) 60%   (b) 8%   (c) $\frac{7}{20}$
5. 7657
6. (a) £3·60   (b) £75·60
7. 50
8. £54

ANSWERS MODULE 3

ANSWERS MODULE 5

AS1 More number

Check in AS1

1. (a) 56   (b) 108   (c) 105   (d) 8   (e) 17   (f) 19
2. (a) $1\frac{1}{2}$ (b) $1\frac{2}{3}$ (c) $1\frac{1}{11}$ (d) $3\frac{1}{7}$ (e) $6\frac{1}{5}$ (f) $4\frac{3}{4}$

Exercise 1A

1. (a) 1, 2, 4, 8   (b) 1, 2, 3, 6, 18, 9   (c) 1, 2, 5, 10
   (d) 1, 2, 3, 4, 6, 12   (e) 1, 3, 9, 27   (f) 1, 2, 4, 7, 14, 28
   (g) 1, 23   (h) 1, 2, 3, 4, 6, 9, 12, 18, 36   (i) 1, 5, 7, 35
   (j) 1, 31   (k) 1, 2, 4, 5, 8, 10, 20, 40   (l) 1, 2, 3, 4, 6, 8, 12, 16, 24, 48
   (m) 1, 2, 5, 10, 25, 50   (n) 1, 3, 17, 51   (o) 1, 2, 4, 8, 16, 32, 64
2. (a) 16, 18, 20, 22, 24   (b) 24, 26, 28, 30, 32   (c) 38, 40, 42, 44, 46
   (d) 110, 112, 114, 116, 118   (e) 202, 204, 206, 208, 210
3. (a) 19, 21, 23, 25, 27   (b) 23, 25, 27, 29, 31   (c) 55, 57, 59, 61, 63
   (d) 73, 75, 77, 79, 81   (e) 313, 315, 317, 319, 321
4. (a) 3 is a factor   (b) 3 is a factor
   (c) 2, 3, 5, 7, 11, 13, 17, 19, 23, 29, 31, 37, 41, 43, 47
5. (a) 4, 8, 12, 16, 20, 24   (b) 5, 10, 15, 20, 25, 30   (c) 6, 12, 18, 24, 30, 36
   (d) 7, 14, 21, 28, 35, 42   (e) 8, 16, 24, 32, 40, 48   (f) 10, 20, 30, 40, 50, 60
   (g) 12, 24, 36, 48, 60, 72   (h) 15, 30, 45, 60, 75, 90   (i) 20, 40, 60, 80, 100, 120
   (j) 50, 100, 150, 200, 250, 300
6. (a) 18   (b) 9   (c) 15   (d) 12   (e) 17
7. (a) 14   (b) 5   (c) 9   (d) 1   (e) 2
8. (a) 24   (b) 25   (c) 20   (d) 3   (e) 11
9. (a) 1, 5   (b) 1, 7   (c) 1, 2, 3, 4, 6, 12
   (d) 1, 2, 3, 6   (e) 1, 5   (f) 1, 2, 4, 8

Exercise 1B

1. (a) 8   (b) 25   (c) 9   (d) 7   (e) 15   (f) 11   (g) 12
   (h) 10   (i) 50   (j) 30   (k) 22   (l) 72
2. (a) 12   (b) 15   (c) 7   (d) 13   (e) 14   (f) 1   (g) 25
   (h) 1   (i) 14   (j) 6   (k) 4   (l) 36

Exercise 1C

1. (a) 30   (b) 60   (c) 210   (d) 140   (e) 315   (f) 70   (g) 210
   (h) 30   (i) 40
2. (a) 120   (b) 126   (c) 168   (d) 280   (e) 168   (f) 315   (g) 770
   (h) 90   (i) 120

Exercise 1D

1. $\frac{1}{3}$ 2. $\frac{1}{2}$ 3. $\frac{3}{4}$ 4. $\frac{2}{5}$ 5. $\frac{4}{5}$ 6. $\frac{1}{2}$ 7. $\frac{1}{2}$ 8. $\frac{2}{3}$

Exercise 1E

1. $\frac{9}{12}$ 2. $\frac{4}{6}$ 3. $\frac{20}{25}$ 4. $\frac{4}{8}$ 5. $\frac{6}{12}$ 6. $\frac{10}{15}$ 7. $\frac{9}{15}$ 8. $\frac{15}{20}$ 9. $\frac{16}{20}$
10. $\frac{7}{42}$ 11. $\frac{18}{42}$ 12. $\frac{7}{14}$ 13. $\frac{8}{14}$ 14. $\frac{15}{40}$ 15. $\frac{28}{40}$ 16. $\frac{3}{12}$ 17. $\frac{8}{12}$ 18. $\frac{21}{35}$
19. $\frac{30}{35}$ 20. $\frac{14}{24}$ 21. $\frac{15}{24}$ 22. $\frac{50}{90}$ 23. $\frac{18}{30}$ 24. $\frac{18}{45}$ 25. $\frac{9}{24}$

Exercise 1F

1. (a) $\frac{1}{2}$ (b) $\frac{1}{4}$ (c) $\frac{3}{4}$ (d) $\frac{2}{3}$ (e) $\frac{4}{5}$ (f) $\frac{3}{5}$ (g) $\frac{5}{7}$ (h) $\frac{8}{9}$ (i) $\frac{9}{10}$
   (j) $\frac{7}{11}$ (k) $\frac{1}{3}$ (l) $\frac{6}{7}$ (m) $\frac{1}{2}$ (n) 4   (o) $1\frac{1}{3}$ (p) $\frac{2}{3}$ (q) $1\frac{1}{4}$ (r) $\frac{3}{5}$
   (s) $1\frac{2}{5}$ (t) 1   (u) $\frac{9}{10}$ (v) $\frac{1}{3}$ (w) $\frac{6}{7}$ (x) $\frac{2}{3}$ (y) $\frac{22}{25}$
2. (a) $\frac{1}{2}$ (b) $\frac{1}{6}$ (c) $\frac{1}{4}$ (d) $\frac{1}{3}$ (e) $\frac{1}{12}$

3. (a) $\frac{5}{12}$ (b) $\frac{2}{3}$ (c) $\frac{3}{5}$ (d) $\frac{11}{12}$ (e) $\frac{2}{5}$
4. (a) $\frac{1}{4}$ (b) $\frac{1}{2}$ (c) $\frac{3}{4}$ (d) $\frac{4}{5}$ (e) $\frac{9}{20}$

Exercise 1G

1. (a) $\frac{4}{5}$ (b) 1 (c) $1\frac{1}{5}$ (d) $1\frac{2}{5}$ (e) $2\frac{2}{5}$
2. (a) 1 (b) $1\frac{1}{2}$ (c) 2 (d) $3\frac{1}{2}$ (e) 6
3. (a) $\frac{3}{7}$ (b) $\frac{5}{7}$ (c) 1 (d) $1\frac{1}{7}$ (e) 2
4. (a) 2 (b) $2\frac{1}{3}$ (c) 3 (d) $4\frac{1}{3}$ (e) 5
5. (a) $2\frac{1}{2}$ (b) 4 (c) $7\frac{1}{2}$ (d) $3\frac{1}{4}$ (e) $7\frac{1}{4}$
6. (a) $\frac{6}{11}$ (b) $\frac{8}{11}$ (c) $\frac{10}{11}$ (d) $11\frac{8}{11}$ (e) $5\frac{2}{11}$
7. (a) $2\frac{2}{3}$ (b) 2 (c) $3\frac{2}{3}$ (d) 7 (e) $13\frac{2}{3}$
8. (a) $4\frac{2}{3}$ (b) 4 (c) $4\frac{4}{9}$ (d) 11 (e) $4\frac{1}{3}$
9. (a) $2\frac{1}{4}$ (b) $2\frac{1}{2}$ (c) 3 (d) $6\frac{1}{2}$ (e) $6\frac{3}{4}$
10. (a) $3\frac{2}{3}$ (b) 4 (c) $3\frac{5}{6}$ (d) $4\frac{1}{3}$ (e) 7

Exercise 1H

1. (a) $\frac{2}{5}$ (b) $\frac{1}{5}$ (c) $3\frac{2}{5}$ (d) 6 (e) $1\frac{1}{5}$
2. (a) $\frac{1}{2}$ (b) $\frac{1}{4}$ (c) $3\frac{1}{2}$ (d) 8 (e) $9\frac{1}{4}$
3. (a) $\frac{1}{7}$ (b) $\frac{2}{7}$ (c) $1\frac{1}{7}$ (d) $4\frac{3}{7}$ (e) 7
4. (a) $3\frac{2}{9}$ (b) $1\frac{5}{9}$ (c) $\frac{1}{3}$ (d) $4\frac{2}{3}$ (e) $\frac{1}{9}$
5. (a) $1\frac{1}{2}$ (b) 3 (c) $5\frac{1}{2}$ (d) $1\frac{1}{4}$ (e) $\frac{1}{4}$
6. (a) $1\frac{1}{11}$ (b) $\frac{5}{11}$ (c) $3\frac{6}{11}$ (d) $5\frac{4}{11}$ (e) $\frac{8}{11}$
7. (a) $6\frac{1}{9}$ (b) 1 (c) $\frac{8}{9}$ (d) $\frac{7}{9}$ (e) $\frac{5}{9}$
8. (a) $4\frac{1}{4}$ (b) 4 (c) $3\frac{3}{4}$ (d) $3\frac{1}{2}$ (e) $3\frac{3}{8}$
9. (a) $1\frac{1}{2}$ (b) $2\frac{1}{2}$ (c) $3\frac{3}{4}$ (d) $10\frac{1}{4}$ (e) $-1\frac{1}{2}$
10. (a) $2\frac{3}{8}$ (b) $1\frac{3}{4}$ (c) $3\frac{1}{2}$ (d) $4\frac{3}{8}$ (e) $4\frac{7}{8}$

Exercise 1I

1. (a) $\frac{19}{20}$ (b) $1\frac{1}{4}$ (c) $\frac{13}{15}$ (d) $1\frac{1}{6}$ (e) $1\frac{13}{14}$ (f) $1\frac{7}{15}$ (g) $1\frac{13}{28}$ (h) $1\frac{29}{70}$ (i) $1\frac{13}{20}$
(j) $1\frac{1}{4}$ (k) $2\frac{5}{6}$ (l) $3\frac{13}{20}$ (m) $2\frac{1}{3}$ (n) $3\frac{1}{10}$ (o) $3\frac{4}{5}$ (p) $4\frac{7}{12}$ (q) $4\frac{7}{15}$ (r) $6\frac{7}{20}$
(s) $5\frac{11}{20}$ (t) $5\frac{1}{18}$ (u) $5\frac{1}{9}$ (v) $8\frac{3}{8}$ (w) $7\frac{21}{22}$ (x) $5\frac{3}{4}$ (y) $6\frac{1}{6}$
2. (a) $\frac{1}{10}$ (b) $\frac{1}{8}$ (c) $\frac{1}{4}$ (d) $\frac{1}{9}$ (e) $\frac{1}{16}$ (f) $\frac{1}{6}$ (g) $\frac{1}{3}$ (h) $\frac{7}{20}$ (i) $\frac{1}{20}$
(j) $\frac{2}{3}$ (k) $3\frac{1}{3}$ (l) $2\frac{1}{6}$ (m) $3\frac{7}{20}$ (n) $2\frac{7}{15}$ (o) $3\frac{3}{20}$ (p) $1\frac{1}{10}$ (q) $4\frac{2}{3}$ (r) $4\frac{11}{21}$
(s) $3\frac{1}{4}$ (t) $1\frac{7}{18}$ (u) $2\frac{7}{12}$ (v) $3\frac{11}{12}$ (w) $5\frac{3}{8}$ (x) $1\frac{13}{15}$ (y) $\frac{1}{2}$

Exercise 1J

1. (a) 2 (b) 5 (c) 25 (d) 50 (e) 200
2. (a) 5 (b) 11 (c) 16 (d) 25 (e) 150
3. (a) 6 (b) 2 (c) 1 (d) 12 (e) 100
4. (a) 25 (b) 9 (c) 22 (d) 36 (e) 48
5. (a) 2 (b) 1 (c) 10 (d) 100 (e) 200
6. (a) 7 (b) 9 (c) 8 (d) 11 (e) 12
7. (a) 2 (b) 3 (c) 8 (d) 9 (e) 100
8. (a) 5 (b) 7 (c) 21 (d) 45 (e) 60
9. (a) 12 (b) 27 (c) 15 (d) 90 (e) 1 200
10. (a) 18 (b) 30 (c) 15 (d) 66 (e) 375
11. (a) 8 (b) 14 (c) 20 (d) 32 (e) 100
12. (a) 24 (b) 6 (c) 18 (d) 28 (e) 40
13. (a) 3 (b) 9 (c) 240 (d) 93 (e) 135
14. (a) 30 (b) 55 (c) 40 (d) 200 (e) 150
15. (a) 16 (b) 20 (c) 40 (d) 48 (e) 480
16. (a) 14 (b) 28 (c) 245 (d) 350 (e) 700

17. 72   **18.** 9 000

19. (a) £20, £40   (b) £15, £30   (c) £10, £20   (d) £12, £24
     (e) £6, £12   (f) £16, £32   (g) £4, £8   (h) 80p, £1·60

20. Marianna 210, Barry 192

Checkout AS1

1. (a) 1, 2, 4, 5, 10, 20   (b) 1, 5, 25
    (c) 1, 2, 3, 6, 14, 21, 42   (d) 1, 2, 3, 6, 9, 18, 27, 54

2. (a) 44, 46, 48, 50, 52   (b)   266, 268, 270, 272, 274

3. (a) 53, 55, 57, 59, 61   (b)   379, 381, 383, 385, 387

4. 7, 23, 31, 37, 53

5. (a) 4, 8, 12, 16, 20   (b)   12, 24, 36, 48, 60

6. (a) $\frac{9}{12}$ (b) $\frac{12}{24}$ (c) $\frac{6}{16}$ (d) $\frac{20}{25}$

7. (a) $\frac{3}{4}$ (b) $\frac{2}{5}$ (c) $\frac{5}{8}$ (d) $\frac{1}{3}$

8. (a) $1\frac{1}{2}$ (b) $1\frac{2}{5}$ (c) $1\frac{3}{11}$ (d) $4\frac{1}{3}$ (e) $\frac{1}{2}$ (f) $\frac{2}{3}$ (g) $\frac{1}{3}$ (h) $\frac{1}{3}$
    (i) $1\frac{7}{15}$ (j) $1\frac{7}{12}$ (k) $1\frac{8}{9}$ (l) $5\frac{3}{10}$ (m) $\frac{2}{15}$ (n) $\frac{1}{8}$ (o) $1\frac{1}{2}$ (p) $2\frac{4}{9}$

9. (a) 5   (b) 8   (c) 50   (d) 120

10. (a) 12   (b) 48   (c) 75   (d) 225

Revision exercise AS1

1. (a) 9, 13, 15, 29, 35   (b) 15, 35   (c) 8, 16   (d) 13, 29

2. (a) 49   (b) 72   (c) 2, 28   (d) 17, 23

3. £1·58   **4.** 50%

5. (a) 10, 12   (b) 9, 12, 15   (c) 7, 13, 17   (d) 12

6. (a) 5, 7, 15, 23   (b) 5, 7, 23   (c) 8, 16, 20

7. (a) $\frac{5}{8}$ (b) $\frac{3}{8}$ (c) 80

8. (a) 2, 3   (b) $2 \times 2 \times 3 \times 3 \times 3$ or $2^2 \times 3^3$

9. (a) 2×12 or 12×2 or 4×6 or 6×4 or 24×1 or 1×24 (b) 1, 2, 3, 4, 6, 8, 12, 24   (c) 2, 2, 2, 3

10. $2 \times 2 \times 2 \times 3 \times 3$ or $2^3 \times 3^2$

11. (a) (i) 12, 34   (ii) 9, 12   (b) 19, 31

12. (a) 3, 15, 17   (b) 18, 24   (c) 2, 3, 17

AS2 Shape and space 1

Check in AS2

1. (a) $\frac{3}{8}$ (b) $\frac{5}{8}$ **2.** (a) clockwise   (b) anticlockwise

Exercise 2A

1. (a) $\frac{1}{2}$ turn   (b) $\frac{1}{2}$ turn   (c) $\frac{1}{4}$ turn   (d) $\frac{1}{4}$ turn   (e) $\frac{1}{2}$ turn   (f) $\frac{1}{8}$ turn   (g) $\frac{3}{8}$ turn   (h) $\frac{3}{4}$ turn
    (i) $\frac{3}{4}$ turn   (j) $\frac{3}{4}$ turn   (k) $\frac{1}{8}$ turn   (l) $\frac{3}{8}$ turn   (m) $\frac{7}{8}$ turn   (n) $\frac{5}{8}$ turn   (o) $\frac{3}{4}$ turn   (p) $\frac{5}{8}$ turn

2. (a) $\frac{1}{2}$ turn   (b) $\frac{1}{2}$ turn   (c) $\frac{3}{4}$ turn   (d) $\frac{3}{4}$ turn   (e) $\frac{1}{2}$ turn   (f) $\frac{7}{8}$ turn   (g) $\frac{5}{8}$ turn   (h) $\frac{1}{4}$ turn
    (i) $\frac{1}{4}$ turn   (j) $\frac{1}{4}$ turn   (k) $\frac{7}{8}$ turn   (l) $\frac{5}{8}$ turn   (m) $\frac{1}{8}$ turn   (n) $\frac{3}{8}$ turn   (o) $\frac{1}{4}$ turn   (p) $\frac{3}{8}$ turn

Exercise 2B

1. (a) 90°   (b) 90°   (c) 180°   (d) 270°   (e) 180°   (f) 90°   (g) 270°   (h) 180°
    (i) 270°   (j) 90°   (k) 180°   (l) 270°   (m) 45°   (n) 45°   (o) 45°   (p) 45°

2. (a) 270°   (b) 270°   (c) 180°   (d) 90°   (e) 180°   (f) 270°   (g) 90°   (h) 180°
    (i) 90°   (j) 270°   (k) 180°   (l) 90°   (m) 315°   (n) 315°   (o) 315°   (p) 315°

Exercise 2C

1. A 20°   B 70°   C 170°   D 120°   E 105°   F 35°   G 135°
   H 155°   I 94°   J 58°   K 141°   L 87°

2. A 30°   B 80°   C 160°   D 100°   E 115°   F 5°   G 145°
   H 55°   I 62°   J 139°   K 146°   L 153°

Exercise 2D

1. *a*   30° acute   *b*   50° acute   *c*   80° acute   *d*   160° obtuse   *e*   120° obtuse
   f   35° acute   *g*   75° acute   *h*   135° obtuse   *i*   95° obtuse   *j*   48° acute
   k   20° acute   *l*   70° acute   *m*   110° obtuse   *n*   150° obtuse   *o*   25° acute
   p   45° acute   *q*   145° obtuse   *r*   62° acute   *s*   88° acute   *t*   162° obtuse

Exercise 2F

1. Angle *x* can be called angle RQP or angle PQR. Angle *y* can be called angle QPR or angle RPQ. Angle *z* can be called angle PRQ or angle QRP.
2. Angle *x* can be called angle GEF or angle FEG. Angle *y* can be called angle EFG or angle GFE. Angle *z* can be called angle EGF or angle FGE.
3. Angle *x* can be called angle ACB or angle BCA. Angle *y* can be called angle BAC or angle CAB. Angle *z* can be called angle ABC or angle CBA.
4. Angle *x* can be called angle RTS or angle STR. Angle *y* can be called angle SRT or angle TRS. Angle *z* can be called angle RST or angle TSR.
5. Angle *x* can be called angle JKL or angle LKJ. Angle *y* can be called angle KJL or angle LJK. Angle *z* can be called angle JLK or angle KLJ.
6. Angle *x* can be called angle MON or angle NOM. Angle *y* can be called angle OMN or angle NMO. Angle *z* can be called angle MNO or angle ONM.

Exercise 2H

1. (c)   86 m   2. (b)   5·4 m   4. (b)   35 m
5. (b)   43 km   6. (b)   45 km   8. (c)   34 km

Exercise 2I

7. (b)   045°   8. (d)   163°

Checkout AS2

1. (a) $\frac{3}{4}$ turn   (b) $\frac{5}{8}$ turn
2. (a)   45°   (b)   270°
3. (a)   acute   (b)   obtuse
4. A   60°   B   130°
6. Angle *x* can be called angle BAC or angle CAB. Angle *y* can be called angle ABC or angle CBA. Angle *z* can be called angle ACB and or BCA.
8. (b)   120 m

Revision exercise AS2

1. (a)   31 or 32 km
2. (a)   (i) 038°   (ii) 250°   (b) 3·6 km
3. (a)   Doddington   (b) NE   (c) 296°
4. (a)   (i) 110°   (ii) Obtuse   (b) 92 m
5. (a)   1.5 m   (b) (i) 2100 mm   (ii) 42 mm
6. 29°, 107°
7. (b)   7.4 cm

AS3 Algebra 1

Check in AS3

1. (a) 11   (b) ⁻5   (c) ⁻11   (d) 5   (e) 5   (f) ⁻11   (g) ⁻5   (h) 11

Exercise 3A

1. (a) $m - 15$ (b) $m + 2$ (c) $m - 6$ (d) $m + 8$ (e) $m + 1$ (f) $m - 10$
2. (a) $y + 2$ (b) $y - 4$ (c) $y + 7$ (d) $y + 1$ (e) $y - 9$ (f) $y - 2$
3. (a) $h + 15$ (b) $h - 12$ (c) $h + 10$ (d) $h - 4$ (e) $h + 1$ (f) $h - 11$
4. (a) $c + 5$ (b) $c - 16$ (c) $c + 3$ (d) $c - 1$ (e) $c + 6$ (f) $c - 2$

Exercise 3B

1. (a) $2a$ (b) $\frac{a}{3}$ (c) $3a$ (d) $\frac{a}{4}$ (e) $5a$ (f) $\frac{a}{20}$

2. (a) $4m$ (b) $\frac{m}{7}$ (c) $\frac{m}{9}$ (d) $3m$ (e) $6m$ (f) $\frac{m}{2}$

3. (a) $4d$ (b) $2d$ (c) $16d$ (d) d (e) $5d$ metres   (f) $\frac{d}{2}$ litres

4. (a) $\frac{b}{4}$ (b) $\frac{b}{6}$ (c) $\frac{b}{8}$ (d) $\frac{b}{12}$ (e) $\frac{b}{16}$ (f) $\frac{b}{15}$

Exercise 3C

1. (a) (i) £55   (ii) £75   (iii) £105   (iv) £215   (b) $b = r + 25$
2. (a) (i) £22·50   (ii) £45   (iii) £90   (iv) £67·50   (b) $w = 4·5n$
3. (a) (i) £5 800   (ii) £3 400   (iii) £8 200   (iv) £4 600   (b) $T = 24M + 1\,000$
4. (a) (i) 90°F   (ii) 110°F   (iii) 130°F   (iv) 230°F   (b) $F = 2C + 30$
5. (a) (i) 540p   (ii) 790p   (iii) 440p   (iv) 1 290p   (b) $C = 25w + 40$
6. (a) (i) £4   (ii) £2   (iii) £2·50   (iv) £1·25   (b) $c = \frac{20}{p}$
7. (a) (i) 5   (ii) 11   (iii) 8   (iv) 2   (b) $S = 3L - 25$
8. (a) (i) £18   (ii) £13   (iii) £12   (iv) £11   (b) $c = \frac{120}{n} + 8$

Exercise 3D

1. (a) 10   (b) 11   (c) 16   (d) 4   (e) 1   (f) 21   (g) 26
   (h) 18   (i) 15   (j) 13
2. (a) 12   (b) 21   (c) 2   (d) 6   (e) 0   (f) 18   (g) 14
   (h) 17   (i) 4   (j) 6
3. (a) 15   (b) 17   (c) 3   (d) 2   (e) 0   (f) 15   (g) 19
   (h) 5   (i) 15   (j) 5
4. (a) 21   (b) 31   (c) 10   (d) 10   (e) 40   (f) 40   (g) 60
   (h) 60   (i) 37   (j) 37
5. (a) 32   (b) 32   (c) 32   (d) 2   (e) 10   (f) 48   (g) 48
   (h) 48   (i) 8   (j) 2
6. (a) 10   (b) 20   (c) 9   (d) 8   (e) 17   (f) 11   (g) 5
   (h) 5   (i) 14   (j) 19
7. (a) 5   (b) 9   (c) 9   (d) 7   (e) 2   (f) 16   (g) 9
   (h) 3   (i) 6   (j) 0
8. (a) 11   (b) 15   (c) 15   (d) 21   (e) 21   (f) 16   (g) 16
   (h) 29   (i) 2   (j) 1
9. (a) 30   (b) 30   (c) 60   (d) 0   (e) 65   (f) 65   (g) 0
   (h) 15   (i) 0   (j) 0
10. (a) 24   (b) 36   (c) 36   (d) 0   (e) 10   (f) 30   (g) 60
    (h) 90   (i) 6   (j) 12

Exercise 3E

1. (a) 12   (b) 60   (c) 16   (d) 15   (e) 24   (f) 24   (g) 8
   (h) 14   (i) 21   (j) 35
2. (a) 2   (b) 6   (c) 4   (d) 3   (e) 9   (f) 6   (g) 6
   (h) 9   (i) 9   (j) 2
3. (a) 20   (b) 40   (c) 40   (d) 8   (e) 10   (f) 3   (g) 3
   (h) 45   (i) 45   (j) 45
4. (a) 50   (b) 50   (c) 6   (d) 3   (e) 2   (f) 30   (g) 30
   (h) 15   (i) 15   (j) 10
5. (a) 21   (b) 21   (c) 10   (d) 4   (e) 4   (f) 400   (g) 400
   (h) 24   (i) 24   (j) 28
6. (a) 50   (b) 10   (c) 20   (d) 52   (e) 100   (f) 45   (g) 30
   (h) 30   (i) 40   (j) 25
7. (a) 6   (b) 8   (c) 12   (d) 12   (e) 4   (f) 10   (g) 20
   (h) 20   (i) 6   (j) 5·5
8. (a) 6   (b) 6   (c) 12   (d) 12   (e) 4   (f) 5   (g) 15
   (h) 15   (i) 9   (j) 9

9. (a) 12 (b) 23 (c) 20 (d) 60 (e) 23 (f) 32 (g) 32
(h) 54 (i) 54 (j) 65
10. (a) $^-1$ (b) 12 (c) 0 (d) 21 (e) 21 (f) 45 (g) 45
(h) 9 (i) 9 (j) 6

Exercise 3F

1. (a) 1 (b) 4 (c) 9 (d) 1 (e) 8 (f) 27 (g) 1
(h) 16 (i) 81 (j) 1 (k) 1
2. (a) 25 (b) 36 (c) 49 (d) 125 (e) 216 (f) 343 (g) 625
(h) 1 296 (i) 2 401 (j) 3 125 (k) 2·2
3. (a) 64 (b) 61 (c) 100 (d) 512 (e) 729 (f) 1 000 (g) 4 096
(h) 6 561 (i) 10 000 (j) 32 768 (k) 3 (l) 3·2
4. (a) 50 (b) 72 (c) 98 (d) 180 (e) 150 (f) 294 (g) 252
(h) 245 (i) 175 (j) 121 (k) 4
5. (a) 8 (b) 54 (c) 48 (d) 18 (e) 32 (f) 64 (g) 6
(h) 12 (i) 18 (j) 13
6. (a) 1 (b) 8 (c) 5 (d) 1 (e) 1 (f) 2 (g) 2
(h) 4 (i) 8 (j) 16
7. (a) 16 (b) 41 (c) 189 (d) 50 (e) 32 (f) 82 (g) 82
(h) 9 (i) 9 (j) 48
8. (a) 12 (b) 36 (c) 24 (d) 12 (e) 216 (f) 49 (g) 60
(h) 60 (i) 12 (j) 12
9. (a) 5 (b) 4 (c) 29 (d) 30 (e) 12 (f) 36 (g) 512
(h) 128 (i) 256 (j) 343
10. (a) 15 (b) 5 (c) 18 (d) 50 (e) 101 (f) 2 (g) 5 000
(h) 1 250 (i) 1 125 (j) 225

Exercise 3G

1. (a) $^-4$ (b) $^-3$ (c) 2 (d) $^-10$ (e) 15 (f) $^-21$ (g) $^-16$
(h) $^-24$ (i) $^-13$ (j) $^-15$
2. (a) 0 (b) 9 (c) $^-10$ (d) 18 (e) $^-12$ (f) $^-18$ (g) $^-22$
(h) $^-7$ (i) $^-44$ (j) 30
3. (a) 5 (b) 7 (c) 13 (d) $^-8$ (e) 10 (f) $^-15$ (g) $^-11$
(h) $^-15$ (i) $^-5$ (j) 45
4. (a) $^-19$ (b) $^-9$ (c) $^-30$ (d) 50 (e) $^-40$ (f) $^-40$ (g) $^-60$
(h) $^-60$ (i) $^-43$ (j) $^-43$
5. (a) 0 (b) $^-32$ (c) $^-32$ (d) 34 (e) $^-22$ (f) $^-48$ (g) $^-48$
(h) $^-16$ (i) $^-88$ (j) 98
6. (a) 9 (b) 12 (c) 6 (d) $^-8$ (e) $^-2$ (f) $^-6$ (g) 10
(h) $^-10$ (i) 5 (j) $^-7$
7. (a) 0 (b) $^-4$ (c) $^-4$ (d) $^-12$ (e) $^-12$ (f) 4 (g) 16
(h) $^-28$ (i) $^-10$ (j) 6
8. (a) 1 (b) $^-3$ (c) $^-3$ (d) 15 (e) 15 (f) $^-16$ (g) $^-16$
(h) 7 (i) 22 (j) $^-9$
9. (a) $^-30$ (b) 10 (c) $^-20$ (d) $^-40$ (e) $^-5$ (f) 25 (g) 20
(h) 45 (i) $^-120$ (j) 80
10. (a) $^-24$ (b) $^-36$ (c) $^-36$ (d) 0 (e) $^-110$ (f) $^-30$ (g) $^-60$
(h) $^-90$ (i) $^-6$ (j) $^-12$

Exercise 3H

1. (a) 4 (b) 6 (c) 9 (d) 26 (e) 51 (f) 32
2. (a) 12 (b) 9 (c) 6 (d) 3 (e) 4·5 (f) 6·3
3. (a) 16 cm (b) 26 cm (c) 6 cm (d) 36 cm (e) 15 cm (f) 12 cm
4. (a) 200 (b) 150 (c) 240 (d) 250 (e) 240 (f) 175
5. (a) 4 (b) 10 (c) 5 (d) 0 (e) 10·5 (f) $^-2$
6. (a) 6 (b) 16 (c) 10 (d) 20 (e) 20 (f) 3
7. (a) 34 (b) 36 (c) 38 (d) 32 (e) 30 (f) 28
8. (a) 3 (b) 4 (c) 7 (d) 10 (e) 24 (f) 1·5
9. (a) 12 (b) 27 (c) 3 (d) 48 (e) 75 (f) 6·75
10. (a) 10 (b) 2 (c) 19·5 (d) 8 (e) 4·5 (f) 17·5

Exercise 3I

1. $11a$	**2.** $10y$	**3.** $3w$	**4.** $6x$	**5.** $13m$	**6.** $4q$	**7.** $2v$	**8.** $11r$	**9.** $20b$	**10.** $10g$
11. $5w$	**12.** $3x$	**13.** t	**14.** $3e$	**15.** $6u$	**16.** u	**17.** $3y$	**18.** $6i$	**19.** r	**20.** x
21. $14x$	**22.** $12y$	**23.** $9t$	**24.** $19a$	**25.** $9b$	**26.** $4x$	**27.** $8w$	**28.** $6d$	**29.** $11e$	**30.** $18r$
31. $8x$	**32.** $3a$	**33.** $4q$	**34.** $2b$	**35.** x	**36.** x	**37.** $3x$	**38.** z	**39.** $2e$	**40.** $7a$
41. $3x$	**42.** $2y$	**43.** $4m$	**44.** $3u$	**45.** y	**46.** $6z$	**47.** b	**48.** $3d$	**49.** $3h$	**50.** $4a$

Exercise 3J

1. $7x + 3y$	**2.** $9t + 6s$	**3.** $9m + 3n$	**4.** $4a + 4b$	**5.** $9y + 3z$	**6.** $11r + 5s$
7. $10y + 4$	**8.** $7u + 4v$	**9.** $6n + 11$	**10.** $5e + 6f$	**11.** $4x + 3y$	**12.** $a + 8b$
13. $2x + y$	**14.** $5f + 1$	**15.** $m + 3n$	**16.** $2x + 2y$	**17.** $4v + 5$	**18.** $3p + 2q$
19. $2r + 3s$	**20.** $a + 4b$	**21.** $3x + 4y$	**22.** $a + 1$	**23.** $e + 2f$	**24.** $s + 1$
25. $3x + 2y$	**26.** $3r + 2s$	**27.** $5x + y$	**28.** $4u + 2$	**29.** $3a + b$	**30.** $y + z$
31. $4a - 2b$	**32.** $7x - 2y$	**33.** $7e - 3f$	**34.** $15u - 5t$	**35.** $8y - z$	**36.** $2a - 3b$
37. $2m - n$	**38.** $2a - 1$	**39.** $7y - 20$	**40.** $3x - 5y$		

Exercise 3K

1. $6a$	**2.** $3b$	**3.** $4x + 2y$	**4.** $12a$	**5.** $5x + 4y$	**6.** $8m$
7. $15a$	**8.** $4a + 8$	**9.** $8x + 4y$	**10.** $4m + 6n$	**11.** $12e + 10$	**12.** $6e + 4f$

Checkout AS3

1. (a) $s + 3$ (b) $s - 3$ (c) $3s$ (d) $\frac{s}{2}$

2. (a) (i) £110 (ii) £185 (b) $C = 20H + P$

3. (a) 3 (b) 2 (c) 12 (d) 16 (e) 11 (f) 2 (g) 6
(h) 60 (i) 14 (j) 20 (k) 2 (l) 30 (m) 4 (n) 64
(o) 18

4. (a) $^{-}1$ (b) 5 (c) 6 (d) $^{-}12$ (e) 4 (f) 21 (g) 5
(h) $^{-}4$ (i) 0 (j) 6 (k) $^{-}3$ (l) $^{-}9$

5. (a) (i) 22 (ii) 10 (iii) 4 (b) (i) 7 (ii) 1

6. (a) (i) $12t$ (ii) $12y$ (iii) $6a$ (iv) $6a + 7b$ (v) $2x + 8y$ (vi) $5d + e$
(vii) $7x - y$ (viii) $5a - 2b$ (ix) $7p - 6q$ (x) $3u - 5v$ (b) $2x + 2y + 8$

Revision exercise AS3

1. (a) $9a$ (ii) $6a + b$ (iii) $3b^2$

2. (a) 8 (b) (i) $p + 5$ (ii) $2p$ (iii) $2p - 3$

3. (a) $4x + 11$ (b) 54

4. (a) $x + 3$ (b) $\frac{3}{4}y$

5. $3S - 4 = F$ **6.** $59°F$

7. (a) £184 (b) $40 + 2M$ (c) (i) $124 = 40 + 2M$ (ii) 42

8. 7

9. (a) (i) £130 (ii) 9 (b) $T = 25d$ (c) Belinda's by £3.

AS4 Shape and space 2

Exercise 4A

Name	Plane faces	Curved surfaces	Vertices	Edges
Cube	6	0	8	12
Cuboid	6	0	8	12
Cylinder	2	1	0	2
Triangular prism	5	0	6	9
Cone	1	1	1	1
Sphere	0	1	0	0
Square pyramid	5	0	5	8
Triangular pyramid	4	0	4	6

Exercise 4B

1. (a), (b), (d), (e), (f), (g) and (i) are nets for a cube

Exercise 6D

1.

2.
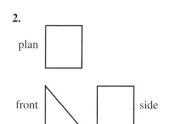

3.
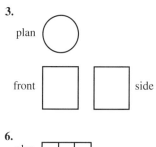

4.
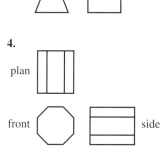

5.
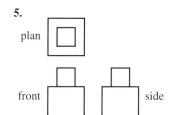

6.
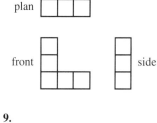

7.
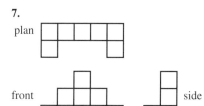

8.
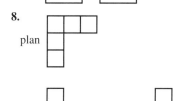

9.
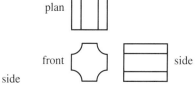

Checkout AS4

1. (a) 0 curved surfaces, 6 plane faces, 12 edges, 8 vertices   (b) 1 curved surface, 2 plane faces, 2 edges, 0 vertices

4. (a)
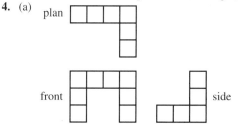

Revision exercise AS4

2. (b) B, C

AS5 Shape and space 3

Check in AS5

1. (a) 180°   (b) 90°   (c) 225°   (d) 45°   (e) 135°   (f) 135°°

Exercise 5A

1. 50°   **2.** 10°   **3.** 45°   **4.** 65°   **5.** 85°   **6.** 28°   **7.** 56°   **8.** 33°
9. 35°   **10.** 35°   **11.** 45°   **12.** 40°   **13.** 115°   **14.** 148°   **15.** 69°   **16.** 96°

17. 47° **18.** 152° **19.** 35° **20.** 50° **21.** 60° **22.** 160° **23.** 295° **24.** 198°
25. 237° **26.** 90° **27.** 45° **28.** 286° **29.** 50° **30.** 40°

Exercise 5B

1. $a = 100°, b = 80°, c = 100°$
2. $d = 145°, e = 35°, f = 35°$
3. $g = 85°, h = 85°, i = 95°$
4. $j = 76°, k = 104°, l = 104°$
5. $m = 122°, n = 58°, o = 58°$
6. $p = 139°, q = 41°, r = 41°$
7. $s = 100°, t = 60°, u = 100°$
8. $v = 60°, w = 60°, x = 90°$
9. $y = 50°, z = 130°, a = 50°$

Exercise 5C

1. $a = 60°, b = 60°, c = 120°, d = 120°, e = 60°, f = 60°, g = 120°$
2. $h = 100°, i = 100°, f = 80°, k = 100°, l = 80°, m = 100°, n = 80°$
3. $o = 115°, p = 65°, q = 65°, r = 115°, s = 65°, t = 115°, u = 65°$
4. $v = 135°, w = 45°, x = 135°, y = 45°, z = 45°, a = 135°, b = 135°$
5. $c = 288°$
6. $d = 55°, e = 125°$
7. $f = 60°, g = 60°, h = 60°, i = 240°, j = 120°, k = 240°$
8. $l = 125°, m = 235°$

Exercise 5D

1. 30° **2.** 78° **3.** 55° **4.** 25° **5.** 78° **6.** 140° **7.** 100° **8.** 63°
9. 133° **10.** 90° **11.** 79° **12.** 111°

Exercise 5E

1. $a = 70°$
2. $b = 62°$
3. $c = 78°$
4. $d = 35°$
5. $e = 26°$
6. $f = 78°, g = 24°$
7. $h = 116°, i = 32°$
8. $y = 82°, k = 16°$
9. $l = 45°, m = 90°$
10. $n = 75°, o = 30°$

Exercise 5G

1. $p = 45°, q = 135°$
2. $m = 40°, n = 140°$
3. $c = 36°, d = 144°$
4. $a = 30°, b = 150°$

Exercise 5H

1. $x = 130°$
2. (a) 360° (b) 110°
3. (a) 720° (b) 115°
4. (a) 1 080° (b) 110°

Checkout AS5

1. $a = 20°, b = 58°, c = 85°$
2. $e = 140°, f = 40°, g = 140°$
3. $e = 68°, f = 68°, g = 112°, h = 112°, i = 68°, j = 68°, k = 112°$
4. $a = 16°$
5. $a = 74°, b = 48°, c = 84°$
7. $p = 60°, q = 120°$
8. (a) 720° (b) 115°

Revision exercise AS5

1. 60°, 120°, 120°
2. (a) 65°, alternate angles AB parallel to DC
    (b) 70°, the required angle and the 110° angle are supplementary angles
3. (a) 50°, 40° (b) (i) kite (ii) 100°, 118°
4. (a) pentagon (b) all 60° (c) identical (d) 90°, 60°
5. (a) congruent (b) (i) 180° (ii) $3a$ (iii) 60°
6. (a) (i) 33° (ii) 35° (iii) 68° (b) 72°

AS6 Algebra 2

Check in AS6

1. (a) 11   (b) 3   (c) $^-3$ (d) $^-11$ (e) 3   (f) $^-11$ (g) 11   (h) $^-3$
2. (a) 9   (b) 12   (c) 25   (d) $^-14$ (e) 43   (f) 20   (g) 16   (h) $^-2$

Exercise 6A

1. $^-8$	2. $^-15$	3. $^-6$	4. $^-6$	5. $^-16$	6. $^-18$	7. $^-16$	8. $^-27$
9. $^-20$	10. $^-6$	11. $^-24$	12. $^-12$	13. $^-28$	14. $^-40$	15. $^-9$	16. $^-21$
17. $^-32$	18. $^-35$	19. $^-18$	20. $^-30$	21. 9	22. 3	23. 7	24. 48
25. 45	26. 63	27. 36	28. 30	29. 5	30. 14	31. 54	32. 42
33. $^-64$	34. $^-81$	35. $^-72$	36. 8	37. $^-24$	38. $^-36$	39. $^-4$	40. 49

Exercise 6B

1. $^-4$	2. $^-2$	3. $^-4$	4. $^-7$	5. $^-5$	6. $^-7$	7. $^-4$	8. $^-3$
9. $^-3$	10. $^-9$	11. $^-8$	12. $^-7$	13. $^-5$	14. $^-2$	15. $^-9$	16. $^-3$
17. $^-4$	18. $^-9$	19. $^-2$	20. $^-2$	21. 2	22. 5	23. 5	24. 8
25. 7	26. 2	27. 2	28. 3	29. 2	30. 4	31. $^-5$	32. $^-5$
33. 5	34. $^-2$	35. $^-2$	36. 2	37. $^-4$	38. $^-4$	39. 6	40. 8

Exercise 6C

1. $8x$	2. $18y$	3. $14p$	4. $25a$	5. $36z$	6. $24u$	7. $20m$	8. $21b$
9. $21q$	10. $36w$	11. ^-12e	12. ^-30t	13. ^-6x	14. ^-3y	15. ^-4u	16. ^-5x
17. ^-a	18. ^-18d	19. ^-40r	20. ^-36y	21. ^-6x	22. ^-20c	23. ^-42p	24. ^-3x
25. ^-4y	26. ^-2z	27. ^-15t	28. ^-t	29. ^-x	30. ^-16z	31. $4x$	32. $15m$
33. $12p$	34. $8x$	35. $10y$	36. $2t$	37. t	38. $3e$	39. e	40. $16x$

Exercise 6D

1. $4ab$	2. $15st$	3. $4ab$	4. $49uv$	5. $16cd$	6. $6ab$	7. $7xy$	8. $30rs$
9. $24xy$	10. $35pq$	11. $6z^2$	12. $7u^2$	13. $5x^2$	14. $6a^2$	15. $4x^2$	16. $9y^2$
17. $8r^2$	18. $12e^2$	19. $25t^2$	20. $21w^2$	21. ^-6ab	22. ^-10mn	23. ^-3ab	24. ^-2xy
25. ^-2xy	26. $^-6z^2$	27. $^-6a^2$	28. $^-4r^2$	29. $^-3x^2$	30. $^-12b^2$	31. $6ef$	32. $8xy$
33. ef	34. rs	35. $12mn$	36. $2x^2$	37. $6y^2$	38. $12a^2$	39. x^2	40. $^-y^3$

Exercise 6E

1. $3x + 6$	2. $5y + 5$	3. $8w + 24$	4. $21 + 7e$	5. $6a + 24$	6. $4x - 4$
7. $5t - 15$	8. $9e - 45$	9. $12 - 3w$	10. $5x - 20$	11. $6a + 12$	12. $20b + 12$
13. $30e + 18$	14. $6x + 4$	15. $30t + 20$	16. $21r - 28$	17. $16x - 24$	18. $8 - 6m$
19. $5 - 5w$	20. $24 - 12w$	21. $10a + 15b$	22. $6a + 24b$	23. $14x + 14y$	24. $18e + 24f$
25. $24t + 20u$	26. $12x - 15y$	27. $10a - 15b$	28. $15b - 10a$	29. $12w - 24x$	30. $25m - 25n$

Exercise 6F

1. $7x + 18$	2. $9y + 17$	3. $14a + 27$	4. $24z + 17$	5. $30q + 24$	6. $7x + 19$
7. $14w + 7$	8. $13w + 20$	9. $14w + 7$	10. $9x$	11. $7x + 5$	12. $6a + 2$
13. $18w - 3$	14. $15e - 1$	15. $7x + 1$	16. $7x - 5$	17. $11y - 7$	18. $8x - 10$
19. $13w - 16$	20. $23z - 22$				

Exercise 6G

1. $3b + 5ab$	2. $5a - 3ab$	3. $2y - 5xy$	4. $x^2 + 2x$	5. $y^2 + 7y$	6. $2z^2 + z$
7. $2m^2 - m$	8. $3d + 2d^2$	9. $5a^2 - 3a$	10. $2b^2 - 2b$	11. $2b^2 - 2b$	12. $3s^2 - 3s$
13. $10r^2 + 15r$	14. $a + ab$	15. $2x - xy$	16. $a^2 + ab$	17. $d^2 + 2de$	18. $3m - 2mn$
19. $6a^2 + 8ab$	20. $8xy + 12x^2$	21. $6uv + 9u^2$	22. $16r^2 + 8rs$	23. $16r^2 - 8rs$	24. $10x^2 - 6xy$
25. $12pq - 8p^2$					

Exercise 6H

1. $^-2a - 6$ 2. $^-4x - 4$ 3. $^-4b - 6$ 4. $^-6 - 4z$ 5. $^-20 - 30t$ 6. $^-18w - 9$
7. $^-10 - 10r$ 8. $^-12b - 12$ 9. $^-3x - 15$ 10. $^-7x - 7x$ 11. $2 - 2x$ 12. $2x - 2$
13. $4 - 4s$ 14. $4s - 4$ 15. $3 - 6w$ 16. $8w - 4$ 17. $25 - 15x$ 18. $15x - 25$
19. $12 - 8p$ 20. $8p - 12$ 21. $^-x - 2$ 22. $^-y - 3$ 23. $^-a - b$ 24. $^-2a - 3b$
25. $^-2x - y$ 26. $1 - x$ 27. $2x - y$ 28. $3b - 2a$ 29. $2y - 3x$ 30. $5q - 3p$
31. $^-a^2 - ab$ 32. $^-2x^2 - xy$ 33. $^-3d - 2d^2$ 34. $^-4v^2 - 2v$ 35. $^-2s^2 - st$ 36. $st - t^2$
37. $6w - 4w^2$ 38. $8xy - 8x^2$ 39. $6ab - 6a^2$ 40. $20m^2 - 10mn$

Exercise 6I

1. $3(x + 3)$ 2. $5(x + 3)$ 3. $6(a + 3)$ 4. $4(m + 3)$ 5. $7(b + 2)$ 6. $4(r - 4)$
7. $5(t - 4)$ 8. $9(w - 2)$ 9. $3(w - 5)$ 10. $4(y - 6)$ 11. $3(w + 7)$ 12. $6(m - 6)$
13. $7(y + 3)$ 14. $11(a - 2)$ 15. $12(w + 2)$ 16. $3(2e + 3)$ 17. $4(2u + 3)$ 18. $5(3a + 4)$
19. $6(2b + 3)$ 20. $3(4w + 5)$ 21. $4(3y - 4)$ 22. $5(4v - 5)$ 23. $6(3c - 4)$ 24. $3(2t - 5)$
25. $7(2m - 3)$ 26. $3(5x + 6)$ 27. $8(2t - 3)$ 28. $5(6r + 7)$ 29. $6(5p - 2)$ 30. $7(4z + 3)$

Exercise 6J

1. $a(1 + b)$ 2. $x(2 + y)$ 3. $p(3 + 5q)$ 4. $t(3 + 2s)$ 5. $a(5 + 7b)$ 6. $x(6y + 1)$
7. $t(4s + 3)$ 8. $e(5 - 4f)$ 9. $u(7 - 5v)$ 10. $b(3a - 5)$ 11. $3a(2b + 3)$ 12. $4u(2 + 3v)$
13. $5e(3 + 4f)$ 14. $3x(3 + 4y)$ 15. $4r(3 + 4s)$ 16. $5y(4x - 5)$ 17. $6b(3a - 2)$ 18. $2y(2z - 3)$
19. $3e(5 - 4f)$ 20. $10q(2p - 3)$ 21. $x(x + y)$ 22. $x(x^2 + y)$ 23. $a(2b + a)$ 24. $t(5s + t)$
25. $5t(s + 2t)$ 26. $x(x + 2y)$ 27. $2x(x + y)$ 28. $2x(x + 2y)$ 29. $7a(a^2 + 2b)$ 30. $ab(2 + 3a)$

Exercise 6K

1. $x = 4$ 2. $y = 3$ 3. $a = 7$ 4. $s = 1$ 5. $x = 1$ 6. $y = 0$ 7. $c = 8$ 8. $z = 12$
9. $f = 45$ 10. $m = 8$ 11. $x = ^-1$ 12. $y = ^-4$ 13. $a = ^-5$ 14. $e = ^-6$ 15. $t = ^-5$ 16. $x = ^-6$
17. $d = ^-4$ 18. $z = ^-7$ 19. $y = ^-4$ 20. $d = ^-8$

Exercise 6L

1. $x = 20$ 2. $e = 17$ 3. $a = 11$ 4. $z = 5$ 5. $t = 10$ 6. $u = 10$ 7. $d = 8$ 8. $r = 21$
9. $x = 7$ 10. $d = 22$ 11. $d = 4$ 12. $x = 4$ 13. $t = 2$ 14. $y = 0$ 15. $u = 6$ 16. $x = 0$
17. $b = ^-6$ 18. $z = ^-1$ 19. $p = ^-5$ 20. $g = ^-3$

Exercise 6M

1. $x = 4$ 2. $r = 5$ 3. $w = 9$ 4. $y = 6$ 5. $m = 6$ 6. $a = 8$ 7. $u = 3$ 8. $y = 3$
9. $t = 8$ 10. $c = 3$ 11. $y = ^-5$ 12. $x = ^-3$ 13. $t = ^-5$ 14. $x = ^-9$ 15. $u = ^-4$ 16. $y = ^-3$
17. $r = ^-8$ 18. $y = ^-5$ 19. $z = ^-10$ 20. $t = ^-1$ 21. $x = 2$ 22. $x = 9$ 23. $f = 8$ 24. $v = 2$
25. $x = 4$ 26. $x = 7$ 27. $a = 21$ 28. $s = ^-7$ 29 $r = ^-10$ 30. $m = 20$

Exercise 6N

1. $x = 16$ 2. $c = 15$ 3. $a = 12$ 4. $t = 7$ 5. $y = 9$ 6. $m = 35$ 7. $x = 48$ 8. $z = 10$
9. $t = 24$ 10. $h = 45$ 11. $j = ^-20$ 12. $y = ^-15$ 13. $z = ^-42$ 14. $d = ^-3$ 15. $r = ^-18$ 16. $d = ^-8$
17. $y = ^-30$ 18. $u = ^-30$ 19. $x = ^-30$ 20. $t = ^-12$ 21. $x = 18$ 22. $z = 24$ 23. $r = 45$ 24. $m = 45$
25. $s = 20$ 26. $e = 56$ 27. $e = ^-56$ 28. $e = ^-56$ 29 $e = 56$ 30. $a = ^-48$

Exercise 6O

1. $x = 6$ 2. $x = 4$ 3. $a = 7$ 4. $e = 2$ 5. $m = 1$ 6. $s = 2$ 7. $p = 6$ 8. $x = 3$
9. $s = 8$ 10. $y = 1$ 11. $y = 4$ 12. $x = 3$ 13. $a = 4$ 14. $z = 6$ 15. $x = 2$ 16. $x = 10$
17. $p = 6$ 18. $m = 5$ 19. $t = 1$ 20. $x = 2$ 21. $x = 8$ 22. $x = 2$ 23. $a = 6$ 24. $x = 2$
25. $z = 1$ 26. $q = ^-1$ 27. $y = ^-2$ 28. $z = 3$ 29 $m = 12$ 30. $y = ^-3$ 31. $a = 8$ 32. $z = 9$
33. $p = 20$ 34. $q = 12$ 35. $x = 5$ 36. $y = 15$ 37. $a = ^-4$ 38. $x = ^-14$ 39. $x = 9$ 40. $x = 12$

Exercise 6P

1. $x = 5$ 2. $a = 4$ 3. $z = 1$ 4. $m = 2$ 5. $p = 0$ 6. $z = 8$ 7. $t = 7$ 8. $x = 5$
9. $t = 5$ 10. $q = 4$ 11. $x = 4$ 12. $a = 3$ 13. $z = 1$ 14. $s = 2$ 15. $x = 4$ 16. $x = 6$
17. $x = 3$ 18. $a = 3$ 19. $y = 1$ 20. $z = 2$ 21. $x = 2$ 22. $x = 4$ 23. $y = 6$ 24. $y = 4$
25. $y = 2$ 26. $y = ^-2$ 27. $x = 1$ 28. $a = 4$ 29 $y = ^-1$ 30. $y = ^-3$

Exercise 6Q

1. $p = 3$
2. $a = 2$
3. $w = 3$
4. $t = 1$
5. $w = 3$
6. $x = 2$
7. $x = 5.25$
8. $c = 7$
9. $a = 13$
10. $w = 6$
11. $s = 11$
12. $e = 1$
13. $x = 4$
14. $x = {}^-2$
15. $b = 3.143$
16. $x = {}^-1$
17. $x = 1$
18. $z = {}^-14$
19. $q = 4$
20. $t = {}^-5$
21. $b = 1.875$
22. $x = {}^-2$
23. $m = 2$
24. $q = {}^-0.1$
25. $k = 5$
26. $x = 12$
27. $s = 3$
28. $w = 8$
29. $y = {}^-3$
30. $y = 1.167$

Exercise 6R

1. (a) $y = 3x + 5$ (b) $y = \dfrac{3x - 2}{3}$ (c) $y = 2 - 3x$ (d) $y = \dfrac{2x - 5}{3}$

   (e) $y = \dfrac{2x - 3}{2}$ (f) $y = \dfrac{a}{b} - \dfrac{1}{2}$

2. (a) $t = \dfrac{v - u}{f}$ (b) 10.59 (c) 46.7

3. (a) $s = \dfrac{v^2 - u^2}{2f}$ (b) 14.4 (c) $v = \sqrt{u^2 + 2fs}$ (d) 57.68

   (e) $u = \sqrt{v^2 - 2fs}$ (f) 13.97

Checkout AS6

1. (a) 20 (b) $^-15$ (c) $^-8$ (d) 24 (e) $^-18$ (f) $^-16$ (g) 36 (h) 14
   (i) $^-9$ (j) 4 (k) $^-3$ (l) 3 (m) $^-3$ (n) 5 (o) $^-4$ (p) 8
2. (a) $12d$ (b) $30x$ (c) $18w$ (d) $20y$ (e) ^-6e (f) ^-6y (g) ^-20r (h) $6x$
3. (a) $6xy$ (b) $20rs$ (c) $6wy$ (d) $5ab$ (e) ^-6ef (f) ^-6xy (g) $15st$ (h) $4r^2$
   (i) $6x^2$ (j) $^-2y^2$ (k) $15t^2$ (l) $^-7x^2$
4. (a) $4x + 8$ (b) $3x - 3$ (c) $12x + 18$ (d) $10t - 2$
   (e) $18 - 30j$ (f) $10a + 15c$ (g) $12x + 6y$ (h) $9u - 6v$
   (i) $x^2 + x$ (j) $d^2 + de$ (k) $2z^2 + 5z$ (l) $x^2 + xy$
   (m) $2s^2 + 3st$ (n) $2pq - 3p^2$ (o) $3c^2 + 6cd$ (p) $8xy - 12y^2$
5. (a) $^-2x - 2$ (b) $^-3z - 12$ (c) $^-8x - 12$ (d) $^-7x - 14$
   (e) $3 - 3x$ (f) $8 - 4x$ (g) $5x - 20$ (h) $30x - 12$
   (i) $^-y - 4$ (j) $6 - 2x$ (k) $^-a - b$ (l) $b - a$
   (m) $^-x^2 - 3x$ (n) $2y - y^2$ (o) $2s^2 - 2s$ (p) $12t^2 - 8pt$
6. (a) $3(x + 3)$ (b) $5(t + 3)$ (c) $4(m - 5)$ (d) $7(t - 2)$
   (e) $5(3x + 8)$ (f) $3(3r + 8)$ (g) $3(4x - 5)$ (h) $10(2p - 3)$
7. (a) $x(1 + y)$ (b) $d(c + 2)$ (c) $b(3a - 2)$ (d) $2f(2 - e)$
   (e) $x(2x + 1)$ (f) $x(3x + 2)$ (g) $a(2b - a)$ (h) $5x(1 - 2y)$
8. (a) $x = 25$ (b) $r = 0$ (c) $y = {}^-26$
9. (a) $c = 10$ (b) $u = 7$ (c) $m = 4$
10. (a) $x = 12$ (b) $n = 10$ (c) $v = {}^-20$
11. (a) $m = 10$ (b) $t = 2$ (c) $x = {}^-8$
12. (a) $x = 3$ (b) $e = 10$ (c) $e = 3$
   (d) $x = 15$ (e) $m = 30$ (f) $c = 6$
13. (a) $x = 5$ (b) $x = 4$ (c) $y = 4$ (d) $e = {}^-1$
14. (a) $x = 3$ (b) $y = 3$ (c) $t = 4$ (d) $x = 4$

Revision exercise AS6

1. (a) $1\tfrac{1}{4}$ (b) $1\tfrac{1}{2}$
2. (a) 7 (b) 2
3. (a) $9\tfrac{1}{2}$ (b) 2
4. (a) 2 (b) $\tfrac{1}{2}$
5. (a) 3 (b) 2
6. $^-1$
7. (i) $8\tfrac{3}{4}$ (ii) 27 (iii) 8
8. (a) $4\tfrac{1}{2}$ (b) 2
9. (a) $5x + 1$ (b) (i) 3 (ii) 5
10. (a) $13x - 2$ degrees (b) $73°$
11. (a) 4 (b) $^-1\tfrac{1}{2}$

AS7 Algebra 3

Check in AS7

1. (a) 6   (b) 4   (c) 21   (d) 8   (e) 4   (f) 5   (g) 4
2. (a) $x = 4$ (b) $y = 3$ (c) $y = 20$ (d) $t = 8$ (e) $t = 5$ (f) $r = 7$ (g) $x = 3$ (h) $n = 1$

Exercise 7A

1. 2, 5, 8, 11, 14
2. 1, 3, 9, 27, 81
3. 5, 9, 13, 17, 21
4. 2, 6, 10, 14, 18
5. 100, 97, 94, 91, 88
6. 6, 11, 16, 21, 26
7. 1, 4, 16, 64, 256
8. 2, 7, 12, 17, 22
9. 3, 9, 15, 21, 27
10. 1, 8, 15, 22, 29
11. 100, 90, 80, 70, 60
12. 1, 1, 2, 3, 5

Exercise 7B

1. 32, 37
2. 60, 50
3. 3 125, 15 625
4. 25, 29
5. 29, 47
6. 19, 21
7. 32, 16
8. 16, 22
9. 243, 729
10. 23, 26
11. 40, 36
12. 78, 93
13. 0·01, 0·001
14. 67, 79
15. 43, 39
16. 13, 21
17. 21, 28
18. 56, 67
19. 200, 2 000
20. 0·25, 0·125

Exercise 7C

1. 2, 4, 6, 8, 10
2. 3, 6, 9, 12, 15
3. 4, 8, 12, 16, 20
4. 5, 10, 15, 20, 25
5. 6, 12, 18, 24, 30
6. 7, 14, 21, 28, 35
7. 8, 16, 24, 32, 40
8. 9, 18, 27, 36, 45
9. 10, 20, 30, 40, 50
10. 2, 3, 4, 5, 6
11. 4, 5, 6, 7, 8
12. 5, 6, 7, 8, 9
13. 3, 5, 7, 9, 11
14. 4, 7, 10, 13, 16
15. 5, 9, 13, 17, 21
16. 1, 3, 5, 7, 9
17. 2, 5, 8, 11, 14
18. 3, 7, 11, 15, 19
19. 7, 12, 17, 22, 27
20. 7, 10, 13, 16, 19
21. 1, 5, 9, 13, 17
22. 7, 9, 11, 13, 17
23. 1, 6, 11, 16, 21
24. 3, 9, 15, 21, 27
25. 9, 11, 13, 15, 17
26. 0, 3, 6, 9, 12
27. 9, 13, 17, 21, 25
28. 9, 14, 19, 24, 29
29. 11, 14, 17, 20, 23
30. 3, 13, 23, 33, 43

Exercise 7D

1. $2n + 3$, 103
2. $3n + 3$, 153
3. $4n + 3$, 203
4. $5n - 2$, 248
5. $6n + 2$, 302
6. $2n - 3$, 97
7. $3n - 2$, 148
8. $4n - 2$, 198
9. $5n - 1$, 249
10. $7n - 3$, 347
11. $2n + 5$, 105
12. $3n + 6$, 156
13. $4n + 7$, 207
14. $5n + 3$, 253
15. $10n + 4$, 504
16. $2n - 2$, 98
17. $3n + 2$, 152
18. $4n + 4$, 204
19. $5n + 8$, 258
20. $10n - 1$, 499

Exercise 7E

1. (a) 5   (b)

Fences in metres	1	2	3	4
Metres of wood needed	5	9	13	17

(c) $4n + 1$
(d) 101 m
(e) 10 m

2. (a)

Number of tables	1	2	3	4
Number of seats	4	6	8	10

(b) $2n + 2$ (c) 42   (d) 15

3. (a) 14 cm   (b)

Pattern number	1	2	3	4
Perimeter	8 cm	14 cm	20 cm	26 cm

(c) $6n + 2$ (d) 362
(e) 10th

4. (a) $3n + 4$ (b) 304   (c) 12th

5. (a)

Height of pyramid	1 can	2 cans	3 cans	4 cans
Number of cans in the bottom row	1	3	5	7

(b) $2n - 1$ (c) 49
(d) 30 cans high

Exercise 7F

1. A(1,5)   B(1,2)   C(2,1)   D(2,2)   E(3,3)   F(0,3)   G(2,4)
   H(4,4)   I(4,0)   J(5,3)
2. A(5,8)   B(5,4)   C(7,2)   D(8,0)   E(6,1)   F(4,3)   G(0,3)
   H(2,5)   I(1,2)   J(0,6)   K(2,8)   L(2,7)   M(3,6)

3.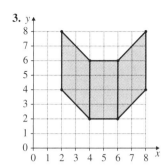

4.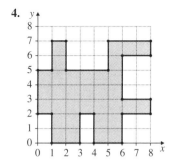

5. (a) isosceles triangle
   (b) quadrilateral
   (c) pentagon
   (d) parallelogram
   (e) square
   (f) kite
   (g) trapezium
   (h) right-angled triangle
   (i) rhombus
   (j) rectangle
   (k) hexagon

6.

Place	Location	Place	Location
Caves	(9,5)	Green Susan's Cabin	(8,2)
Dead Person's Point	$(8\frac{1}{2},7\frac{1}{2})$	Swamp	(4,6)
Stockade	(12,6)	Turtle Beach	(1,5)
Jack's Cabin	(11,5)	First Landing	(2,4)
Treasure	(6,7)	Gold Mine	(2,3)
More Treasure	$(11,2\frac{1}{2})$	Snake Pit	(3,1)
Fresh Water Spring	$(6\frac{1}{2},4\frac{1}{2})$		

Exercise 7G

1. A(3,2)   B(⁻3,2)   C(0,1)   D(⁻2,⁻2)   E(2,3)   F(⁻2,2)   G(1,⁻1)
   H(1,1)   I(⁻3,⁻3)   J(2,⁻2)   K(⁻2,0)   L(0,⁻2)

2. A(2,5)   B(2,3)   C(1,2)   D(3,0)   E(3,⁻4)   F(4,⁻1)   G(5,⁻1)
   H(4,⁻5)   I(⁻2,⁻5)   J(0,⁻4)   K(⁻1,⁻1)   L(0,1)   M(⁻2,3)   N(⁻2,5)
   O(0,4)

3. (a)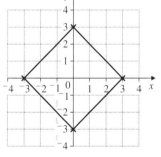

   (b)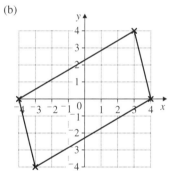

   (c)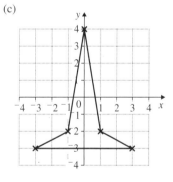

   (d)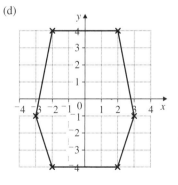

   (e)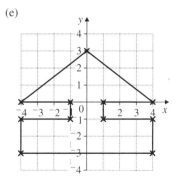

   (f)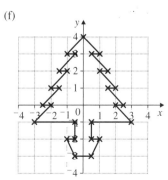

4. (b) ($^-2,^-5$) and (4,$^-5$), or ($^-2,7$) and (4,7)
5. (d) They all have a y-coordinate of 1.
6. (d) They all have an x-coordinate of 1.

Exercise 7H

2. (a)

x	$^-2$	$^-1$	0	1	2
$y = x + 2$	0	1	2	3	4

(b)

x	$^-2$	$^-1$	0	1	2
$y = x + 3$	1	2	3	4	5

(c)

x	$^-2$	$^-1$	0	1	2
$y = x + 4$	2	3	4	5	6

(d)

x	$^-2$	$^-1$	0	1	2
$y = x - 1$	$^-3$	$^-2$	$^-1$	0	1

(e)

x	$^-2$	$^-1$	0	1	2
$y = x - 2$	$^-4$	$^-3$	$^-2$	$^-1$	0

(f)

x	$^-2$	$^-1$	0	1	2
$y = x - 3$	$^-5$	$^-4$	$^-3$	$^-2$	$^-1$

3. (a)

x	$^-2$	$^-1$	0	1	2
$y = x$	$^-2$	$^-1$	0	1	2

(b)

x	$^-2$	$^-1$	0	1	2
$y = 2x$	$^-4$	$^-2$	0	2	4

(c)

x	$^-2$	$^-1$	0	1	2
$y = 3x$	$^-6$	$^-3$	0	3	6

(d)

x	$^-2$	$^-1$	0	1	2
$y = {}^-2x$	4	2	0	$^-2$	$^-4$

(e)

x	$^-2$	$^-1$	0	1	2
$y = {}^-3x$	6	3	0	$^-3$	$^-6$

(f)

x	$^-2$	$^-1$	0	1	2
$y = {}^-x$	2	1	0	$^-1$	$^-2$

4. (a)

x	$^-2$	$^-1$	0	1	2
$y = 3 - x$	5	4	3	2	1

(b)

x	$^-2$	$^-1$	0	1	2
$y = 2 - x$	4	3	2	1	0

(c)

x	$^-2$	$^-1$	0	1	2
$y = 1 - x$	3	2	1	0	$^-1$

(d)

x	$^-2$	$^-1$	0	1	2
$y = 4 - x$	6	5	4	3	2

(e)

x	$^-2$	$^-1$	0	1	2
$y = 8 - 2x$	12	10	8	6	4

6. (a)

x	$^-2$	$^-1$	0	1	2
$y = \frac{x}{2}$	$^-1$	$^-\frac{1}{2}$	0	$\frac{1}{2}$	1

(b)

x	$^-3$	$^-1$	0	1	3
$y = \frac{x}{3}$	$^-1$	$^-\frac{1}{3}$	0	$\frac{1}{3}$	1

(c)

x	$^-4$	$^-1$	0	1	4
$y = \frac{x}{4}$	$^-1$	$^-\frac{1}{4}$	0	$\frac{1}{4}$	1

(d)

x	$^-2$	$^-1$	0	1	2
$y = \frac{-x}{2}$	1	$\frac{1}{2}$	0	$^-\frac{1}{2}$	$^-1$

(e)

x	$^-3$	$^-1$	0	1	3
$y = \frac{-x}{3}$	1	$\frac{1}{3}$	0	$^-\frac{1}{3}$	$^-1$

(f)

x	$^-4$	$^-1$	0	1	4
$y = \frac{-x}{4}$	1	$\frac{1}{4}$	0	$^-\frac{1}{4}$	$^-1$

7. (a)

x	$^-2$	$^-1$	0	1	2
$y = 2x + 1$	$^-3$	$^-1$	1	3	5

(b)

x	$^-2$	$^-1$	0	1	2
$y = 3x - 1$	$^-7$	$^-4$	$^-1$	2	5

(c)

x	$^-2$	$^-1$	0	1	2
$y = 2x - 3$	$^-7$	$^-5$	$^-3$	$^-1$	1

(d)

x	$^-2$	$^-1$	0	1	2
$y = \frac{x}{2} + 3$	2	$2\frac{1}{2}$	3	$3\frac{1}{2}$	4

(e)

x	$^-2$	$^-1$	0	1	2
$y = 3 - 2x$	7	5	3	1	$^-4$

(f)

x	$^-2$	$^-1$	0	1	2
$y = 3x - 4$	$^-10$	$^-7$	$^-4$	$^-1$	2

Exercise 7I

2. (a)

x	$^-3$	$^-2$	$^-1$	0	1	2	3
$y = x^2 + 2$	11	6	3	2	3	6	11

(b)

x	$^-3$	$^-2$	$^-1$	0	1	2	3
$y = x^2 + 4$	13	8	5	4	5	8	13

2. (c)

x	$^-3$	$^-2$	$^-1$	0	1	2	3
$y = x^2 + 6$	15	10	7	6	7	10	15

(d)

x	$^-3$	$^-2$	$^-1$	0	1	2	3
$y = x^2 - 2$	7	2	$^-1$	$^-2$	$^-1$	2	7

(e)

x	$^-3$	$^-2$	$^-1$	0	1	2	3
$y = x^2 - 4$	5	0	$^-3$	$^-4$	$^-3$	0	5

3. (a)

x	1	2	3	4	5	6	7	8	9	10	11	12
$y = \frac{12}{x}$	11	6	4	3	2·4	2	1·7	1·5	1·3	1·2	1·1	1

(b)

x	1	2	3	4
$y = \frac{4}{x}$	4	2	1·3	4

(c)

x	1	2	3	4	5	6
$y = \frac{6}{x}$	6	3	2	1·5	1·2	1

4. (a)

x	$^-3$	$^-2$	$^-1$	0	1	2	3
x^2	9	4	1	0	1	4	9
$2x$	$^-6$	$^-4$	$^-2$	0	2	4	6
$y = x^2 + 2x$	3	0	$^-1$	0	3	8	15

5. (a)

x	$^-3$	$^-2$	$^-1$	0	1	2	3
x^2	9	4	1	0	1	4	9
x	$^-3$	$^-2$	$^-1$	0	1	2	3
$y = x^2 - x$	12	6	2	0	0	2	6

6. (a)

x	$^-3$	$^-2$	$^-1$	0	1	2	3
8	8	8	8	8	8	8	8
x^2	9	4	1	0	1	4	9
$y = 8 - x^2$	$^-1$	4	7	8	7	4	$^-1$

7. (a)

x	$^-3$	$^-2$	$^-1$	0	1	2
x^2	9	4	1	0	1	4
$3x$	$^-9$	$^-6$	$^-3$	0	3	6
5	5	5	5	5	5	5
$y = x^2 - x$	5	3	3	5	9	15

Exercise 7J

1. (b) (i) 25 francs   (ii) 75 francs   (iii) 95 francs
  (c) (i) 50p   (ii) £3·50   (iii) £5·50
2. (b) (i) 0·5 ml   (ii) 4 ml   (iii) 5·5 ml
  (c) (i) 4 months   (ii) 20 months   (iii) 10 months
3. (b) (i) 80p   (ii) 240p   (iii) 360p
  (c) (i) 50 g   (ii) 350 g   (iii) 400 g

4. (a)

Number of people	10	30	50	70	90	
Cost of disco (£)		25	35	45	55	65

  (c) (i) £30   (ii) £37·50   (iii) £52·50
  (d) (i) 80   (ii) 40   (iii) 60

Exercise 7K

1. (a) 9:00   (b) Dover   (c) 1 hour   (d) 310 km
   (e) (i) 125 km   (ii) 70 km   (iii) 280 km
   (f) 14:00   (g) 2 hours   (h) 62·5 km/h
2. (a) 11 km   (b) 30 minutes   (c) 22 km/h   (d) $2\frac{1}{2}$ hours   (e) 30 minutes
   (f) 7 km   (g) 14 km/h   (h) 45 minutes   (i) 45 minutes   (j) 5·3 km/h
3. (a) 14:00   (b) 14:30   (c) 16:00   (d) 15:30   (e) 120 km
   (f) 60 km   (g) 15:00   (h) 60 km/h   (i) 120 km/h   (j) 30 minutes
4. (a) 15 minutes   (b) 6 km   (c) 2 km   (d) 3 km   (e) 8 km
   (f) 10 minutes   (g) 1 km   (h) 15 minutes   (i) 12 km/h   (j) 24 km/h

Checkout AS7

1. (a) 15, 18   (b) 10, 8   (c) 32, 64   (d) 25, 12·5
2. (a) 5, 10, 15, 20, 25   (b)   6, 7, 8, 9, 10   (c) 0, 1, 2, 3, 4   (d) 8, 11, 14, 17, 20
3. (a) $5n-1$ (b) $3n+8$ (c) $2n+7$ (d) $4n+3$
4. (b) ($^{-}$1,1) and ($^{-}$1,$^{-}$1), or (3,1) and (3,$^{-}$1)
5. (a)

x	$^{-}2$	$^{-}1$	0	1	2
$y = x + 5$	3	4	5	6	7

(b)

x	$^{-}2$	$^{-}1$	0	1	2
$y = x - 5$	$^{-}7$	$^{-}6$	$^{-}5$	$^{-}4$	$^{-}3$

(c)

x	$^{-}2$	$^{-}1$	0	1	2
$y = 3x + 1$	$^{-}5$	$^{-}2$	1	4	7

(d)

x	$^{-}2$	$^{-}1$	0	1	2
$y = 2x - 4$	$^{-}8$	$^{-}6$	$^{-}4$	$^{-}2$	0

6. (a)

x	$^{-}3$	$^{-}2$	$^{-}1$	0	1	2	3
$y = x^2 + 3$	12	7	4	3	4	7	12

(b)

x	$^{-}3$	$^{-}2$	$^{-}1$	0	1	2	3
$y = x^2 - 5$	4	$^{-}1$	$^{-}4$	$^{-}5$	$^{-}4$	$^{-}1$	4

(c)

x	$^{-}3$	$^{-}2$	$^{-}1$	0	1	2	3
$y = 9 - x^2$	0	5	8	9	8	5	0

7. (b) (i) £80   (ii) £140   (c) (i) 7 hours   (ii) 4 hours
8. (b) (i) 10.40 a.m.   (ii) 10.30 a.m.   (iii) 9.50 a.m.   (iv) 50 km

Revision exercise AS7

1. (a) (i) 8   (ii) subtracted 5   (b) (i) 24   (ii) all the numbers are being doubled
2. (a) 19   (b) (i) $x + 4$ (ii) $x - 4$
3. (a) (i) square numbers   (ii) 36   (b) (i) 42   (ii) 65
4. (a) $^{-}$3, 1, 5   (c) 1·75
5. (a) 0, $^{-}$1, 3   (b) 1·25
6. (a) 25 km   (b) 30 minutes   (c) 6·25 km

AS8 Shape and space 4

Check in AS8

1. A (2,1), B (5,2), C (1,0), D (3,$^{-}$2), E (5,$^{-}$1), F (0,$^{-}$2), G ($^{-}$1,2), H (0,3), I ($^{-}$3,1), J ($^{-}$4,2), K ($^{-}$2,$^{-}$1), L ($^{-}$4,$^{-}$3), M ($^{-}$5,$^{-}$1), N ($^{-}$2,0)

Exercise 8A

1. A $\begin{pmatrix} +8 \\ +5 \end{pmatrix}$ B $\begin{pmatrix} +10 \\ +2 \end{pmatrix}$ C $\begin{pmatrix} +6 \\ 0 \end{pmatrix}$ D $\begin{pmatrix} +7 \\ -4 \end{pmatrix}$ E $\begin{pmatrix} 0 \\ -3 \end{pmatrix}$

   F $\begin{pmatrix} -6 \\ -5 \end{pmatrix}$ G $\begin{pmatrix} -6 \\ 0 \end{pmatrix}$ H $\begin{pmatrix} -6 \\ +4 \end{pmatrix}$ I $\begin{pmatrix} 0 \\ +3 \end{pmatrix}$ J $\begin{pmatrix} -2 \\ +6 \end{pmatrix}$

2. A $\begin{pmatrix} +7 \\ +5 \end{pmatrix}$ B $\begin{pmatrix} -7 \\ +4 \end{pmatrix}$ C $\begin{pmatrix} -1 \\ +5 \end{pmatrix}$ D $\begin{pmatrix} +3 \\ +3 \end{pmatrix}$ E $\begin{pmatrix} +7 \\ 0 \end{pmatrix}$

F $\begin{pmatrix} +7 \\ -5 \end{pmatrix}$ G $\begin{pmatrix} -5 \\ +1 \end{pmatrix}$ H $\begin{pmatrix} -7 \\ -3 \end{pmatrix}$ I $\begin{pmatrix} -1 \\ -4 \end{pmatrix}$ J $\begin{pmatrix} +3 \\ -6 \end{pmatrix}$

5. (a) $\begin{pmatrix} -14 \\ -1 \end{pmatrix}$ (b) $\begin{pmatrix} -8 \\ 0 \end{pmatrix}$ (c) $\begin{pmatrix} -4 \\ -2 \end{pmatrix}$ (d) $\begin{pmatrix} 0 \\ -5 \end{pmatrix}$ (e) $\begin{pmatrix} 0 \\ -10 \end{pmatrix}$

(f) $\begin{pmatrix} +14 \\ +1 \end{pmatrix}$ (g) $\begin{pmatrix} +10 \\ -1 \end{pmatrix}$ (h) $\begin{pmatrix} +14 \\ -4 \end{pmatrix}$ (i) $\begin{pmatrix} +14 \\ -4 \end{pmatrix}$ (j) $\begin{pmatrix} +10 \\ -10 \end{pmatrix}$

(k) $\begin{pmatrix} -4 \\ -4 \end{pmatrix}$ (l) $\begin{pmatrix} +8 \\ 0 \end{pmatrix}$ (m) $\begin{pmatrix} +8 \\ -5 \end{pmatrix}$ (n) $\begin{pmatrix} -6 \\ -8 \end{pmatrix}$ (o) $\begin{pmatrix} 0 \\ -9 \end{pmatrix}$

(p) $\begin{pmatrix} -6 \\ +1 \end{pmatrix}$ (q) $\begin{pmatrix} +6 \\ -1 \end{pmatrix}$ (r) $\begin{pmatrix} +4 \\ +1 \end{pmatrix}$ (s) $\begin{pmatrix} +12 \\ +4 \end{pmatrix}$ (t) $\begin{pmatrix} -14 \\ +9 \end{pmatrix}$

All shapes are congruent to each other.

Exercise 8C

2. (a) 270° (b) 180° (c) 90° (d) 90° (e) 270° (f) 180° (g) 180° (h) 90°
(i) 270° (j) 270° (k) 180° (l) 90°
3. (a) 90° (b) 270° (c) 180° (d) 270° (e) 180° (f) 90° (g) 90° (h) 180°
(i) 270° (j) 180° (k) 270° (l) 90°

Exercise 8D

1. There is one vertical line of symmetry.
2. There is one horizontal line of symmetry.
3. There is one vertical line of symmetry.
4. There is one vertical and one horizontal line of symmetry.
5. There is one vertical line of symmetry.
6. There is one vertical and one horizontal line of symmetry.
7. There are six lines of symmetry.
8. There is one vertical and one horizontal line of symmetry.
9. There are six lines of symmetry.
10. There are five lines of symmetry.
11. There are four lines of symmetry.
12. There are two lines of symmetry.
13. There are no lines of symmetry.
14. There are four lines of symmetry.
15. There are no lines of symmetry.
16. There are four lines of symmetry.
17. There are eight lines of symmetry.
18. There is one vertical and one horizontal line of symmetry.

Exercise 8E

1. (a) 1 (b) 2 (c) 4 (d) 6 (e) 4 (f) 2 (g) 4 (h) 5
(i) 2 (j) 8 (k) 2 (l) 2 (m) 1 (n) 1 (o) 4
2. (a) 1 (b) 2 (c) 1 (d) 2 (e) 2 (f) 1 (g) 2 (h) 1
(i) 2 (j) 2 (k) 2 (l) 4

Checkout AS8

1. A $\begin{pmatrix} +8 \\ +5 \end{pmatrix}$ B $\begin{pmatrix} +7 \\ 0 \end{pmatrix}$ C $\begin{pmatrix} +5 \\ -4 \end{pmatrix}$ D $\begin{pmatrix} -4 \\ -4 \end{pmatrix}$ E $\begin{pmatrix} -1 \\ -5 \end{pmatrix}$

3. (a) A 90°, B 180°, C 270° (b) A 270°, B 180°, C 90°
4. (b) 1, 2, 2, 4

Revision exercise AS8

1. (a) (ii) hexagon (b) (i) 0 (ii) 3
2. (a) (i) (2, 3) (ii) position is (2, ⁻3)
3. (a) (5, 2) (b) (ii) $x = 8, y = 3.5$ (c) (i) (⁻4, 1) (ii) $\begin{pmatrix} 9 \\ 4 \end{pmatrix}$:9 units to the right and 4 units up.

AS9 Shape and space 5

Check in AS9

1. (a) 7   (b) 12·3   (c) 31   (d) 36   (e) 15·2   (f) 93   (g) 4·08   (h) 79·8
2. (a) 6   (b) 14   (c) 8·7   (d) 17·5   (e) 20·5   (f) 13·7   (g) 43·65   (h) 28·35

Exercise 9A

1. 10 cm   **2.** 14 cm   **3.** 16 cm   **4.** 18 cm   **5.** 12 cm   **6.** 16 cm   **7.** 6·8 cm   **8.** 10·2 cm
9. 14·8 cm   **10.** 11·2 cm   **11.** 13·6 cm   **12.** 17·2 cm   **13.** 14·8 cm   **14.** 13·2 cm   **15.** 16·8 cm

Exercise 9B

1. 4 cm^2 **2.** 8 cm^2 **3.** 10 cm^2 **4.** 7 cm^2 **5.** 9 cm^2 **6.** 7 cm^2 **7.** 8 cm^2 **8.** 5 cm^2
9. 8 cm^2 **10.** 10 cm^2 **11.** 8 cm^2 **12.** 10 cm^2 **13.** 9 cm^2 **14.** 9 cm^2 **15.** 8 cm^2

Exercise 9C

1. 6·8 m^2 **2.** 12·6 cm^2 **3.** 31·5 mm^2 **4.** 25 m^2 **5.** 35 cm^2 **6.** 19 mm^2 **7.** 77 cm^2 **8.** 0·6 m^2
9. 25 m^2 **10.** 1 cm^2, 100 mm^2 **11.** 100   **12.** 1 m^2, 10 000 cm^2 **13.** 10 000

Exercise 9D

1. 36 cm^2 **2.** 39 cm^2 **3.** 128 cm^2 **4.** 168 mm^2 **5.** 41 m^2 **6.** 112 m^2 **7.** 78 cm^2 **8.** 10 m^2 **9.** 650 cm^2

Exercise 9E

1. 9 cm^2 **2.** 24 cm^2 **3.** 80 mm^2 **4.** 17·5 m^2 **5.** 83 cm^2 **6.** 780 mm^2 **7.** 31 m^2 **8.** 90 cm^2
9. 15 750 mm^2 **10.** 17·28 cm^2 **11.** 25·2 m^2 **12.** 66 mm^2 **13.** 79·9 m^2 **14.** 270 cm^2 **15.** 13 m^2

Exercise 9F

1. 20 cm^2 **2.** 18 cm^2 **3.** 49 mm^2 **4.** 7·5 m^2 **5.** 42 mm^2 **6.** 28·5 cm^2 **7.** 38·5 mm^2 **8.** 22·5 cm^2
9. 1·2 m^2 **10.** 1·5 m^2 **11.** 1·8 m^2 **12.** 27·5 mm^2 **13.** 18·75 cm^2 **14.** 64·5 m^2 **15.** 29·24 cm^2

Exercise 9G

1. 15 cm^2 **2.** 1·5 m^2 **3.** 1·875 m^2 **4.** 108 mm^2 **5.** 120 cm^2 **6.** 35 m^2 **7.** 37 m^2 **8.** 11·5 m^2
9. 21 m^2 **10.** 27 cm^2 **11.** 1 020 cm^2 **12.** 480 m^2
13. (a) 25 m^2 (b) 6·25 m^2 (c) 18·75 m^2
14. (a) 2·8 m^2 (b) 8·4 m^2 (c) £21
15. (a) 4 cm × 8 cm rectangle   (b) 5 cm × 6 cm rectangle   (c) 4 cm × 9 cm rectangle

Checkout AS9

1. (a) 17 cm^2 (b) 11·5 cm^2
2. (a) 30 cm^2 (b) 5 m^2
3. 36 m^2 **4.** 3·6 m^2
5. (a) 60 mm^2 (b) 125 cm^2
6. 53 cm^2

Revision exercise AS9

1. (a) 16 cm   (b) eg 4 cm by 4 cm and 1 cm by 7 cm
2. (a) $6x + 10$ cm   (b) $15x$ cm^2 (c) (i) $x = 105$ (ii) 52 cm
3. (a) 24 cm^2 (b) eg 4 cm by 6 cm.
4. 6 cm
5. (a) $3(x + 4)$ or $3x + 12$ cm^2 (b) $5x$ cm^2 (c) 6
6. (a)

(b) (i) 10 cm^2 (ii) 6 cm   **7.** 15.6 cm^2

AS10 Shape and space 6

Check in 10

1. (a) 31·4　　(b) 37·68　　(c) 16·328　　(d) 78·5　　(e) 200·96　　(f) 12·56

Exercise 10A

3. (a) 10 cm　(b) 14 cm　(c) 5 cm　(d) 12·8 cm　(e) 18·6 cm
4. (a) 10 cm　(b) 16 cm　(c) 3·5 cm　(d) 7·5 cm　(e) 8·3 cm

Exercise 10B

1. (a) 12·4 cm　(b) 18·6 cm　(c) 6·2 cm　(d) 24·8 mm　(e) 9·3 m　(f) 7·75 cm
2. (a) 26·38 mm　(b) 3·14 m　(c) 1·57 m　(d) 157 cm　(e) 628 mm　(f) 3·77 m
3. (a) 31 cm　(b) 49·6 mm　(c) 21·7 m　(d) 7·4 m　(e) 74·4 m　(f) 27·9 cm
4. (a) 43·96 cm　(b) 47·1 mm　(c) 37·68 m　(d) 15·07 m　(e) 3·14 m　(f) 314 mm
5. (a) 219·8 cm　(b) 2 198 cm　　　　　6. (a) 22 miles　　　　(b) ~~20 mins~~ *20 mins*

Exercise 10C

1. (a) 12·4 cm²　(b) 77·5 mm²　(c) 111·6 m²　(d) 17·9 m²　(e) 0·78 cm²　(f) 7 750 mm²
2. (a) 3·14 cm²　(b) 201 mm²　(c) 38·5 m²　(d) 4·5 m²　(e) 452 m²　(f) 63·6 cm²
3. (a) 297 m²　(b) 63·6 m²　(c) 233 m²　(d) 16
4. (a) 2·2 m²　(b) 0·5 m²　(c) 0·25 m²　(d) 1·9 m²
5. (a) 78·5 cm²　(b) 314 cm²　(c) The area of the big box label is four times the area of the small box label.

Exercise 10D

1. (a) 222 cm²　(b) 454 mm²　(c) 20 m²
   (d) 19·6 m²　(e) 63 cm²　(f) 288 mm²
2. (a) 700 cm²　(b) 600 cm²　(c) 14p, 12p
3. 150 cm²
4. (a) 96 cm²　(b) 2 400 cm²　(c) 96p

Exercise 10E

1. 12 cm³　　2. 8 cm³　　3. 6 cm³　　4. 16 cm³　　5. 12 cm³　　6. 36 cm³
7. 27 cm³　　8. 16 cm³　　9. 20 cm³　　10. 18 cm³　　11. 14 cm³　　12. 16 cm³

Exercise 10F

1. (a) 60 cm³　(b) 72 cm³　(c) 486 cm³　(d) 9 m³　(e) 9 m³　(f) 0·48 m³
2. (a) 40 cm³　(b) 480 cm³　(c) 6 cm
3. (a) 40 000 cm³　　(b) 40 litres　(c) £30
4. (a) 864 cm³　(b) 810 cm³　(c) 324 cm³
5. (a) cube　(b) 1 cm³, 1 000 mm³
6. 1 000　　7. 750　　8. 1 m³, 1 000 000 cm³　　9. 1 000 000

Exercise 10G

1. (a) 75·3 m³　(b) 9 420 mm³　(c) 603 cm³
   (d) 0·785 m³　(e) 25·1 cm³　(f) 25 120 mm³
2. (a) 36 cm³　(b) 70 cm³　(c) 1 440 mm³
   (d) 1·5 m³　(e) 9 m³　(f) 2·25 m³
3. (a) 48 m²　(b) 15 m²　(c) 63 m²　(d) 1 260 m³
4. (a) 40 m²　(b) 25 m²　(c) 1 625 m³
5. (a) 62 800 cm³　(b) 502

Checkout AS10

2. (a) (i) 24·8 cm　　(ii) 155 mm　(b) (i) 62·8 cm　　(ii) 753·6 mm
3. (a) 201 cm³　(b) 1 256 mm³
4. 430 mm³　　5. 24 cm³　　6. 375 m³　　7. 151 cm³, 0·96 m³

Revision exercise AS10

1. (a) 27   (b) 24   (c) 20
2. (a) $7\,m^3$ (b) $0.2\,m$ (c) $13.9\,m^3$
3. (d) $90°$
4. (a) $19.44\,m^2$ (b) $14.58\,m^2$ (c) $27.36\,m^2$ (d) 76
5. $628\,cm^2$ 6. $9.82\,cm^2$
7. (a) $8\,640\,cm^3$ (b) $1.77\,m^2$
8. (a) 64   (b) $768\,cm^3$
9. (a) $10\,cm^3$ (b) $\frac{1}{3}$

Module 5 Practice calculator test

1. (a) (i) 4, 8   (ii) 4, 8   (iii) 5, 7, 11, 13, 17   (iv) 9
   (b) (i) 9 and 11 or 7 and 13   (ii) 13, 17
2. (a)

   (b) (i) 21, 26   (ii) add 5 more matchsticks for each number
   (iii)   Number of matchsticks = $5 \times$ shape number $+ 1 = 46$
3. (a) (i) 31   (ii) added 4   (b) (i) 3, ⁻1   (c) 28
4. (a) (i) equilateral   (ii) $60°$ (b) (i) regular hexagon   (iii) 6
5. (a) E   (b) $(1, 6)$ (d) $(3, 5)$
6. (a) $.26\,cm^3$ (b) 3 cm   (c) no; volume of box is $20\,cm^3$
7. (a) 2   (b) (i) 2 km   (ii) 12 km/hour   (c) DE
8. $86°$ 9. $4a + 3b$
10. (a) $39.0\,cm$ (b) $121\,cm^2$
11. (a) $2^3 \times 5$ (b) 2×5^2 (c) 10
12. (a) $135°$ 9b) $135°$

Module 5 Practice non-calculator test

1. (a) $\frac{2}{7}$ (b) $\frac{1}{10}$
2. (a) 4, 9, 25   (b) 27
3. (a) 10, 12   (b) 8
   (c) Every extra table seats an extra two people **or** the number of people seated is 2 + 2 times the number of tables
4. (a) (i) 19   (ii) 39   (b) 5, ⁻4
5. (a) 14   (b) $3n - 1$
6. (a) 8   (b) 4
7. (b) Quadrilateral   (c) $13.5\,m^2$ (d) $16.2\,m$
8. (a) DE and CB   (b) CD   (c) angles ABC and AED
9. (a) (i) Pentagon   (ii) angles are not equal   (b) (ii) $147°$
10. (a) ⁻4, ⁻1, 5   (c) $\frac{4}{3}$ or 1.3
11. (a) $090°$ (b) (i) $69°$ (ii) $159°$ (iii) $234°$
12. (a) $3 + 4 = 7$ which is an odd number   (b) (i) $1\frac{1}{4}$ (ii) $\frac{7}{30}$
13. (a) 37   (b) 9   (c) $-1\frac{1}{2}$

INDEX